EDIBLE
WILD PLANTS

ROY GENDERS

EDIBLE
WILD PLANTS

A GUIDE TO NATURAL FOODS

van der Marck Editions

NEW YORK

CONTENTS

A Co-Publication of EMB-Service for
Publishers, Lucerne, Switzerland

US edition copyright © 1988 and published
by VAN DER MARCK EDITIONS
1133 Broadway, Suite 1301
New York, New York 10010

Library of Congress Cataloging-in-
Publication Data

Genders, Roy.
Edible wild plants.

Bibliography: p.
Includes index.
1. Wild plants, Edible.
2. Cookery (Wild foods)
I. Title.
QK98.5.A1G46 1988   581.6'32   88-14199
ISBN 0-912383-84-4

Original Concept and Design by
Emil M. Bührer

Editor: David Baker, Jason Friedman

Captions and Copy Editor:
Rosalind Weaver

Picture Procuration: Rosaria Pasquariello

Production Manager: Franz Gisler

Printed and bound by:
Rotolito Lombarda SpA, Milan, Italy

Typesetting by:
Maihof Druckerei, Lucerne, Switzerland

Photolithography by:
La Cromolito, Milan, Italy

Printed in Italy

p.2:
Woodcut showing the pounding of
horseradish roots, 1493.

Opposite page:
Illustration of asparagus from a herbal of
1543.

XXXIII.

From sunrise to sunset every day the miracle that allows and supports life on earth takes place. When a man eats a freshly picked leaf, he swallows something that eight minutes previously was part of the sun. Eight minutes is the time the light of the sun takes to reach the earth.

The plant collaborates with the sun, using a singular chemical process to transform, in a fraction of a second, the sun's rays into food. Only plants are able to receive sunlight and combine it with earthly material to form the basis of animal and human life. The root, the stalk, the fruit and the flowers of a plant form the first link in a food chain, a process encompassing everything – birth, death and rebirth.

The Power of Plants

Since *Homo erectus erectus,* the ape-man who walked upright on two legs, first appeared on earth some 20 million years ago, man has been dependent on plants for all of his needs. To supply food and medicines, wood for a home; to provide protection against marauding tribes and animals and adverse weather; to provide material for clothing; for shade and to prevent the erosion of soil; and most of all, to give the oxygen we breathe to exist.

The earth's surface as we know it today had, by the advent of man, taken shape. The climate, too, had settled into that of today, with areas of heavy rainfall and barren tundra and desert, so that plants gradually became adapted to the different conditions. By then, most of the cyads or tree ferns and the giant horsetails which covered the earth's surface for millions of years and the dinosaurs which fed on them had long since vanished, though several species of cyad and horsetail are found to this day. In their place had grown grasses, dwarf ferns and conifers, while cacti and palms had made their appearance; each was adapted to the different climatic conditions that had evolved. As primitive man developed, so did he rely upon these plants for his existence. They supplied his total needs. Among the grasses he found cereals, the seeds of barley, wheat and oats which we know as grain or corn, and in the flooded warmer parts of the earth, rice. Grasses also provided food for livestock which in return would yield meat and milk. From fungi and seaweeds which were among the first things edible to inhabit the earth, and from the young shoots of ferns, more nourishing food was obtained. The fronds of ferns also provided food for livestock and when they became too dry to eat, they could be used to protect the body from cold and provided litter for livestock in winter.

Early man made his home in caves, living off the land around him, but when he began to look elsewhere for his food, to travel distances, trees would provide material for his home and ferns and reeds for its thatching. And this has continued until today. Trees are still used the world over to provide timber for building; also fuel for warmth and for cooking; as well as providing pulp for making paper for books. Trees also provide man with timber to make boats for fishing and for travel.

Man also obtained his medicines from plants, in the warmer parts quinine and morphine, among the most important preparations of modern medicine; in cooler climes, he cured himself of simple ailments by herbs which grew in abundance everywhere. Weeds such as nettle and dandelion which were among the first flowering plants of the temperate world are some of the most valuable for food or medicine.

The coming of the insects, together with the first flowering plants and the nectar they produced, meant that bees could find nectar and pollen to produce honey which early man would have found nourishing as well as useful as a sweetener for food and drinks. For the same purpose he would use the sap of the sugar maple in northerly climes and of sugar cane in warmer parts. He lacked nothing for his health and well-being, for nature had provided all his requirements and as he became more adept in the use of tools, so did he make greater use of the plants around him. The hard seeds of corn were ground into flour to bake into bread. As man developed, so did plant life, until today more than 350,000 species cover the earth.

Without green plants, there could be neither man nor animals, for one cannot exist without the other. Seaweeds were the first green plants to appear and several million years later, at the end of the Devonian period, appeared horsetail and the first evergreens in the form of tree ferns. As the first green plants to appear on earth, they perhaps evolved from seaweeds washed up on the sea shore. Like all green plants, they contained chlorophyll which by exposure to sunlight (photosynthesis) enables the plant to convert carbon dioxide into carbohydrates, starches and sugar upon which the plant is able to grow and which man and animals eat to obtain their energy. At the same time, plants give off oxygen required by living creatures to survive. They in turn convert oxygen into carbon dioxide and exhale it for green plants to absorb, and by the light of the sun, convert into oxygen again.

Plants also provide shade against the direct rays of the sun and protection from wind and rain. They prevent soil erosion, and keep soil from being washed away by heavy rains or blown by winds. They prevent moisture evaporation from the soil. Without plants the soil would have long since vanished.

15th century painting by Giovanni di Paolo *(right)* showing the expulsion of Adam and Eve from Paradise. God had created an idyllic garden for the man he had created, full of fruit-bearing trees, only one of which was forbidden. Having eaten from this tree Man was condemned to toil to find his food. Now there are deserts where the Garden of Eden is thought to have stood.

Once Upon a Time

A fossil of a tree ape dating from about 20 million years ago has recently been found in Kenya and was named Proconsul by scientists. From it came Southern Ape (Australopithecus) of Tanzania, believed to be the first mammal to walk upright. He used his hands and feet to climb trees in search of food and shelter, but a million years ago began to use primitive tools in his hunt for food. Half a million years later there were found near Peking in China the remains of a more advanced ape-man who was able to fashion his clothes from the vegetation and to make fires for warmth and for cooking food. During all this time, the Ice Age continued to spread downwards from the Arctic, driving the mammals further south where there was sufficient food for ape-man's needs.

Remains of earliest man had been found only in the warmer parts of the Old World until a century ago, when a skull was discovered by the Neander River in Germany. The oldest man to have been found in northerly latitudes, he lived just south of the ice some 50,000 years ago. With bears and the mammoth, Neanderthal man shared a cave for his home for the next 40,000 years, using their skins for clothes, their flesh for food. During this time our ancestor, Homo sapiens, was living in similar style in other parts of Europe. A recently discovered cave at Lascaux in France, whose walls are covered in beautifully executed drawings of animals, shows him to have been a person of great artistic ability. By then, plant life would be similar to that we know today. In colder parts there would be the fruits of woodland trees such as apples and sloes and the nuts of hazel, beech and oak. Brambles and rose hips, rich in vitamins, would be available in the autumn, while nuts could be stored during winter. In spring and summer, plants of the Cruciferae family would be available. Watercress grew in ponds and streams, the wild cabbage and many of those plants that today we call herbs, on wasteland. There would be edible fungi and seaweeds would be plentiful around the coast where beetroot and asparagus prevailed. On heathlands grew bilberries and bracken, whose young shoots in spring would be a welcome delicacy after a long winter, and the leaf of brooklime and chickweed. The dandelion, its leaves rich in vitamins and mineral salts, enjoys a wide distribution throughout the temperate regions, and nettles are equally widespread and nourishing. There would also be the rising sap of trees to tap. In addition there is archaeological evidence to show that the storage organs of water plants such as arrowhead and bulrush were especially appreciated.

The largest number of food plants available to early man were concentrated in that area known as the Fertile Crescent, an arc of land that runs for almost 3,000 kilometers, from northern Palestine and Syria to Iraq and the Persian Gulf. There, in the rich alluvial deposits washed up by the two mighty rivers, the Tigris and Euphrates, grew wheat and barley, melons and vines, all the foods that early man needed.

The First Book of Moses, called Genesis, tells us that God had said: "Behold, I have given you every herb bearing seed, which is upon the face of all the earth, and every tree, in which is the fruit of a tree-yielding seed; to you it shall be for meat" (food).

"And the Lord God planted a garden eastward in Eden; and there he put the man whom he had formed. And out of the ground made the Lord God to grow every tree that is pleasant to the sight, and good for food."

And from Adam's rib God created woman and forbade her to eat of the fruit of the tree in the midst of the garden to which exhortation she heeded not and gave some fruit to Adam.

Today, some 10,000 years later, exactly as told in the Book of Genesis, these same plants which provide food for man and which God had planted in the garden of Eden can be found growing wild 600 meters above the now arid plains. Deserts have replaced the fertile soil, because of the destruction of millions of trees, and the date palm alone provides the wandering tribes with most of their food.

It is along the valleys of the great rivers that most of the world's food supplies are to be found. Ten thousand years ago, the most progressive of the early civilizations, that of Egypt, prospered from the food produced in the silt of the Nile banks, which was able to sustain a population of perhaps 10 million. There grew cucumbers and melons, grapes and peaches, dates, barley and wheat, peas and broad beans, garlic and onions, lettuce and endive, olives and almonds.

From earliest times the watermelon has been prized in the east both as food and drink. Its season extended from mid-May until the year end when seeds were planted and a fresh crop raised, but large numbers of watermelon seeded themselves everywhere as they do today. The juice was pressed out and mixed with honey and taken as a sustaining drink; the flesh, rich in vitamins, was eaten while the seeds, which are removed before eating, can be roasted and sprinkled with salt to enjoy like salted almonds. Lentils, peas and broad beans grew on wasteland and were dried and made into potage or ground into flour. Highly nutritious, they supplemented figs and dates which were dried to consume during winter. Corn grew in abundance and could be stored for winter use and there were radishes, garlic and onions to sustain the working population.

Gradually, the foods most appreciated by the Egyptians and those of the Fertile Crescent were introduced into southern Europe, perhaps by soldiers of Alexander the Great who founded the Egyptian city which bears his name, and later by the Romans during their occupation of North Africa and Palestine.

The peoples of the New World found different foods available to them and in North America there were many which are also present in northern Europe and Asia. Bilberries and berberries (barberry) are found on heathlands and hawthorn, blackberry and elder covers much of the scrublands. The sugar maple provided early man with syrup for sweetening and from the bark of the red elm, a nourishing drink (slippery elm) was made.

In the deserts of the New World, the prickly pear, a cactus, provides wandering man with thirstquenching fruit. The rain forests of the Amazon yield the Brazil and cashew nut; sassafras and cocoa; mangosteen and avocado pear, among today's most valuable food crops.

Among the most widely distributed plants of edible value in the New World are those of the family Solanaceae which includes poisonous plants but also the tomato and eggplant, the cape gooseberry and potato. These plants of the temperate regions of South America are rich in vitamins and mineral salts. With dahlia, native of Mexico where its tuberous roots are among the most important items of food, they are now grown commercially throughout the temperate world. The potato is also tuberous and with its introduction into Europe during the 16th century, it became, with the cereals, the most important food crop of millions.

Through millions of years the creation of the world by a supreme Deity has continued, all in order, each period in its own time, though man is trying hard to destroy it.

THE BEGINNING OF PLANT LIFE ON EARTH

Plant life began in the seas at least 5,000 million years ago and consisted of nothing more than single-celled objects of microscopic form, swimming organisms which modern science might find difficult to differentiate as either plants or animals. The earliest record we have of plant life is that of the Cambrian age, named after Cambria, the Roman name for Wales, where rocks dating from more than 500 million years have been found. They contained the fossilized remains of trilobites and sea snails, also sponges and primitive seaweeds or algae, known as thallophytes. Nothing has been discovered of fossils dating from earlier times, possibly because the sea and land mass were inhabited only by bacteria and algae which were without any form of bone or shell structure which would fossilize.

Plant life consisted only of single-celled forms which would be almost invisible and which existed only in water. By the end of the pre-Cambrian period, the sea contained many living things important to modern man, including the seaweeds. They contained the green pigment, chlorophyll, which is present in all plants and enables them, with the help of sunlight, to perform a process known as photosynthesis which converts carbon dioxide from the air and water from the soil into starches and sugar to be used by man and animals as food. In addition, various other pigments such as carotene and xanthophyll may also be present, so that some algae are red, yellow or brown while others are found in all shades of green. Algae are present in ponds and pools and wherever there is moisture. They exist in damp soil and marshland, and float on the surface of water in the form

Cambrian fossil remains show a large variety of algae which supported many invertebrate animals. The green alga *(left)* is singlecelled, but forms long chains.

known as plankton. They are the basic food of fish and mammals (the whales) that inhabit fresh and salt water. Without algae in its many forms, there could be no higher animal life. Not only do animals feed on algae, but so do humans; seaweeds such as carrageen and laver provide nourishing soups and drinks.

From a red seaweed with dainty fern-like fronds, known as Gelidium, present in most of the world's sea masses, a gelatine-like substance called Agar is prepared. The fronds are dried and bleached and after the gelatine is extracted, it is dried and powdered. It is employed in making ice-cream and with sugar added, is a demulcent. It is also a culture medium for bacteria and tissue and is used in large quantities by hospitals and laboratories. Fungi also grow in it and experiments with the field mushroom and other edible fungi suggest it may be suitable for growing much of the world's food requirements in the not too distant future. Plankton in the form of tiny shrimps almost invisible to the naked eye, which abound in the Arctic seas, are also being harvested and processed for human consumption. With Gelidium, they would have been present during the pre-Cambrian period perhaps 5,000 million years ago.

Fungi, a separate group of Thallophytes, differ in that they contain no chlorophyll and hence no starch or sugar. They are thus unable to manufacture their own food but instead must exist an material made by decaying vegetable matter or, later, on the droppings of animals. A fungus forms mycelium, thread-like roots which live underground; the part that appears above ground is the fruiting body, formed by a fusion of the mycelium threads. Fungus requires no light to grow and it reproduces itself by spores produced on the gills beneath the cap.

The Cambrian period lasted until about 500 million years ago, when the Ordovician era began and lasted 100 million years. It too carries a Welsh name for it was named after a Celtic tribe inhabiting Wales early in history; rocks were first discovered there that showed fossilized objects of more advanced form including bivalves such as oysters and clams and large sea snails. Fossilized algae show seaweeds with branched fronds as seen today. On land appeared slime molds and the earliest fungi, living matter without chlorophyll.

One hundred million years later began the Devonian period when the first green plants appeared on land. It lasted for about 60 million years. It was perhaps the most important period in the development of plant and marine life, for the first vertebrates, animals with a backbone, appeared. These were lobe-finned fishes covered in large scales from which the "fringe-fins" evolved. They were fishes which walked. Tiny appendages had appeared in place of fins, like legs and feet which enabled them to leave the lakes and pools as they dried up and to move over land in search of food and water. They were the first amphibians or walking fishes, the first creatures to appear on dry land. They would find these simple ferns and other green plants that reproduced themselves by seed spores. Through their "fringe fins", the amphibians could take in air to a lung or bladder inside the body.

By the end of the Devonian period, the "fringe fins" began to remain for much of their life on dry land and laid their eggs there. The first reptiles had emerged, cold blooded creatures which did not need water for their survival, for the development of scales kept moisture in their body.

During the Devonian period, mosses and liverworts, more advanced forms of plant life, appeared. They produced stalked heads in both male and female forms and were the first plants to increase by reproduction. This is by means of spores which are released from the female capsule. Mosses are a further advancement, for, although difficult to detect with the naked eye, they have tiny stems and leaves. They are plants of damp places, the important sphagnum mosses growing entirely submerged.

As the land masses formed and mountain ranges became established, more land plants made their appearance. With the Carboniferous period came tree ferns, scale trees and giant horsetails, trees with fern-like leaves, produced at the top of tall unbranched stems which were often covered in hard scales. They reproduced themselves by spores which are present on the underside of the leaves, contained in small capsules. When the capsules ripen, the spores are released to alight on damp ground where new growth develops. Several of the horsetails survive from this period which, like the Devonian, lasted for about 50 million years when

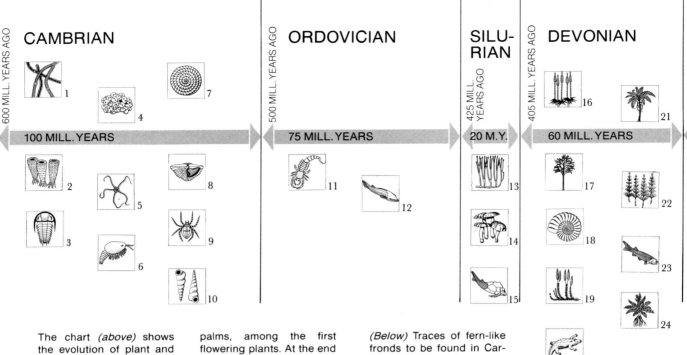

600 MILL. YEARS AGO

100 MILL. YEARS

ORDOVICIAN

500 MILL. YEARS AGO

75 MILL. YEARS

SILU-RIAN

425 MILL. YEARS AGO

20 M.Y.

DEVONIAN

405 MILL. YEARS AGO

60 MILL. YEARS

The chart *(above)* shows the evolution of plant and animal life on Earth, from the Cambrian period, from which fossils of the earliest forms of life have been found, to the arrival of the palms, among the first flowering plants. At the end of the Cretaceous period plant life was more or less as we know it today but man had yet to make his appearance.

(Below) Traces of fern-like fronds to be found in Carboniferous coal seams.

(Opposite) Ferns as they are today. The young shoots are edible.

the cyads first made their appearance. They were similar to the tree ferns but differed in that they were cone-bearing and were the first plants to bear pollen. Pollen of the male organ or catkin fertilized the female part, the ovary which is naked or uncovered in the case of the most primitive spermatophytes, the gymnosperms. In those plants of a higher order, the Angiospermes, flowering plants which came later, the ovules are enclosed.

The Carboniferous period saw the formation of the great coal deposits of North America, Britain and northern Europe which have provided fuel for industry for the past 150 years, during which time much of the natural plant life of the earth has been destroyed for industry and to grow large concentrations of food to feed the people employed in industry. The balance of nature has been upset. Insects necessary for pollination and for healthy plant life have been destroyed and food crops under cultivation have fallen prey to those harmful pests which continue to increase without predators to control them. There has arisen the need for spraying, with the result that food crops have become contaminated by chemicals which accumulate in the body to dangerous levels, causing most of the modern world's most troublesome diseases.

The Carboniferous period also saw the beginning of the giant reptiles which during the next

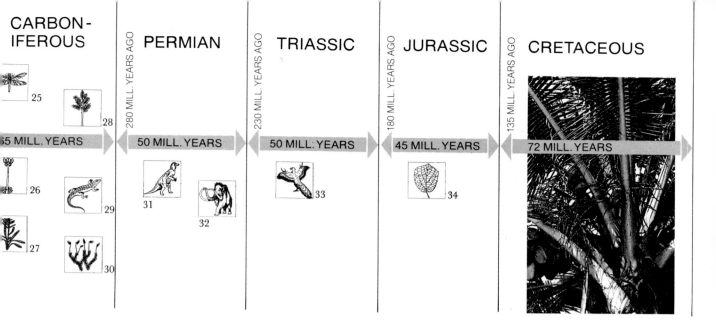

CARBON-IFEROUS	PERMIAN	TRIASSIC	JURASSIC	CRETACEOUS
	280 MILL. YEARS AGO	230 MILL. YEARS AGO	180 MILL. YEARS AGO	135 MILL. YEARS AGO
65 MILL. YEARS	50 MILL. YEARS	50 MILL. YEARS	45 MILL. YEARS	72 MILL. YEARS

1 BLUE-GREEN ALGAE
2 PORIFERA
3 TRILOBITA
4 ALGAE
5 ECHINODERMATA
6 CRUSTACEA
7 PROTOZOA
8 BRACHIOPODA
9 ARACHNOIDEA

10 GASTROPODA
11 EURYPTERIDA
12 AGNATHA
13 PSILOPHYTA
14 FUNGI
15 PLACODERMI
16 CALAMITES
17 LEPIDODENDRONS
18 AMMONITES

19 LYCOPSIDA
20 AMPHIBIA
21 PTERIDOPHYTA
22 ARTICULATAE
23 OSTEICHTHYES
24 FILICES
25 INSECTA
26 SIGILLARIA
27 CONIFERA

28 CORDAITES
29 REPTILIAE
30 BRYOPHYTA
31 DINOSAURIA
32 MAMMALIA
33 AVES
34 ANGIOSPERMAE

100 million years, during what is known as the Permian and Triassic periods, were to inhabit the earth. Some were carnivorous, living on each other, but among them some were plant eaters, the Diplodocus having an extended neck to enable it to reach the fresh green of the tree ferns and cyads. Several of the cyads are still with us, to be found in Australasia; the genus Encephalartos is present in tropical and South Africa, and there are four genera in Mexico and tropical South America. Fossilized fronds have been found in strata dating from the beginning of the Permian era. A number of the horsetails also persist in Australasia to this day. They rely on wind pollination for reproduction.

By the end of the Jurassic period, the broad outlines of the earth's surface as we know it today had taken shape. The great land masses of North America and Greenland had not then separated but the Atlantic Ocean had divided South America from Africa; Europe and Asia covered much of the earth's surface and Australia had become separated from the land mass of south-east Asia by the Indian Ocean.

Deserts and rain forests had formed over much of the earth's surface, which had cooled appreciably, causing much of the vegetation to die. As there was insufficient plant food for the dinosaurs

13

Some forms of animal life, such as the Archeopteryx *(right)*, one of the first birds, were destined to become extinct. Only three examples have been found. They have a long reptilian tail and claws at the end of the wings.

to feed upon, the millions that inhabited the earth, on land and in sea, perished.

From the cyads came the conifers, trees of more advanced form, and the palms which more nearly resembled the cyads in their habit and their scale-covered stems although they were true flowering plants.

Until now, insects were few. There were dragonflies and midges upon which they fed and which spent most of their time over water though they were not pollinators. Until the emergence of pollinating insects, flowering plants did not appear, pollination being by wind agency only. With conifers, pollen from male cones dispersed by the wind fertilized the egg cells in the ovules present on the scales of female cones, where they form seeds but are not enclosed in an ovary. With flowering plants, the Angiospermes, the ovary grows into fruit.

With their tiny leaf surface, the conifers were adapted to the changing climate, being well able to survive in the rarefied atmosphere of mountainous slopes at high altitudes and in the colder regions where, as today, they would have to tolerate long periods of snow and ice. As colder conditions prevailed, the number of conifers increased, until by the end of the Cretaceous period, they accounted for most tree life.

Grasses, too, had by now covered large parts of the land surface and were able to survive drought and arid conditions. Their flowers are naked or have a perianth reduced to scales, enclosed in scale-like bracts, and are borne in large inflorescences. They are pollinated by wind or are self-pollinated, relying on no other pollinating agent. They provided early man with seeds for food and since they first appeared on earth have been plants of the greatest economic importance. They yield cereals for flour; sugar cane; bamboos for food, and provide shelter for man and animals; while rice, which grows in water, feeds millions of Asiatic people. Their genera number about 500 and there are more than 4,000 species distributed over the earth's surface from the Arctic Circle to the tropics, mostly on dry ground. They vary in height from dwarf meadow grasses to bamboos which grow more than 10 ft (3 m) tall. With the grasses appeared sedges, of the family Cyperaceae with about 70 genera and 3,000 species, distributed throughout the earth as marsh-plants, growing in soils which are too acid to support the grasses. Many are plants of extreme hardiness and make up more than 10% of the vegetation of the Arctic Circle.

Among the first flowering plants to appear were the palms, mostly trees, often reaching a great height with an unbranched stem bearing a crown of leaves of considerable size. The stem is marked by rings which are the scale-like bases of dead leaves. In many respects they resemble the cyads but bear flowers instead of cones.

As the cone-bearing conifers mostly confined their habitat to the colder parts where pollinating insects are few, the palms appeared in the warmer parts of the world, for they are well adapted to withstand considerable warmth and with their vigorous rooting system, are able to search for every drop of moisture in the ground. They are plants of the desert and sandy coastlines, their stems often covered in thorns as protection from marauding animals. They are evergreen but after several years the leaves begin to decay and fall, leaving a broad sheathing base which later falls to the ground, leaving its mark on the stem. The flowers are borne in a large simple or compound spike, the males releasing large quantities of pollen which by wind agent fertilizes the females. However, as the flowers are sweetly scented and very conspicuous, those of a number of genera are entomophilous, i.e. are also pollinated by insects. It could be that the palms were the first plants on earth with scented flowers, for by the time of their appearance, insects were more numerous. They were also the earliest fruit-bearing plants, the flowers being replaced by a berry as with the date palm, or a drupe as with the coconut, one of the largest of all fruits, the plant being present on the

Other animals, of which the Eohippus (right) is an example, were to evolve further. Remains of this animal have been found in America and Europe. The Eohippus, which was about 38 cm in height, is the ancestor of the shire horse.

The ape-man, *Homo erectus erectus* or *Pithecanthropus*, of Java made primitive stone tools chipped only on one side and used sticks or clubs as weapons. He had a small wide

coasts of tropical Africa as well as the South Sea islands. There are more than 1200 species of palm and 140 genera. Most are found in Africa, South China and Japan, the islands of the Pacific and tropical America. Next to the grasses, they are plants of the greatest economic importance. Since man first walked on earth, the date palm has provided him with food and timber; the terminal buds of the cabbage palm yield a vegetable; and the oil palm yields oil for cooking.

Other flowering plants that appeared soon after the palms are those of the order Liliflorae which include Juncaceae, the rushes whose flowers are adapted for wind pollination; but in the closely related Liliaceae family, there is elaboration of the perianth, the flowers showing considerable size and color range and some have outstanding perfume to attract pollinating insects. The flowers also secrete nectar and must have been among the first plants to do so and to be visited by bees. With their nutritious honey, they prepared the way for the arrival of man on earth and his appearance in the garden of Eden.

Of the lily family, those plants of the genus Allium which includes the onion, garlic, leek and chive also provide man with valuable food. They are plants of temperate and cooler regions (chiefly the Near East) and have persisted for millions of years. They must have been among the most valuable of all food plants for early man, for they were able to store up food in their bulbous roots (really an extension of underground stems) which could be used in winter when other foods were scarce, exactly as today. Potatoes and dahlias with their tuberous roots are their counterpart in the New World.

By the end of the Cretaceous period which finished about 50 million years ago and which had lasted for almost 150 million years, most of the reptiles had perished and were being replaced by mammals, animals with warm bodies and with fur which covered them and which they needed for additional warmth as the earth cooled. They also breast-fed their young, hence their name which comes from the Latin mamma, the breast.

While tropical rain forests still persisted, large areas were covered in mountains and glaciers so that a large part of the earth's surface was now dry and cold. The mammals, some of which lived in

nose, a receding forehead, prominent jaws and no chin. According to Darwin's theory he was to develop into man (below).

holes in the ground for safety and greater warmth, varied in size from tiny shrews to enormous hoofed animals with head horns, which resembled the bison. The Eohippus, of about the size of a small dog, developed into the shire horse which was to become man's greatest asset in commercial food production during modern times until machines took over. In the trees lived small monkey-like animals called tarsioids. They were the first primates and during the next 50 million years became apes; then ape-man, who first walked upright on two legs.

The 251 most important edible wild plants

REFERENCE SECTION I

The following pages show the 251 most important edible wild plants, and describe their principal uses in the kitchen. The reader can discover which plants are most suitable for the various methods of preparation and preservation.

This selection of plants offers a fascinating overall picture of the incredible variety of foods provided by nature. Some readers may be surprised at how many wild plants it is actually possible to use in the kitchen, but those shown here are only a sample of more than a thousand edible wild plants.

It is now a well-known fact that most of the food we find in the shops has been deprived of its nutritional content for ation to generation. Besides constituting a major source of nutrition we tend to forget that, to almost the turn of the century, plants occupied a leading place in medicine in the form of herbal remedies. In recent years drugs have been produced that are less effective and more toxic than the original herbal medicine. Collecting wild food is an enjoyable activity which not only supplies us with nutritious and free food, but

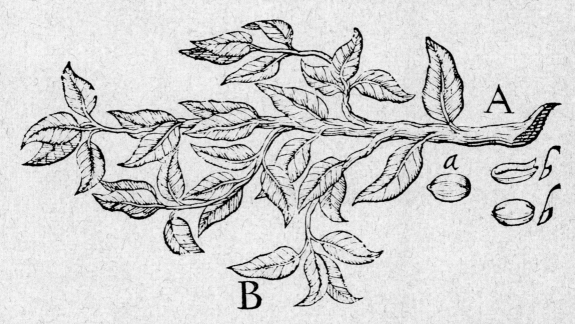

Opposite page:
A field of bear's garlic. Garlic has long been considered healthy and curative. It is in fact a kind of natural antibiotic and is widely used in herbal medicine, besides of course being an excellent flavoring.

the sake of presentation and preservation, and that the quality of what we eat is far more important than the quantity. We actually require a very small quantity of food to remain alive and healthy, but often lack the ability or the knowledge to select the substances most useful to us. Recent studies show that wild plants contain as much as twice the amount of protein, vitamins and minerals as do those cultivated for general consumption. All the elements we require can be obtained from wild foods.

The information provided here is based on the cumulative experience of the ages. Much of this wisdom was acquired the hard way, by trial and error, and has been handed down from gener-

brings us closer to a part of life which, in our concrete jungles, we tend to forget, and provides us with much needed physical exercise. Our fields, hedgerows, woods and mountains are crammed with trees and plants which are not only pleasing to the eyes but whose fruit, leaves and roots can be used in a variety of ways to nourish, delight and cure us. Care should be taken, however, not to destroy these gifts of nature but to take only what we need, leaving plants to develop or reproduce. One day we may have to depend on these foods for our survival.

Plant Lexicon Number	Plant Name	Principal Uses	Plant Lexicon Number	Plant Name	Principal Uses
4	AGRIMONY	Salads; drinks; wine making.	128	BALM	Salads; "teas."
211	ALEXANDERS	Salads; soups; sauces.	25	BAMBOO	Salads; vegetable.
127	ALFALFA	Sprouting seeds for salads.	137	BANANA	Dessert.
164	ALLSPICE	Pickles; chutneys; soups; sauces.	35	BARBERRY	Preserves; drinks.
10	ALMOND	Confectionery; salted for dessert.	103	BARLEY	Bread and cakes; drinks.
9	AMERICAN AMARANTH	Salads; vegetable.	143	BASIL	Salads; stuffings.
14	ANGELICA	Salads; to flavor stewed fruit and drinks.	33	BAUHINIA	Salads; stuffings.
165	ANISE	To flavor cakes and bread; soups and stews.	114	BAY LAUREL	Marinades; stuffings.
178	APRICOT	Dessert fruit fresh or canned.	84	BEECH	Flour for bread and cakes; salted.
198	ARROWHEAD	Salads; vegetable.	37	BEET	Vegetable; pickles.
126	ARROWROOT	Beverage.	132	BERGAMOT	Salads; "teas."
28	ASPARAGUS	Salads; vegetable.	19	BETELNUT PALM	Dessert.
120	ASPARAGUS PEA	Vegetable.	173	BISTORT	Vegetable; stuffings.
158	AVOCADO PEAR	Dessert; hors d'œuvres.	110	BITANG	Salads; vegetable.
			194	BLACKBERRY	Preserves; dessert.
			134	BLACK MULBERRY	Preserves.

Plant Lexicon Number	Plant Name	Principal Uses
209	BLACK MUSTARD	Condiment.
240	BLUEBERRY	Tarts and flans; preserves.
130	BOGBEAN	Salads; drinks.
38	BORAGE	Salads; drinks.
36	BRAZIL NUT	Dessert; confectionery.
23	BREAD FRUIT	Vegetable; for bread.
245	BROAD BEAN	Vegetable.
243	BROOKLIME	Salads; vegetable.
18	BURDOCK	Vegetable; drinks.
176	BURNET	Salads; drinks.
228	CACAO	Confectionery; drinks.
162	CAPE GOOSEBERRY	Dessert.
42	CAPER	Pickles; sauces.
47	CARAWAY	To flavor bread; cakes.
80	CARDAMOM	To flavor bread; curry powders; liqueurs.

Plant Lexicon Number	Plant Name	Principal Uses
50	CAROB	Sweetening; drinks.
52	CARRAGEEN MOSS	Vegetable; drinks.
75	CARROT	Vegetable.
11	CASHEW	Dessert; hors d'œuvres.
125	CASSAVA	Soups; stews; flour for bread.
54	CASSIA	Pickles; for seasoning.
91	CHECKERBERRY	Sauces; preserves; "teas."
16	CHERVIL	Sauces; in salads.
220	CHICKWEED	Salads; vegetable.
53	CHICORY	Salads; vegetable.
219	CHINESE ARTICHOKE	Vegetable.
6	CHIVE	Salads.
206	CHOCHO	Dessert; preserves.
58	COCONUT PALM	Confectionery; drinks.
59	COFFEE	Drinks, flavoring.

Plant Lexicon Number	Plant Name	Principal Uses
60	COLA	Drinks; flavoring.
39	COLEWORT	Vegetable.
88	COMMON ASH	Pickles.
30	COMMON ORACH	Vegetable.
195	COMMON SORREL	Salads; soups; stews.
62	CORIANDER	Flavoring soups; curries.
241	CORN SALAD	Salads; vegetable.
223	COSTMARY	Salads; soups and stews.
135	COWAGE	Vegetable.
177	COWSLIP	Salads; wine making.
123	CRAB APPLE	Preserves; drinks.
151	CRANBERRY	Preserves; drinks.
167	CUBEB	Condiment.
68	CUCUMBER	Salads; pickles.
70	CUMIN	Pickles; chutneys; curries.
136	CURRY LEAF TREE	Pickles; curries.

Plant Lexicon Number	Plant Name	Principal Uses
99	CURRY PLANT	Soups; stews; curries.
74	DAHLIA	Vegetable.
61	DALO	Vegetable.
225	DANDELION	Salads; wine making.
161	DATE PALM	Dessert; confectionery; jams and chutneys.
100	DAY LILY	Salads; pickles; sauces.
13	DILL	Sauces; stews; pickles.
189	DULSE	Vegetable; soups.
32	EARLY WINTER CRESS	Salads; vegetable.
212	EGGPLANT	Salads; vegetable.
201	ELDERBERRY	Pies and tarts; chutneys; preserves; wine making.
186	ENGLISH OAK	Flour for bread; cakes.
144	EVENING PRIMROSE	Salads; vegetable.
86	FENNEL	Salads; soups; sauces.
233	FENUGREEK	Salads; curries.

Plant Lexicon Number	Plant Name	Principal Uses	Plant Lexicon Number	Plant Name	Principal Uses
29	FERN	Salads; vegetable.	17	GROUND NUT	Preserves; salted; fritters.
116	FIELD CRESS	Salads; vegetable.	157	GUARANA	Drinks; "teas."
182	FIELD MUSHROOM	Vegetable; pickles.	183	GUAVA	Dessert; preserves; drinks.
85	FIG	Dessert; jams; chutneys.	65	HAWTHORN	Preserves; drinks.
7	GALANGAL	Soups and stews; flavoring.	63	HAZEL	Dessert; confectionery.
5	GARLIC	Flavoring.	113	HENBIT	Salads; vegetable; "teas."
93	GENTIAN	Beer; drinks.	104	HOP	Salads; beer.
226	GERMANDER	Beer; "teas."	20	HORSERADISH	Sauces.
250	GINGER	Preserves; flavoring.	43	HOT PEPPER	Pickles; sauces.
153	GINSENG	Flour for cakes; dessert.	92	HUCKLEBERRY	Pies; tarts; preserves.
73	GLOBE ARTICHOKE	Vegetable; salads.	105	HYSSOP	Soups; stews; stuffings.
51	GOOD-KING-HENRY	Salads; vegetable.	98	JERUSALEM ARTICHOKE	Vegetable.
191	GOOSEBERRY	Dessert; wine making.	251	JUJUBE	Confectionery; drinks.
247	GRAPE	Dessert; wine making.	109	JUNIPER	Flavoring sauces; drinks.
239	GREATER NETTLE	Vegetable.	76	KALINGA	Dessert; preserves; drinks.

Plant Lexicon Number	Plant Name	Principal Uses
168	KAVA	Pickles; curries; drinks.
89	KIE-KIE	Dessert; preserves.
44	LADY'S SMOCK	Salads; vegetable.
174	LAVER	Vegetable.
56	LEMON	Flavoring; drinks.
115	LENTIL	Soups; stews; bread.
230	LIME TREE	Syrup; ''teas''.
232	LING	Salads; confectionery; bread and cakes.
96	LIQUORICE	Beer; drinks.
119	LITCHEE	Dessert; preserves.
142	LOTUS LILY	To flavor bread, cakes.
118	LOVAGE	Salads; soups; stews.
94	MAIDENHAIR TREE	In bread; Chinese dishes.
124	MANGO	Dessert; chutney; preserves.
90	MANGOSTEEN	Dessert; chutney; preserves.

Plant Lexicon Number	Plant Name	Principal Uses
40	MARIGOLD	Soups; stews.
148	MARJORAM	Stuffings; to flavor sausage meat.
8	MARSH MALLOW	Salads; vegetable.
171	MAY APPLE	Dessert; preserves.
131	MEDLAR	Dessert; chutneys.
46	MELON TREE	Dessert; drinks.
111	MILK CAP	Vegetable.
27	MILKWEED	Vegetable.
216	MILLET	Vegetable; flour for bread.
133	MOREL	Vegetable.
213	NARANJILLA	Dessert, preserves; drinks.
31	OAT	Cakes; porrage.
101	OKRA	Salads; pickles; chutneys.
145	OLIVE	Cooking oil; pickles.
122	OREGON GRAPE	Tarts and flans; preserves.
207	ORPINE	Salads; pickles.

Plant Lexicon Number	Plant Name	Principal Uses	Plant Lexicon Number	Plant Name	Principal Uses
15	PAPAW	Dessert; drinks.	146	PRICKLY PEAR	Dessert; preserves.
106	PARAGUAY TEA	For "teas."	175	PURSLANE	Salads; pickles.
159	PARSLEY	Sauces; garnishing.	72	QUINCE	Dessert; preserves.
155	PASSION FRUIT	Dessert; preserves; drinks.	187	RADISH	Salads; hors d'œuvre.
170	PEA	Vegetable.	41	RAMPION	Salads; vegetable.
181	PEACH	Dessert; preserves.	238	RED ELM	Beverage.
185	PEAR	Dessert; preserves.	154	RED POPPY	Flavoring bread and cakes.
48	PECAN	Confectionery.	237	REED MACE	Salads; vegetable.
78	PERSIMMON	Preserves; puddings.	188	RHUBARB	Dessert; preserves; tarts and flans.
12	PINEAPPLE	Dessert; confectionery; preserves.	150	RICE	Vegetable; confectionery; flour.
166	PINE-NUT	Dessert; confectionery.	82	ROCKET	Salads; vegetable.
169	PISTACHIO	Dessert; confectionery.	193	ROSEMARY	Stuffings; for flavoring.
163	POKEWEED	Vegetable.	215	ROWAN	Preserves; drinks.
160	POLE BEAN	Vegetable.	196	RUE	Salads; for flavoring.
184	POMEGRANATE	Dessert; drinks.	67	SAFFRON	Flavoring cakes; pies.
214	POTATO	Vegetable; salads.	200	SAGE	Stuffings; drinks.

Plant Lexicon Number	Plant Name	Principal Uses	Plant Lexicon Number	Plant Name	Principal Uses
147	SALOP	Beverage.	152	SORREL TREE	Stuffings; soups; drinks.
231	SALSIFY	Vegetable.	95	SOYA BEAN	Vegetable; cooking oil; salads.
66	SAMPHIRE	Vegetable; pickles.	129	SPEARMINT	Sauces; confectionery; liqueurs.
202	SASSAFRAS	Flavoring; beer.	217	SPINACH	Vegetable.
203	SAVORY	Salads; stuffings.	69	SQUASH	Vegetable.
204	SCOLYMUS	Vegetable.	190	STAGHORN	Drinks.
205	SCORZONERA	Vegetable; sweetmeat.	149	STAR-OF-BETH-LEHEM	Vegetable.
57	SCURVY GRASS	Salads; beer.	87	STRAWBERRY	Dessert; preserves.
102	SEA BUCKTHORN	Sauces; preserves.	197	SUGAR CANE	Sweetening.
83	SEA HOLLY	Vegetable; in salads; sweetmeat.	1	SUGAR MAPLE	Sweetening.
64	SEAKALE	Vegetable.	97	SUNFLOWER	Vegetable oil.
199	SEA SPINACH	Vegetable; pickles.	49	SWEET CHESTNUT	Dessert; vegetable; sweetmeat.
208	SESAME	Confectionery; cooking oil.	139	SWEET CICELY	Salads; sweetmeat; drinks.
210	SKIRRET	Vegetable.	249	SWEET CORN	Vegetable; sweetmeat.
26	SNAKEROOT	Flavoring; sweetmeat.	107	SWEET POTATO	Vegetable; salads.
172	SOLOMON'S SEAL	Vegetable.	3	SWEET RUSH	Beer; sweetmeat.

Plant Lexicon Number	Plant Name	Principal Uses	Plant Lexicon Number	Plant Name	Principal Uses
221	TAMARIND	Preserves; drinks.	140	WATERCRESS	Salads; drinks.
222	TAMARISK	Sweetening.	55	WATERMELON	Dessert; drinks.
224	TANSY	Stuffings; sausage meat.	234	WHEAT	Bread and cakes.
22	TARRAGON	Sauces; stuffings.	24	WILD ARUM	Beverage.
34	TAWA	Tarts and flans; preserves.	179	WILD CHERRY	Preserves; tarts and flans.
227	TEA	Drinks.	112	WILD LETTUCE	Salads.
117	TEA TREE	Drinks.	156	WILD PARSNIP	Vegetable.
45	THISTLE	Vegetable.	180	WILD PLUM	Preserves; tarts and flans.
229	THYME	Stuffings; soups; stews.	244	WILD RAISIN	Preserves; chutney.
121	TOMATO	Salads; chutneys; soups.	192	WILD ROSE	Preserves; tarts and flans.
236	TRUFFLE	Stuffings; paté.	81	WILLOW HERB	Vegetable; "teas."
71	TURMERIC	Curries; flavoring.	21	WORMWOOD	Stuffings; beer; liqueurs.
242	VANILLA	Flavoring.	218	WOUNDWORT	Vegetable.
246	VIOLET	Confectionery; sweetening.	77	YAM	Vegetable; chutney.
108	WALNUT	Confectionery; pickles.	248	YUCCA	Vegetable.
79	WATER CHESTNUT	Salads; soups; canned.	2	ZAPODILLA	Dessert, preserves.

Die Eschen von Byrenbeumen holtz gebrandt/soll denen helffen/so erstrunen wöl=
len/wann sie Schwemme gessen haben/sagt Diosco.lib.j.cap.cxxvij.

Eusserlich.

Auß dem Birbeumen laub/desigleichen von den rauhen wilde Biren/macht man
nützliche fomenta oder Bäder/für die fürgehende Mütter vnd anders/2c.
So man die Byren kocht vnd pflasters weiß auff legt/stopffen sie/hefften auch
die wunden/sonderlich die wilden vnnd gebachnen.

Maulbeeren. Cap.xlvj.

Der blütig safft/waher der selbig erstmals
den Maulbeeren sey kommen/zeiget an die Fabel von Tisbe vnd Py=
ramo inn dem Poeten Ouidio/lib. iiij. Metamor. das befelhen wir de
Knaben in den Schülen. Vnd sprechen/dz man zweierley Maulbeer
findet/weiß vnd schwartz/dise beyde findet man im Etschland wachsen.
Aber auff dem Rheinstrom hatt man allein die schwartzen Maul=
beeren/die seind in der erst auch weiß/werden darnach rot/vñ zületst braüschwartz/
ein gantz safftigs Obs/das nicht lang weret.

Maulbeerbaum.

Vnder allen Obsbeu=
me ist der Maulbeerbaum
der klügest/dañ er laßt seine
junge bletter (welche gantz
rumpffecht seind) nicht ehe
herfür schlieffen/es seye daß
kein schädliche kelte od reyff
mehr dahinden/vnd dz hab
ich selbs war genomen. Vñ
die bletter werde gantz rüd/
rauch vñ vo farbe schwartz
grün/der baum würt sehr
groß/wachßt gern inn den
Höfen vnnd Stattgärten/
bey den Mawren/nicht ferr
von den Reben/bey den sel=
ben hat er sonderlich ein lust
zü wachsen/sagt Palladius
im Februario cap.xxv.
Etliche Lehrer schreiben/
man möge junge Maul=
beerbeum auch mit impf=
fen auffbringen/also/das
man die junge zweyg auff
Büchen stemm oder Rü=
sten holtz/Castanien vnnd
wilde Byrbeum impffe.
Vnnd so man die Maul=
beer zweyglein auff Bellen

vnnd Sarbaum impffet/sollen sie weisse Maulbeer tragen.

Left margin notes:
Erstrummen.
Fürgehende müt=ter.
Bauchstopffen.
Wunden hefften.
Ouidius.
Etschland.
Plin.lib.16. cap. 26.
Tempus.
Forma.
Cultura.
Weisse Maul=beer.

The Great Writers Bear Witness

The Chinese and Egyptians were already writing about the medicinal properties of plants four thousand years ago. The Ancient Greeks, the Romans and the Arabians developed herbal medicine, strongly influencing many mediaeval herbalists.

Opposite page:
A page from a German "Kreuterbuch" (herbal), 1557, illustrated by Hieronymus Bock, describes the properties of the mulberry tree. Originally from China, where it has been cultivated since earliest times for breeding silkworms, which feed on its leaves, this tree was introduced into Greece in the 4th century, but arrived in France and Italy only in the 14th century. In Europe the cultivation of the mulberry tree declined with that of the silk industry. The fruit, of which the black variety is the more flavorful, besides being excellent to eat, can also be used to make a gargle for the treatment of throat infections, while an infusion of the leaves lowers blood pressure.
The illustrations on the following pages are from the same "Kreuterbuch".

Through the centuries, many famous people have extolled the virtues of those fruits and vegetables which grew in the countryside, and their words have come down to us, for at least 2,000 years, from Roman times until the present day. Those same plants continue to provide man with nourishment and pleasure. Kings and queens, bishops and churchmen of all denominations, and writers of our first books on gardening and natural history have given us their observations of these wild foods and their recommendations on how to use them. We should do well to heed them, for they are as valuable as they were in ancient times.

Nicholas Monardes, a 16th century apothecary of Seville, was the first to describe the scorzonera, a Spanish vegetable of considerable delicacy still found there in the wild:
"The roots preserved in sugar as I have done often, to eat almost as delicate as eringoe roots." The latter are the roots of sea holly which when candied make a delicious sweetmeat.

Anise was widely used as a spice during the time of the Roman Empire, as Virgil reported:
"His chimney side could boast no gammon, salted well and dried and hook'd behind him but sufficient store of bundled anise, and a cheese it bore."

Of alexanders, Pliny wrote:
"It should be digged or gathered 'once or twice' (a year), at any time from the blowing of the western wind Favonius in February until the later Equinox in September be past."

Of fenugreek, Galen said:
"It should be eaten as lupins. Egyptians eat the seeds yet to this day as pulses or meat."

Grimm has told that in German mythology, Good-King-Henry was one of the plants appropriated to Heinz or Heinrich, the household *"goblin"* who helped the maids with their work in return for a bowl of cream and a dish of Good-King-Henry.

John Evelyn wrote that
"the tops may be eaten as asparagus, or sodden in pottage"
and said there was
"a white and red form much used in Spain and Italy."

In the Book of Job it says of the mallow:
"In times of want and famine, they cut up mallows by the bush."

The Frenchman De la Quintinye, who supervised the kitchen garden of Louis XIV and the vegetables served to him, wrote that
"the thick stalks of purslane that run to seed are good to pickle in salt and vinegar for winter salads."

Of the rampion, John Parkinson said:
"The roots may be eaten in salads or boiled and stewed with butter and oil and with some black pepper cast on them."

An Italian writer of the 14th century who was anonymous, named the plant samphire, Finocchio marino, and said it was
"of delightful smell and pleasant taste, and hath many fat and thick leaves, somewhat like those of the Purslane … of a spicie taste, with a certain saltness."

John Evelyn said that skirrets were *"so wholesome, nourishing and delicate"* that the Emperor Tiberius accepted them for tribute and had them regularly sent to him from Gelduba on the Rhine.

In ancient German mythology it was supposed to be unlucky to use cumin seed to bake bread, hence caraway is almost always used instead:
Bake no cumin in bread,
And God will help thee in thy need.

The Countess of Hainault, wrote from France to her daughter, Philippa, Queen of England (the letter is now in the British Museum) describing the many virtues of rosemary and exhorting her to plant some in the Royal Gardens:
"Take the flowers or else the leaves,"
she wrote:

Mushrooms of the woods *(right)* include *Cantharellus cibarius,* a yellow mushroom to be found at the foot of trees. It is delicious and much sought after.

The oak *(below)* was a sacred tree for the Gauls and has long been attributed with magical powers. The leaves and acorns have a high tannin content and can be used to treat all kinds of hemorrhages.

The stages of growth of the hazel tree during the four seasons. A tiny squirrel is seen harvesting nuts, in the same way as early man, who collected and stored nuts in his cave to survive the winter. The hazel nut is one of the most

nutritious nuts and, if gathered when fully mature, can be easily stored all winter. It is a tree of woods and hedgerows whose «lambstails» delight children in spring. .

"both is better to put in brews, in stews, and in baked meats and roast meats … It is a holy tree and with folk that have been just and rightful, gladly it groweth and thriveth."

Fortunatus, bishop of Poitiers in the 6th century, wrote:
"Of all the fragrant herbs, none can compare in nobleness with the purple violet"
and he described its perfume, beauty and its many culinary and medicinal uses.

Of the pumpkin, Walfred Strabo, who wrote the first Life of Charlemagne for the Emperor Charles III, said:
"It casts its tendrils far and wide … slim is the stem from which it hangs, but huge the bulk which it attains"
and he writes of its value as a vegetable with its many uses.

Bartholomeus Anglicus, in DE PROPRIETATIBUS RERUM, printed in Basle in 1470, which was a description of the natural history of the Middle Ages, extols the virtues of the apple tree in these words:
"It is a tree with good fruit and noble, and is gracious in sight and in taste … virtuous in medicine (good to eat). Some bear sourish fruit and hard, and some right sour, and some right sweet with a good savour and merry it is."

Of the Sompnour in the Prologue to the CANTERBURY TALES (1380), Geoffrey Chaucer said:
"Well loved be garlic, onions and the leek."

In the Clerk's Tale, speaking of Griseldis, Chaucer said:
"When she homeward came she would bring worts and other herbs time oft
to which she shredde and seeth for her living."

In William Langland's PIERS THE PLOUGHMAN (1394) the old lady says to the priest:
"I have pepper and piones and a pound of garlic, and a farthingworth of fennel seed for fasting days."
Langland told of how the people of the 14th century lived on
"Beans and baken apples brought in her lappe

cibolles (onions) and chervils and ripe cherries many."

William FitzHerbert, writing in 1544, said:
"It is necessary and also a pleasure to have peares and apples of diverse sorts. Also cherries, filberts, bullaces, damsons, plums, walnuts and such others."

In Shakespeare's HENRY IV, it was Falstaff who said of Prince Hal, later to become Henry V of England:
"He plays at quoits well; and eats conger and fennel."

In Thomas Fuller's ANTHEOLOGIA (1655), he writes of the marigold:
"We all know the many and sovereign virtues of its leaves, the herb general in all pottage";
hence it came to be called pot marigold.

Writing of lady's smock in THE WORLD OF WORDS (1696), Thomas Phillips said:

"It is a kind of water cress of whose virtue it partakes."

In BRITANNIAS PASTORALS, William Browne wrote of the nourishment to be obtained from thistles:
*"And for the chiefest cherisher she lent
The Royal thistles' milky nourishment."*

Michael Drayton, the 16th century poet, said in the POLYOLBION:
"Hyssop is a herb most prime."

The poet Alexander Pope observed:
*"For want of rest,
Lettuce and cowslip wine: probatum est."*

In William Shakespeare's A WINTER'S TALE, Perdita says:
*"Here's flowers for you:
Hot lavender, mints, savory, marjoram;
The marigold that goes to bed with the sun,
And with him rises weeping."*
And in the same play, the Clown asks:
"What am I to get for our sheep-shearing feast? I must have saffron to colour the warden pies …"
(These were pies made with wild or warden pears.)

John Parkinson, botanist to Charles I of England, wrote in 1629:
"Without doubt it (rue) is a most wholesome herb, although bitter and strong."
And of black mustard powder he said:
"With some vinegar added to make it liquid and running, it was served as a sauce both for fish and flesh."

The ROXBURGHE BALLADS of 16th century London described the plants sold in the streets:
*"Here's fine rosemary, sage and thyme,
Come buy my ground ivy.
Here's featherfew, gillyflowers and rue,
Come buy my knotted marjoram too!
Let none despise the merry, merry cries
Of famous London town."*

Of cress, Parkinson said the
"Dutchmen used to eat the cresses familiarly, with their butter and bread, as also stewed or boiled, either alone or with other herbs."

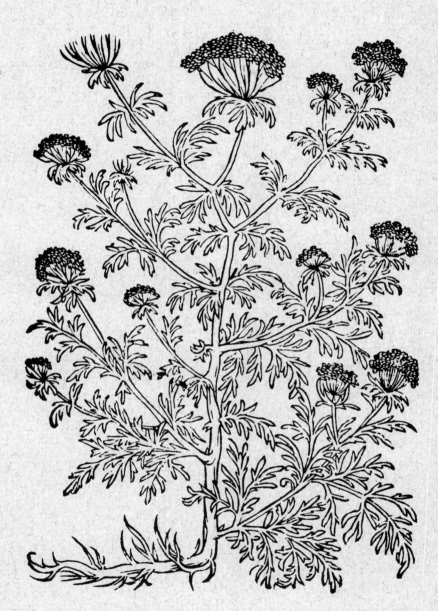

Of caraway, Parkinson said:
"The seed is much used to be put amongst baked fruit and into bread and cakes, to give them a relish (flavour)."

The German monk Walfred Strabo, writing in the 9th century from his monastery near the shores of Lake Constance, said:
"Amongst herbs, sage holds place of honour, of good scent it is and full of virtue."

Both the leaves and the seeds of wild fennel *(above)* can be eaten. The leaves are particularly good for breast-feeding mothers. The seeds, which have a strong flavor, are used as a spice in many parts of the world for flavoring meat, fish, cheese and bread.

29

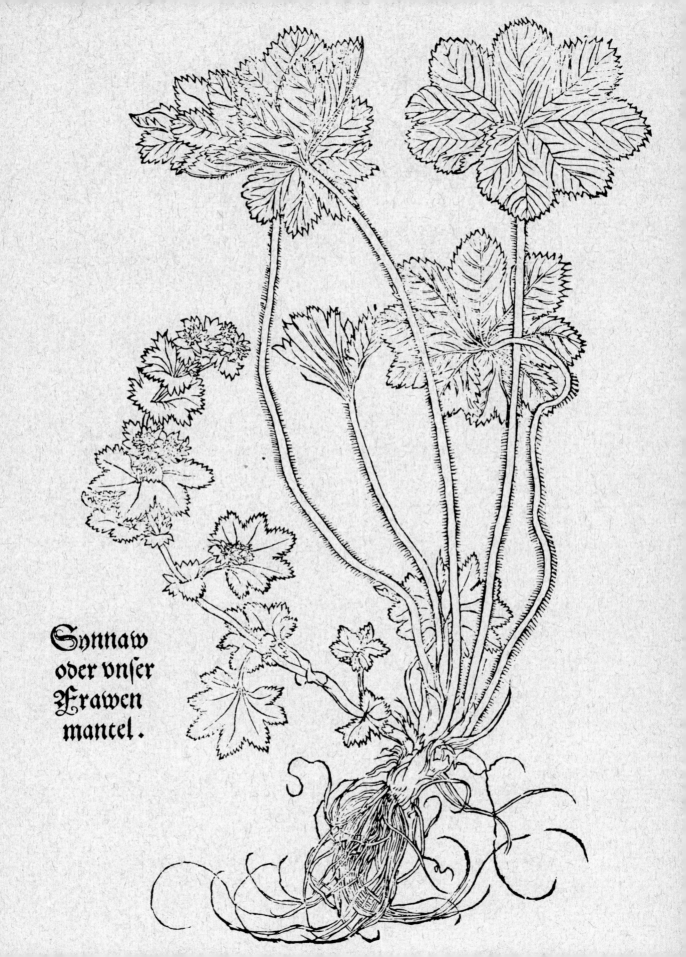

Synnaw
oder vnſer
Frawen
mantel.

And of mint he had this to say:
"I know as many mints as there are sparks from Vulcan's anvil."

The French garden writer of the 17th century De la Quintinye said that chervil gave a *"perfuming relish"* to all salads. And of Good-King-Henry he said:
"This humble plant will confer a more lasting duration on the memory of King Henry IV

The chestnut tree *(above)*. Chestnuts, which were the staple diet of country folk in many regions of Europe for months every year, are rich in minerals and vitamins and highly nutritious. With their spiky husk they resemble the hedgehog who is eating them.

(who discovered its valuable culinary properties) than the statue of bronze placed on the Port Neuf, though fenced with iron."

The 17th century writer John Evelyn spoke of *"gherkins muriated with the seeds of dill"* and of rampions that were more nourishing than radishes and had a pleasant nutty flavor.

Of sorrel, Evelyn said that the leaves
"sharpened the appetite ... and gave so grateful a quickness to a salad, supplying the want of oranges and lemons, that it should never be omitted."

The 16th century poet Edmund Spenser wrote in Muiopotmos of
"Sound savory and basil, hartie-hale,
Fat coleworts and comforting parsley,
Cold lettuce and refreshing rosemary."

Virgil, in the 2nd Eclogue of his Buco-lics, wrote:
"Thestilis, for mowers tir'd with parching heat, Garlic, wild thyme, strong smelling herbs doth beat."

The English herbalist John Gerard, who published his Herbal in 1597, wrote:
"We know lamb's lettuce as loblollie and it serves in winter as a good salad herb."
Of horseradish he said that
"stamped with a little vinegar is commonly used in Germany for sauce to eat fish and such like meats as we do mustard."

Antonius Musa, physician to the Emperor Augustus, published a work entirely on the virtues of wood betony.
"Sell your coat and buy betony,"
he wrote.

Pliny extolled the virtues of coriander and said that *"the best seed came from Egypt."*
He called borage Euphrosinum
"because it maketh a man merry and joyful"
and has told of the Emperor Tiberius having parsnips brought from the banks of the Rhine where the best grew wild.

The 17th century English herbalist Culpeper said of the burnet,
"two or three of the stalks and leaves put into wine are known to quicken the spirits, refresh and cheer the heart and drive away melancholy."
And of yellow gentian he wrote:
"The herb (root) steeped in wine, and the wine drunk, refreshes those who be weary with travelling."

The date palm, *Phoenix dactylifera*, is easily confused with its ancestor the wild date palm, *P. Sylvestris*, which provided early man with food and timber. Dates are an important food in North Africa and the Middle East, being rich in sugar, vitamins and fiber, besides being a principal export item. They also contain nicotinic acid. The artist had probably never seen this tree.

Anything green that grew
out of the mould,
Was an excellent herb
to our fathers of old.

RUDYARD KIPLING

I know a bank
where the wild thyme blows,
Where oxlips and the
nodding violet grows,
Quite over-canopied
with luscious woodbine,
With sweet musk-roses and
with eglantine.
There sleeps Titiana
sometime of the night
Lulled in these flowers with
dances and delight.

WILLIAM SHAKESPEARE
(A Midsummer Night's
Dream)

Woodcut by Brunfels from an ancient herbal *(above)* shows an early example of fruit tree grafting. Today many varieties of fruit can only be obtained by using this method.

LEXICON OF EDIBLE WILD PLANTS

Schlehendorn.
Prunus spinosa.

Fig.2.

Weinrose. Rosa rubiginosa.

Gem. Eberesc
Sorbus aucupa
Fig.5.

Fig.6. Gem. Himmbeere.
Rubus Jdaeus

Plant Lexicon

This section includes basic descriptions, primarily botanical in nature, of the 251 wild food plants that constitute the basic material of the book.

SELECTION CRITERIA FOR THE 251 PLANTS

• Priority was given to the most important and widely used food plants that grow in the wild.

• This was arrived at by consideration of the value of the plants to those tribes who

Pistachio, almond and pecan nuts *(above)*. These are nuts which grow in warm climates. Nuts, which are technically known as drupes, are a valuable source of protein.

Opposite page:
The chestnut tree in flower is a familiar sight in Europe. It provides us with delicious, energy-giving food.

Root crops such as the parsnip, carrot and turnip *(top right),* growing secretly underground, offer us another valuable source of nutrition.

continue to use them in various parts of the world and also the nutritional value of the plants.

• Certain plants that are edible but are used only for flavoring (some spices) and have little nutritional value are omitted, as are those plants now used only for medicinal purposes.

• Those plants are also omitted that, though at one time used for food, have poisonous qualities which make them dangerous to use without knowledge of special preparation techniques. Some poisonous plants, of course, have parts which are safe to use and these are included.

• Edible plants that are no longer found in the wild but are grown only under cultivation are also excluded. Destruction of the environment adds to their number each year.

• The geographical distribution of wild food plants has been considered, and the more important plants of one part of the world given preference over the less important food plants of other parts.

CONTENTS OF THE PLANT LEXICON

For each plant we provide the Latin name, common English names, the plant family to which it belongs, and indications of its geographical distribution. Classification of plants is by no means as simple as it was in the day of Linnaeus. An attempt has been made to adhere as closely as possible to his classification, but other systems of nomenclature are also used at times and the re-classification of plants goes on endlessly.

The text on each plant explains its name and gives a detailed account of its appearance and characteristics (growth, blooming, seed-bearing, and so on).

Indications of the plant's nutritional value and the parts that are edible are also given. The reader will find further information in Reference Sections I and III.

Indispensable to any plant description is, of course, an illustration that can guide us in recognizing and identifying the healing plant in its natural site. Particular care has been given to the selection of photographs, and of handpainted illustrations from herbal guidebooks of the last century, which are both accurate and beautiful.

HOW TO LOCATE A PLANT IN THE LEXICON

Because English common names of the plants are so unstandardized and variable, the 251 plants of the Lexicon have been arranged in alphabetical order according to their standard Latin names and each plant has been assigned a number from 1 to 251. This number can be located in the list of English names on the next two pages. The reader can look up the more common English names in this list; if a particular name is not listed, it can be sought in the English Plant Index at the end of the book, where a further range of alternative English names are given, with cross-references to their number in the Lexicon.

Index and Key of the Plant Lexicon

Common English names of the 251 plants are listed here with the number designating each plant's location in the Lexicon.

Each text in the Plant Lexicon includes the following information in its heading: Latin name, English name, plant familiy, plant number (in color box; in other reference sections, circled), and references to the plant's geographical distribution. The distribution is indicated in two lines. The first line gives the plant's original habitat or place of provenance; the second, in italics, indicates areas in which the plant has been introduced by man. The following abbreviations are used:

N	North
S	South
W	West
E	East
C	Central
–	parts of (Example: W–C Asia = western part of Central Asia)

Af	Africa
Am	America
Aus	Australia
Eur	Europe
NZ	New Zealand
Medit	Mediterranean Region

trop	tropical
subtrop	subtropical

A

4	AGRIMONY
211	ALEXANDERS
127	ALFALFA
164	ALLSPICE
10	ALMOND
9	AMERICAN AMARANTH
14	ANGELICA
165	ANISE
178	APRICOT
198	ARROWHEAD
126	ARROWROOT
28	ASPARAGUS
120	ASPARAGUS PEA
158	AVOCADO PEAR

B

128	BALM
25	BAMBOO
137	BANANA
35	BARBERRY
103	BARLEY
143	BASIL
33	BAUHINIA
114	BAY LAUREL
84	BEECH
37	BEET
132	BERGAMOT
19	BETELNUT PALM
173	BISTORT
110	BITANG
194	BLACKBERRY
134	BLACK MULBERRY
209	BLACK MUSTARD
240	BLUEBERRY
130	BOGBEAN
38	BORAGE
36	BRAZIL NUT
23	BREAD FRUIT
245	BROAD BEAN
243	BROOKLIME
18	BURDOCK
176	BURNET

C

228	CACAO
162	CAPE GOOSEBERRY
42	CAPER
47	CARAWAY
80	CARDAMOM
50	CAROB
52	CARRAGEEN MOSS
75	CARROT
11	CASHEW
125	CASSAVA
54	CASSIA
91	CHECKERBERRY
16	CHERVIL
220	CHICKWEED
53	CHICORY
219	CHINESE ARTICHOKE
6	CHIVE
206	CHOCHO
58	COCONUT PALM
59	COFFEE
60	COLA
39	COLEWORT
88	COMMON ASH
30	COMMON ORACH
195	COMMON SORREL
62	CORIANDER
241	CORN SALAD
223	COSTMARY
135	COWAGE
177	COWSLIP
123	CRAB APPLE
151	CRANBERRY
167	CUBEB
68	CUCUMBER
70	CUMIN
136	CURRY LEAF TREE
99	CURRY PLANT

D

74	DAHLIA
61	DALO
225	DANDELION
161	DATE PALM
100	DAY LILY
13	DILL
189	DULSE

E

32	EARLY WINTER CRESS
212	EGGPLANT
201	ELDERBERRY
186	ENGLISH OAK
144	EVENING PRIMROSE

F

86	FENNEL
233	FENUGREEK
29	FERN
116	FIELD CRESS
182	FIELD MUSHROOM
85	FIG

G

7	GALANGAL
5	GARLIC
93	GENTIAN
226	GERMANDER
250	GINGER
153	GINSENG
73	GLOBE ARTICHOKE
51	GOOD-KING-HENRY
191	GOOSEBERRY
247	GRAPE
239	GREATER NETTLE
17	GROUND NUT
157	GUARANA
183	GUAVA

H

65	HAWTHORN
63	HAZEL
113	HENBIT
104	HOP
20	HORSERADISH
43	HOT PEPPER
92	HUCKLEBERRY
105	HYSSOP

ACER SACCHARUM	ACHRAS ZAPOTA	ACORUS CALAMUS	AGRIMONIA EUPATORIA
SUGAR MAPLE	ZAPODILLA	SWEET RUSH	AGRIMONY
Aceraceae	Sapotaceae	Araceae	Rosaceae
1 E–N Am *North Temperate Zones*	**2** S Am, West Indies *Tropical America*	**3** SE Asia *Eur, E Af, E–N Am*	**4** Eur, N Af, W Asia *N Am*

Tree 60–100 ft (10–30 m)

The sugar maple is indigenous only to N. America. Several species are present in the Himalayas and in C. China and Japan; in the Balkans and Caucasus, with A. platanoides, in Scandinavia. The sugar maple grows erect rather than spreading and has white bark. The wood is also white, with a close grain. The leaves are long-stalked with palmate lobes; the flowers borne in a leafy inflorescence. Syrup (the sap) is tapped from the bark of several species; that obtained from trees growing on low lying ground yielding the largest quantity. Tapping is done early in spring before the sap rises, a deep notch being made in the stem 3–4 ft (1 m) above ground, through which the sap flows through a tube and into a bowl below. The flow is greatest by day, especially after a night's frost, and it continues for 6 weeks, to yield 20–30 gallons (72–98 liters) of the finest quality syrup.

Tree 60–100 ft (20–30 m)

A genus of a single species, native of tropical America and the West Indies, where it grows in rain forests and may reach a height of 100 ft (30 m). It has smooth bark and alternate, simple leathery leaves which are mostly borne in tufts at the end of short branches. The flowers appear solitary in the leaf axils and are erect at first, pendulous after fertilization. They are followed by plum-like fruits with hard, brittle brown skins like litchis which enclose a deliciously flavored yellow flesh in which the large nut-like seeds are enveloped. The tree yields an unflavored latex gum which is chewed by the people as an alternative to tobacco. It is known as chicle and is shipped to the United States, where it is flavored, usually with mint, and sold as chewing gum.

Perennial 4–5 ft (1.5–2 m)

A genus of a single species, native of N. temperate regions where it grows by the side of rivers and ponds. It is present throughout Europe and Asia, especially in the Himalayan valleys. The plant forms a thick creeping rhizome, covered with the old leaf scars, which may grow to 2 ft (60 cm) in length. The sword-like leaves are narrow and the flower is a pale brown spadix 3 in. (7.5 cm) long, made up of numerous tiny flowers. They appear in mid-summer but set no fruit. The roots are lifted in autumn, washed clean of soil and the small rootlets trimmed off. The root is brown, reddish inside and spongy with a sweet aromatic taste and smell. The roots should not be peeled as the scented oil ducts are on the outside. The dried root, powdered, is used to flavor cakes as an alternative to cinnamon.

Perennial 2 ft (50 cm)

A common plant of hedgerow and field, it is present in the British Isles and across C. Europe into W. Asia; also N. America. From its tall, elegant flower spikes it is called "church steeples" but its botanical name is derived from the Greek *argemone,* "shining", for it was thought that a decoction of the leaves, used for bathing the eyes, would remove cataract. A slender plant whose stems are covered with small soft hairs, the leaves are composed of 3–6 pairs of leaflets with toothed edges while the small, bright yellow flowers are borne in long racemes. It blooms during July and August. In the garden, plant about 16 in. (40 cm) apart in a light well drained soil. It is readily grown from seed, or by root division. A decoction of the plant is used as a gargle to ease a sore throat for it contains tannin and countrymen would use it as an astringent application for wounds.

ALLIUM SATIVUM	ALLIUM SCHOENOPRASUM	ALPINIA OFFICINARUM	ALTHAEA OFFICINALIS
GARLIC	CHIVE	GALANGAL	MARSH MALLOW
Alliaceae	Alliaceae	Zinziberaceae	Malvaceae
5 C Asia *Warm Temperate Zones*	**6** Eur, N+C+E Asia, N–N Am *Temperate Zones*	**7** SE Asia, Polynesia *Warm Temperate Zones*	**8** SE Eur *S+W Eur, W Asia, NE–N Am*

Perennial 8–10 in. (20–25 cm)

A genus of more than 450 species, spread over the temperate regions of Europe and Asia with onion, shallot and garlic native of Egypt, Ethiopia and the near east. A. sativum is the garlic which grows in sandy soil and is used in S. Europe and Asia to flavor stews and roast meats. A garlic bulb forms a number of white bulblets called cloves which overlap the base of the central stem, the cloves being flat on one side, rounded on the other. The leaves are flat, about 1 in. (2.5 cm) broad and 16 in. (40 cm) long. The base of the leaves forms the tunic of the bulb. Garlic stimulates the digestive juices and contains vitamins C and those of the B complex.
The broad-leaf garlic or ransom, A ursinum, is native of N. Europe where it grows in open woodlands. It has large lance-shaped leaves which are used to flavor fish dishes where garlic is not obtainable.

Perennial 10–14 in. (25–32 cm)

Chives have been found growing in all parts of Europe and Asia since earliest times and are endemic to large areas. They form clums of up to 100 or more bulbils from which arise thin hollow leaves that die down in winter and come again in spring. They are cut and used in summer after chopping into small pieces to sprinkle into omelettes, soups and stews or into salads. They contain oils of sulphur, vitamins A, B₃ and C and a high percentage of mineral salts. They have a delicate onion flavor. Chives are found in damp woodlands and by the side of streams. In spring they form small globular flowers of intense purple on 8 in. (20 cm) stems. They are increased by division of the roots in winter.

Perennial 3–4 ft (1.5 m)

The large genus Alpinia, indigenous to tropical S.E. Asia, was named in honor of the 17th century Italian botanist Prospero Alpino and its name, galangal, is from the Chinese meaning "mild ginger." The plant is common in Thailand and on the island of Java where it grows 4–5 ft (1.5 m) tall with long, narrow lanceolate leaves terminating in a long point and flowers borne in a terminal spike. They are white, veined with crimson, and are followed by small red fruits. But it is the rhizomatous root that is used in cooking, and has been exported to N. Europe for centuries. The fibrous reddish-brown cylindrical roots are cut when freshly lifted. They are about 2 in. (5 cm) long and are of finger thickness. They show the scars of old leaves. When dried they become dark brown and have the aromatic taste of ginger but in a milder form.

Perennial 3–4 ft (1 m)

A genus of 12 species, native of the British Isles, N. Europe and Siberia. Included in the genus is the common and musk mallow. Marsh mallow, found in damp woodlands and on river banks, makes a brached plant with lobed leaves 2–3 in. (5–7.5 cm) long which are downy on both sides. The plants contain mucilage and are demulcent. The pale pink flowers, about 1 in. (2.5 cm) across, are followed by flat round fruits known as "cheeses". The plant is distinguished from other mallows by the thick down on the stems. It takes its botanical name from the Greek *altho,* to cure, on account of its healing properties. The common mallow, A. sylvestris, with its ivy-shaped leaves and pinkish-purple flowers, is a plant of open woodlands and waste ground and can be used in the same way but is not nearly so effective.

AMARANTHUS RETROFLEXUS

AMERICAN AMARANTH

Amarantaceae

9 | N+S Am
Temperate Zones

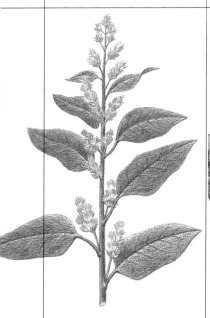

Annual 1−2 ft (30−40 cm)

It is closely related to the Chenopodium family which includes beet and samphire, both valuable food plants which are present in temperate parts. Amaranthus is mostly found in the warmer parts of America and India, several of the 50 species being edible plants. Included are A. polygonoides and A. oleraceus, both common garden weeds of India, the shoots and young leaves being highly nutritious. A. retroflexus, a common weed of N. America, is especially prevalent in the S.E. half of the country. It has alternate long-stalked pointed leaves. Like most of the family, they are pale green with a reddish tinge and bear their tiny greenish flowers in small spikes from the leaf axils. They are followed in autumn by small black seed pods which are used to flavor pickles.

AMYGDALUS COMMUNIS

ALMOND

Rosaceae

10 | W−C Asia, Medit
Warm Temperate Zones

Tree 15−18 ft (3−4 m)

It is native of Persia and Palestine, where it has survived in the hot arid land by its ability (like the red rose) to send down its roots deep into rock crevices by which it obtains moisture. In their native lands, the small twiggy deciduous trees bloom in January, the pale pink blossom appearing before the leaves. Seen from a distance it is as if the trees were covered in snow. The fruit is born on the young wood in short spurs. It is oval in shape with a downy green covering enclosing the shell which is yellow and pitted with holes. This protects the edible kernel – the nut which is narrow, elongated and pointed at one end. It is enclosed in an edible rough, brown skin. The sweet almond is that used in confectionery, to make almond paste and also to extract oil of almonds used in beauty preparations. The fruit of the bitter almond (var. amara) is now rarely used, for it has poisonous properties.

ANACARDIUM OCCIDENTALE

CASHEW

Anacardiaceae

11 | Trop Am
Tropical Af, SE Asia

Tree 40−60 ft (10−15 m)

This spreading tree is indigenous to tropical S. America, especially the Amazon Valley and the West Indies, where it is found in the rain forests and is also grown commercially. It has blunt alternate leaves and bears panicles of purple scented flowers followed by a yellow fleshy pear-shaped drupe, the juice of which is made into drinks and preserves. The fruit contains pectin and is used to set jams and jellies. It is also rich in vitamins C and B_2. At the end of the fruit is the kidney-shaped nut which from a distance has the appearance of a snail with its hard grey shell marked with circular stripes. The nuts are rich in protein and fat and highly nutritious. From the shell, cashew oil is extracted and from incisions made in the bark of the tree, a gum, similar to gum-arabic is obtained.

ANANAS COMOSUS

PINEAPPLE

Bromeliaceae

12 | Trop + subtrop Am
SE Asia, Hawaiian Isles

Perennial 3−4 ft (1 m)

The Order, comprising 50 genera and about 1000 species, is named in honor of Olaf Bromel, the Swedish botanist of the 17th century. Most are plants of the tropics of the New World. Now cultivated in Hawaii, the Philippines and Malaysia, A. comosus supplies the fruits for dessert throughout the world, both fresh and canned. The plant takes its name from the likeness of its fruits to pine-cones which at one time were known as pine-apples. The plant forms a short leafy stem about 3 ft (1 m) long, at the end of which is a terminal inflorescence which forms the fleshy fruit mass, the axis growing beyond, to form a tuft of jagged leaves at the top or crown of the fruit. Each fruit is about 12 in. (30 cm) long with a diameter of about 16 in. (40 cm). It ripens to a deep golden-orange, the skin being covered with tubercles in which the seeds are lodged. The plant is now rare in the wild.

ANETHUM GRAVEOLENS	ANGELICA ARCHANGELICA	ANNONA TRILOBA	ANTHRISCUS CEREFOLIUM
DILL	ANGELICA	PAPAW	CHERVIL
Umbelliferae	Umbelliferae	Annonaceae	Umbelliferae
13 SE Eur, SW Asia *Temperate Zones*	**14** N+E Eur, N Asia *N–N Am*	**15** S Asia *Trop + Warm Temperate Zones*	**16** C Eur, C Asia *N Am*

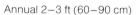

Annual or biennial
16 in. (40 cm)

It is native of all parts of Europe and W. Asia, and is present in meadows and on wasteland. It takes its botanical name from *cheiri* and *phyllum*, "that which rejoices the heart", because of its warming smell which resembles aniseed. It forms a low bushy plant, its hollow stems covered in silky hairs, its tripinnate leaves being pubescent on the underside. If growing in the garden, it should be treated as a biennial, seed being sown late in summer previous to the year in which it is required to produce its leaves. Roots must be boiled, since they can be mildly poisonous.

Annual 2–3 ft (60–90 cm)

A half-hardy annual, native of N. Africa and the Near East and grown commercially in the Iberian peninsula, Italy and Yugoslavia for its seeds which are used as a condiment and exported to all parts of the world. The plant was probably introduced into N. Europe by the Romans. Dioscorides wrote of its carminative qualities and it takes its name from the Saxon *dilla,* to lull, for the water, after steeping the seed overnight, was rubbed on women's breasts to lull babies to sleep after feeding. The plant has finely cut foliage, like fennel. In mid-summer it bears pale yellow flowers in flat heads followed by oval light brown seeds which are bitter and pungent. Long hours of sunshine are necessary to ripen the seed. Grown commercially, an acre will yield ⅓ ton of seed.

Perennial 5 ft (1.5 m)

It is distributed across N. Europe, including the Scandinavian countries, and is present in Iceland and Greenland. It differs from the more widely dispersed A. sylvestris in that its smooth stems are free of purple coloring and it is taller growing. The plant was given its name because it had so many uses that it was thought to be of heavenly origin. It is not fully perennial, as it usually dies after seeding for the first time in its third year, when it will reproduce itself by self-sown seedlings. The leaves, which are divided into numerous segments, measure 2–3 ft (60–90 cm) across and the umbels of tiny greenish-white flowers appear in July. The plant gives off a pleasant muscatel scent. It is a plant of wasteland rather than woodlands. It is a carminative and aids the digestion.

Tree, shrub 6–20 ft (1–6 m)

The genus, closely related to the magnolia, has large, entire leaves and solitary purple flowers, which appear in spring and are borne along the branches of the old wood. The shiny leaves have prominent veins and may grow up to 12 in. (30 m) long. They appear in clusters at the ends of the branches. A. squamosa, the custard apple, is distributed in the Canary Isles and along the N. African coast; A. triloba, the papaw, in the eastern United States from Nebraska to Florida. The trees are found in moist woodlands and ravines. The papaw has more pointed leaves than most of the family. The fragrant fruit is almost pear-shaped, 5–6 in. (12–15 cm) long and ripens to a golden brown. Three large seeds are embedded in the yellow, fleshy mass which tastes and looks like thick custard.

ARACHIS HYPOGAEA	ARCTIUM LAPPA	ARECA CATECHU	ARMORACIA RUSTICANA
GROUND NUT	BURDOCK	BETELNUT PALM	HORSERADISH
Leguminosae	Compositae	Arecaceae	Cruciferae
17 S Am *Tropical Zones*	**18** Eur, NW Asia *Temperate Zones*	**19** SE Asia, Polynesia, N Aus *Tropical Zones*	**20** Eur, Asia *Temperate Zones*

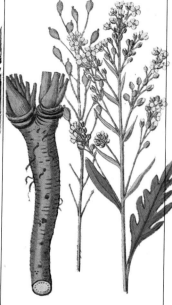

Perennial 8–10 in. (20–25 cm)

A genus of 15 species, mostly native of Brazil, the most important of which, the ground nut or peanut, is cultivated in tropical Africa, S.E. Asia and the southern USA. The ground nut forms a spreading plant which is present on wasteland, growing in sandy soil, but is now cultivated in the tropics everywhere. It has compound leaves divided into 5 pairs of opposite oblong leaflets and bears purple pea-like flowers. The flower stalks bend downwards, burying the young fruits which ripen underground. They produce 2 seeds or fruits, rather larger than pea-size, which are juicy and nut-like. They are white but covered in a thin brown outer skin and are enclosed in a tubular fibrous case about 1½ in. (4 cm) long, grey in color, and which is readily opened with the fingers. The plants also bear aerial flowers and fruits which are usually single-seeded.

Biennial 2–3 ft (60–90 cm)

A stoutly growing much branched plant with alternate, heart-shaped leaves, wavy at the edges and bearing purple thistle-like flowers in late summer. The plant is found on wasteland and at the side of fields throughout temperate Europe and Asia. Its reproduction is dependent on the burs being carried on the coats of browsing animals, for the sepal-like bracts have short hooks which cause the seed heads to adhere to anything rough. In this way the plant's reproduction is scattered over large areas. It takes its name from the Greek *arktos,* a bear, from the long hairs of the burs and the word bur itself is a corruption of bear. The plants are grown commercially in England and the USA and the dried roots boiled with those of the dandelion to make a nourishing beer. The roots are reputedly excellent as blood purifiers.

Tree 50–80 ft (15–20 m)

Native of Indonesia, the Solomon Isles, N. Australia and New Zealand, usually growing near the seashore and making tall, upright trees whose trunks show the scars of fallen leaves. A. dicksonii, present in the West Indies, is known as the cabbage palm, the terminal buds being eaten as cabbages. The leaves fold over to form a large white head, but damage to the tree may result. A. catechu produces the areca nut. The fruits are of walnut size, the brown nut being conical and rounded at the top, somewhat like an acorn. The aromatic nuts are cut into strips and rolled in betel leaves which are the leaves of piper betel. Hence their name betel nuts, though they are not those of the betel tree. Chewed by the natives, they are sustaining and have a narcotic effect.

Perennial 2 ft (60 cm)

It is present over the entire temperate world but is nowhere more plentiful than C. Europe. It was formerly known as coarse-radish, to distinguish it from the refined salad radish. Parkinson, botanist to Charles I of England, tells that its roots were found and mixed with vinegar to accompany meats for they contain the same bitter principle as mustard and are a help to their digestion. The plant is found on wasteland and by the side of fields. It has large, dark green leaves and in summer bears small white flowers in long spikes. It forms a large forked root which is lifted in autumn or when required, washed clean of soil and scraped. An infusion of the fresh root and mustard seed and a wineglassful taken daily is as beneficial to the kidneys as asparagus and barley-water.

ARTEMISIA ABSINTHIUM	ARTEMISIA DRACUNCULUS	ARTOCARPUS ALTILIS
WORMWOOD	TARRAGON	BREAD FRUIT

ARTEMISIA ABSINTHIUM

WORMWOOD

Compositae

21 C+S Eur, N Af, C Asia
Temperate Zones

ARTEMISIA DRACUNCULUS

TARRAGON

Compositae

22 Eur, N+E Asia
Warm Temperate Zones

ARTOCARPUS ALTILIS

BREAD FRUIT

Moraceae

23 SE Asia
Tropical Zones

Perennial 3–4 ft (1 m)

A plant of N. temperate regions including W. USA and the USSR, it has branching stems and smooth pointed lance-shaped leaves about 2 in. (5 cm) long, while the drooping white flowers are borne in flat heads in June and July but rarely open. The disc florets are tubular. It is the French tarragon, though native of C. Asia where it is found in hedgerows and on wasteland, that is the most used in cooking; the Russian variety, native of Siberia, has less flavor. Its botanic name is derived from its serpent or dragon-like roots. When grown in the garden, the plant requires a well drained, sandy soil and an open situation.

Propagation is by root division in autumn. After lifting and dividing, plant 20 in. (50 cm) apart. Also by cuttings removed in late summer and rooted in a cold frame; or in boxes covered with transparent polythene. The cuttings will root in 6 weeks but are not planted out until spring. The plant is rich in mineral salts and iodine, so necessary to keep the thyroid gland healthy and which is provided by few plants. The plant has many culinary uses. Tarragon vinegar makes the best "sauce tartare" to serve with fish. Tarragon can be frozen to use in winter.

Perennial 2–3 ft (60–90 cm)

A genus of more than 400 species native of Europe, Siberia and the USSR, Africa and the United States, found on waste ground everywhere and growing in sandy soil, often close to the sea. The plant forms woody stems which are covered in silky hairs, as are the leaves which are divided into numerous narrow segments, the entire plant having a grey-green fern-like appearance. The dull greenish-yellow flowers which appear late in summer are borne in leafy panicles. Large areas of Texas and Mexico are now covered with the plant, to form a jungle of interlacing stems which give the countryside a greyish hue. The closely related mugwort, A. vulgaris, grows to a similar height and has dark green leaves divided into numerous segments. Less bitter than wormwood, the dried leaves are used in stuffings and are used fresh in omelettes.

Tree 30–50 ft (10–15 m)

A genus of about 50 species native of India, S.E. Asia, the Fiji and other Pacific islands, being closely related to the fig and mulberry. The trees form a spreading crown with dark green leathery lobed leaves about 2 ft (60 cm) long with prominent yellow veins. The male flowers are borne in a club or truncheon-shaped spike 8–12 in. (20–30 cm) long, the females in large round heads in which the perianth-leaves and axis are united into a fleshy mass 6–8 in. (15–20 cm) in diameter. As they ripen, the green fruits turn yellow, then golden-brown. Then they are harvested and are boiled or roasted; or they are preserved underground in their hard covering, to be used as required. When baked they make a kind of bread, for they have a high starch content and inside have the "open" appearance of well-made bread. The fruits are highly nourishing.

Perennial 16 in. (40 cm)

It is the only species of a large family to grow in the British Isles (mostly south of the Thames) and is one of 12 species present in most European countries. The wild arum grows in hedgerows and copses, usually in shade. The glossy green leaves are net-veined and often spotted with brown or purple. It blooms in April and May, the greenish spathe being larger than the yellow spadix. As the spathe opens, a remarkable rise in temperature occurs, often reaching as much as 20° F (65° C) above the surrounding air, and it gives off an unpleasant smell. This is to attract midges (psychoda) for its pollination. Afterwards, the spadix loses heat and smell. The flowers are followed by a bunch of green berries which turn brilliant red. All parts are poisonous, but the roots are edible if peeled and soaked in water for several days before baking.

Perennial 6–20 ft (2–6 m)

A genus of 70 species, mostly native of the Himalayas, China and Japan. A. gigantea, the tallest growing, with canes reaching 20 ft (6 m) tall, is native of S. USA where it forms dense thickets in swamplands and on river banks. Bamboos grow in dense clumps, continually forming new shoots all around the plants. The leaves are long and narrow, bright green above, paler beneath with A. viridastriata showing yellow and green variations. They require a moist soil and prefer some shade. The young shoots produce stems up to 20 ft (6 m) long and when ripe become hard and woody. They are cut and marketed as bamboo canes to support garden plants. If removed when about 4 in. (10 cm) tall, when succulent and juicy, they are simmered until tender and served with melted butter to eat like asparagus; or when cold are sliced into salads. A. japonica is the species most widely planted in European gardens.

Perennial 10–12 in. (25–30 cm)

A genus distributed throughout N. temperate regions but mostly the New World, with creeping rhizomatous roots from which arise each year a pair of leaves, and on the rhizome, scale leaves. The deeply veined dark green leaves are heart-shaped and measure about 6 in. (15 cm) across. Early in summer a purple bell-shaped flower appears between the leaves on a short stem. The horizontal rhizome, which increases in length each year, is formed just below the surface and is easily lifted in late summer. The roots can be used as a substitute for tropical ginger. A volatile oil and a bitter principle obtained from the rhizomes is a tonic and stimulant if taken sparingly. A. canadense is found in moist woodlands across S. Canada and south from the Great Lakes to Alabama and Texas.

Perennial 3–4 ft (1 m)

A. syriaca, the common milkweed, is the most widely dispersed of more than 100 species most of which are native to the USA and Canada, where they grow from the Great Lakes south to Georgia. They are usually found on wasteland or by the side of fields. The plant grows 3–4 ft (1 m) tall with opposite leaves about 3 in. (7.5 cm) long, terminating to a point. The tiny fragrant greenish-purple flowers are borne through summer in small heads at the end of the stems. But it is the young shoots that are in demand, when about 6 in. (15 cm) tall and while the leaves still clasp the stems. They are cut and served like asparagus. Later, the young leaves can be boiled as a vegetable, as can the small heads of the shoots when in bud but before the flowers open. The plant will die down in winter but comes into new growth early in spring.

ASPARAGUS OFFICINALIS

ASPARAGUS

Liliaceae

28   C+S Eur, SW+N Asia
Warm Temperate Zones

ASPIDIUM FILIX-MAS

FERN

Filices

29   Eur, Asia, N Af, N+S Am
Temperate Zones

ATRIPLEX PATULA

COMMON ORACH

Chenopodiaceae

30   Eur, C Asia
Temperate Zones

Perennial 2—4 ft (60—100 cm)

After the bracken, Pteris aquilina, Aspidium filix-mas is the most widely distributed of all ferns, appreciated since earliest times for its culinary and medical uses. It has a creeping rootstock and grows best in a moist soil and semi-shade which are the conditions enjoyed by most ferns. Its fronds arise to a height of 3—4 ft (1 m) from the crown, which is a mass of brown fibers, the bases of the leaves in which the pinnae or leaflets are arranged alternately along the mid-rib. The pinnae decrease in size all the way along the fronds, which are about 6 in. (15 cm) wide at the base. The young shoots before the leaves unfold are removed when about 6 in. (15 cm) high and are eaten like asparagus. Pteris aquilina, the brake or bracken, the most widely distributed fern, is used in the same way. The roots contain starcha and are also used for food after roasting and remo-ving the outer skin. In New Zealand where it is plentiful, the root of Pteris esculenta was at one time a favorite food of the aborigines.

Perennial 3—4 ft (1 m)

One of 300 or more species of mostly maritime plants growing in dry, sandy soils and native of the Old World, especially the Mediterranean regions, with A. officinalis, an edible plant, a rare native of the British Isles, Denmark and Holland. It is now naturalized in parts of the New World, on wasteland and by the road-side throughout the USA and by the shores of the Great Lakes in Canada. From the rhizome-like roots arise the thick stems early in summer which are composed of greenish-purple overlapping leaf scales at the top. The spear-like shoots are cut from just below soil level, when about 8 in. (20 cm) tall, before they begin to form leaf or fern. The leaves are small, narrow and pointed, while the small greenish male and female flowers are borne on separate plants. They are fol-lowed by small red berries.

Annual 8 in. — 2 ft (20— 60 cm)

The common orach (A. patula), of the seashore and wastelands, is a member of a genus which is found as far apart as the Australian salt-plains and the shores of the Red Sea. A. patula grows up to 2 ft (60 cm) high with spreading branches and tri-angular leaves covered in reddish meal. The small greenish flowers are borne in late summer in leafy spikes. The mountain spinach is present throughout the N. temperate regions on moun-tainous slopes, usually close to the sea. It is widely culti-vated in France and Italy. It is more upright in growth than A. patula, with arrow-shaped leaves which are used fresh or from the freezer and made into a purée to accompany meats. The reddish coloring of the leaves disappears when cooking though it is attractive when the young leaves are included in salads. A. hostata is a more compact species with leaves that are less downy.

AVENA SATIVA	BARBAREA VERNA	BAUHINIA PURPUREA	BEILSCHMIEDA TAWA
OAT	EARLY WINTER CRESS	BAUHINIA	TAWA
Gramineae	Cruciferae	Leguminosae	Lauraceae
31 Eur, Asia *Temperate Zones*	**32** SW Eur *W Eur, N Am, S Af,* *E Asia, NZ*	**33** S+E Asia *Warm Temperate Zones*	**34** S Asia, N Aus, NZ *Australasia*

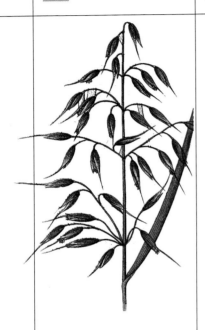

Annual or perennial 3—4 ft (1 m)

The oats, which number 70 species, are the hardiest of the grains. Distributed throughout the temperate world as far north as 70° N, they are the staple food of the people. A. sativa is the cultivated form of the wild oat, A. fatua, which is found in arable land or by the wayside. It has broad, rough leaves and spreading branched flower heads, each spikelet having a tuft of brown hairs. The heads dangle and rustle in the wind. A. sativa has smooth stems and rough lanceolate leaves. The pendulous spikelets are 2-flowered. A. strigosa is cultivated and found in the wild on the west coast of Ireland. It grows less tall and its flowers are without the tuft of brown hairs. Oat seeds when harvested are enclosed in a protective cover, a paleae which is removed by winnowing before used.

Perennial 8 in. (20 cm)

An evergreen plant, one of a genus of 20 species native of N. temperate regions and closely related to watercress, nasturtium and ladies smock. The plants are rich in sulphur compounds and mineral salts. They also contain vitamins C, A and E and should be included in salads all the year and to impart their appetizing bitterness to cream cheese sandwiches. The plant is known as land cress for it grows without running water. It is widespread in the E. United States and Canada, where it grows on wasteland and in hedgerows, anywhere that the plants are shaded from strong sunlight. It will stay green all year except during a severe winter. The plant grows 8 in. (20 cm) tall with shiny dark green leaves and stems. B. vulgaris comes later and has a more bitter taste. Like watercress, the stems and leaves can be put through a juicer to make a chlorophyll "cocktail."

Tree 12—20 ft (4—6 m)

A genus of 300 or more species distributed about the sub-tropical parts of the old world. A deciduous tree flowering in winter before (or after) the leaves, it is rare in nature, where it is usually found on sparse hillsides. It has smooth ash-grey bark and 2-lobed leaves as broad as they are long and covered with small hairs on the underside. Linnaeus named the genus in honor of the 16th century botanists Jean and Caspar Bauhin, remarking that "the 2-lobed leaves recall the noble pair of brothers." The flower stems and calyces are covered with a brown powdery pubescence, and the bark if cut exudes a sticky substance. The large purple flowers are borne in racemes at the ends of the branches and are vanilla-scented. The flowers are followed by laburnum-like seed pods often 12 in. (30 cm) long.

Tree 60—70 ft (18—20 m)

A genus of about 200 species, indigenous to the warmer parts of Australia and New Zealand, several of which form large forest trees. Two species, B. tawa and B. tarairi, are endemic to New Zealand, being especially prevalent in North Island where they grow in hilly parts. They have slender branches and narrow glossy leaves 4 in. (10 cm) long. The greenish-white flowers, which appear in November and December, are borne in large panicles and are followed by oval purple fruits like large damsons which make delicious preserves and tarts. B. tarairi is distinguished from B. tawa in that its twigs and leaf stalks are covered in rust-colored down. The fruits of this species, unless boiled first, and the water drained away, may act as a mild poison.

Perennial 6–8 ft (2 m)

One of a large genus of hard wooded plants distributed throughout the temperate regions of the world, especially the Himalayas, N. and S. America and N. Europe. The common barberry is a deciduous, thorny bush with toothed oval leaves and in May and June bears clusters of small yellow flowers. It is found in open woodlands and copses but as it acts as a "host" for rust disease of wheat, plants have been eradicated from most corn growing areas. The fruit is a ½ in. (1 cm) long oval, translucent red berry which when ripe makes a pleasant preserve to serve with meat and poultry for it has the slight acidity needed to correct any richness. The fruits contain vitamins A and C and act as a stimulant. The plant takes its name berberis from the Arabic for "a shell" on account of the high gloss of the leaves resembling the inside of a shell.

Tree 40–60 ft (12–20 m)

A genus of a single species, it is an evergreen tree native of tropical S. America, where it grows in the rain forests of the Amazon basin. The large entire leaves are alternately arranged and crowded at the ends of the branches. They are without stipules. The large bisexual flowers, borne in compound racemes, have 4–6 free sepals which persist in the fruit which is a drupe or large woody 3-sided capsule with sharp edges. It contains seeds or nuts which are white and oily and covered in a hard woody testa. At one end of the almost stone-hard capsule, a plug which is the hard calyx comes away readily when in contact with the warmth and moisture of the soil. The nuts are about 1½ in. (4 cm) long and slightly curved, rounded at one end. They are sweet and juicy, like coconut, and highly nutritious.

Annual or biennial 6–20 in. (15–50 cm)

No group of plants, with the exception of the onion and cabbage family, are of greater importance to mankind than this small genus of only 6 species. Native of the Mediterranean coastal areas of S. Europe and N. Africa, B. maritima grows in sandy marshlands. From it was evolved the garden beetroot, sugar beet and the mangold, fed to sheep and cattle. B. maritima grows about 20 in. (50 cm) tall, has large glossy leaves with crimson stems and veins, and bears leafy spikes of tiny green flowers. Its small fleshy root is hard and woody and unsuited to culinary use but roots of the garden beets from which it was evolved are cooked to a deep crimson and are sweet and fleshy, non-nitrogenous substances taking the form of sugar. When hot, the roots are served with white sauce to accompany meats or when cold are sliced into salads. As the roots can be stored during winter in boxes of sand, they are available all year. They are lifted at the end of summer when the leaves are screwed off. If cut off, the roots bleed.

From a white rooted beet, the valuable sugar beet was evolved. Yielding about 20% sugar from its roots, it has been cultivated world wide and especially in Europe as an alternative to cane sugar. The Dutch were the first to take up the crop commercially in the 1920's.

A beet of a different type is seakale beet, B. cicla, also known as silver beet or Swiss chard. It grows 20 in. (50 cm) tall and forms long unbranched stems about 1 in. (2.5 cm) wide which resemble celery. They are crisp and succulent and there are red and white stemmed varieties. The stems and leaves contain valuable mineral salts and vitamins and can be used in summer.

BORAGO OFFICINALIS

BORAGE

Boraginaceae

38 W Asia
Eur, N Am

BRASSICA OLERACEA

COLEWORT

Cruciferae

39 N+C Eur, Asia
Temperate Zones

Annual or biennial 20 in. (50 cm)

It is naturalized in most parts of Europe and the Near East, also N. America, but is of Mediterranean origin. All parts of the plant are covered in bulbous hairs which give it a grey appearance. Its name is derived from the Latin *burra,* rough hair. The pointed, wrinkled leaves are about 3 in. (7.5 cm) long with toothed margins, and throughout summer it bears its flowers in forked cymes. They are sky-blue with black anthers which fold over to form a unique central cone. The flowers are much visited by bees and can be candied like violets and used in confectionery, dipping them in a solution of gum arabic and rose water. The flowers can also be included in salads. Plants are found on wasteland and in hedgerows and because of their ability to revive and stimulate in warm weather, the leaves were eaten by working men. ''I borage, always brings courage'' was an old saying and modern science has substantiated this, for the plant is rich in manganese and potassium salts which the body needs to maintain its vigor and give it a sense of wellbeing. Propagation is from seed sown in July for the plants to mature the following year.

Annual or biennial 12–30 in. (30–90 cm)

A genus of important edible plants which includes the cabbage, cauliflower, kale, savoy and Brussels sprouts, each of them derived from B. oleracea, native of most parts of Europe and Asia and usually present on wasteland, often close to the sea. It is a hairless plant with a woody stem and fleshy leaves which fold over each other to form a head or heart. From it, the garden cabbage was evolved, some with a rounded, ball-like head, others (spring cabbages) with a pointed head. Garden cabbages are available all the year. Brussels sprouts, which grow 3 ft (90 cm) tall, form tight heads or sprouts in the axils of the leaves. Kale, its name a corruption of cole, is often called curly kale and has crinkled leaves formed all the way up the stem which grows 2 ft (60 cm) tall. It too crops all winter and is completely hardy, being a favorite vegetable of Scandinavian people. Also a derivative of the colewort is the savoy, a hardy plant of N. Italy which forms a large head like a cabbage and has crinkled leaves. This allows excess winter wet to drain away quickly, as otherwise the plants would decay. The cauliflower, with its fleshy white inflorescence, and the sprouting broccoli, which forms small cauliflower-like growths at the axils of the leaves, are suitable for pickling and for boiling to serve as a vegetable. Kohl rabi or cole rabi (from rapa, a turnip) is a cabbage with a swollen stem root which grows as large as a grapefruit and provides a delicious vegetable when boiled or stewed. It resembles the turnip, B. rapa. The hardy swede, known as rutabaga in the United States, forms a large yellow-fleshed root with a purple skin often weighing 6 lb. (2 kg) or more. It can be left in the ground all winter for the roots improve with frost.

CALENDULA OFFICINALIS

MARIGOLD

Compositae

 40 S Eur, N Af, W Asia
Temperate Zones

Annual 10–12 in.
(25–30 cm)

It is a plant of S. Europe but has been grown in gardens in all European countries since earliest times. Though annual, it will bloom for 12 months of the year, on the calends, the first day of each month, hence its botanical name. Its country name "golds" is a reference to its radiating golden petals similar to the rays of gold shown around the head of the Virgin, after whom it is named, in mediaeval paintings. The petals and young leaves are anti-scorbutic and are used sparingly in salads for they have a pungent, bitter taste. The marigold makes a bushy plant and has pale green oblong sessile leaves and flowers of about 2 in. (5 cm) in diameter with orange or yellow ray petals and brown disc florets.

CAMPANULA RAPUNCULUS

RAMPION

Campanulaceae

 41 Eur, N Af, SW+N Asia
Temperate Zones

Perennial 2–3 ft (60–90 cm)

Campanula rapunculus is a handsome unbranched member of the Campanula family, so many being attractive garden plants. Rampion is no exception, for in mid-summer it bears large slender panicles of purple or blue bell-shaped flowers on stems covered in stiff white hairs. The stem leaves are narrow and about 3 in. (7.5 cm) long. But it is the roots for which the plant is famed and from which it was named, from the Latin *rapa,* a turnip, for the roots grow as thick as a turnip and are white after cooking. Rampion is a plant of roadsides and hedgerows. There is a charming old Calabrian story of a maiden who dug up a rampion root and found a stairway leading down to a golden palace where lived her prince charming.

CAPPARIS SPINOSA

CAPER

Capparidaceae

42 S Eur, W Asia
Warm Temperate Zones

Perennial 3–4 ft (1 m)

A low growing trailing shrub with long slender stems, native of S. Europe where it grows on rocky slopes, usually near the sea. It is also cultivated commercially for its unopened flower buds which are the capers of hors d'œuvres and sauces. As long ago as the 15th century, Matthiolus recommended that the buds be eaten before a meal to stimulate the appetite and this is how they have since been used. The plant grows in dry places and has oval or heart-shaped leaves about 1 in. (2.5 cm) long and the same in width at the base where it joins the long foot-stalk. The stipules are represented by short spines. The large pale pink flowers are also held on long foot-stalks which arise from the axils of the leaves. The flowers appear in July and August.

CAPSICUM ANNUUM

HOT PEPPER

Solanaceae

 43 C+S Am
Torrid + Warm Temperate Zones

Annual or perennial 2–3 ft (60–90 cm)

A genus of 30 species native of S. and C. America, C. baccatum is the sweet pepper, a perennial which when grown under glass in colder climes is usually treated as an annual. It grows about 3 ft (90 cm) tall with thin, stems and grey-green long stalked leaves about 3 in. (7.5 cm) long, terminating to a point and covered with short down. The purple flowers are also long stalked and grow from the stem opposite to the leaf stems. They are replaced by large, conical fruits which are green at first but later turn bright red. The fruits have a glossy skin and a thick wall of flesh which encloses the seeds. C. annuum provides red peppers. The plant is of sturdier habit with smaller crinkled leaves and it bears single white flowers followed by long, red pointed fruits. The variety microcarpum has smaller leaves and fruits that yield paprika.

CARDAMINE PRATENSIS

LADY'S SMOCK

Cruciferae

44   N+C Eur
Temperate Zones

CARDUUS BENEDICTUS

THISTLE

Compositae

45   Medit, Asia
Temperate Zones

CARICA PAPAYA

MELON TREE

Caricaceae

46   C+N−S Am, C Am
Torrid Zones

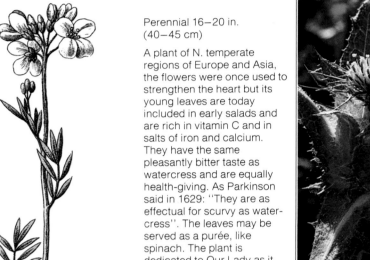

Perennial 16−20 in.
(40−45 cm)

A plant of N. temperate regions of Europe and Asia, the flowers were once used to strengthen the heart but its young leaves are today included in early salads and are rich in vitamin C and in salts of iron and calcium. They have the same pleasantly bitter taste as watercress and are equally health-giving. As Parkinson said in 1629: "They are as effectual for scurvy as watercress". The leaves may be served as a purée, like spinach. The plant is dedicated to Our Lady as it blooms at Lady-tide. It is in bloom from April to June when the cuckoo calls. It is an unbranched plant of damp meadows usually growing near rivers and streams, with dark green lanceolate leaves, and flowers borne in clusters. They are like pieces of metallic silver seen from a distance, being of an unusual silvery-mauve color, like the smocked dresses worn by ladies during mediaeval times. It is readily grown from seed sown in spring and is also propagated by root division in winter. It also reproduces itself from tiny plantlets which frequently appear on the leaves.

Annual or biennial 2 ft
(60 cm)

The thistle has since earliest times been the symbol of barren and ill-cultivated land, and yet the thistle ranks next to the rose in heraldic importance. It first appeared on the coinage of Scotland in 1474, during the reign of James III. In 1540 it was recognized in the founding of the Order of the Thistle. A slender much-branched plant, with long, narrow leaves with wavy edges ending in spines, it bears its yellow flowers in July and August. The flowers are enclosed by large leafy bracts covered in sharp spines. The plant grows in all parts of Europe and C. Asia, also the Near East, and may have received its name because it is one of more than 120 species of thistle growing in the Holy Land. Another is C. marianus, the milk thistle, also called Our Lady's thistle for its white leaf veins which tradition says are the milk of the Virgin.

Tree 25−30 ft (8 m)

One of a small genus of trees native of tropical and subtropical America with succulent stems and palmate leaves 2 ft (60 cm) across and arranged spirally at the top. The stem or trunk is hollow at the center and carries the marks of fallen leaf petioles. The flowers, formed in the axils of the leaf petioles, are followed by large fruits resembling melons, being round or oval and up to 12 in. (30 cm) in length. They are green at first, turning yellow, then orange as they ripen. The fruits are covered by a hard rind or skin and have a hollow cavity filled with blackish-brown seeds which when dried have a "hot" taste. The seeds are enclosed by a soft pulp (like melons) 2−3 in. (5−7.5 cm) thick which is also orange when ripe. It contains an enzyme, papain, similar to pepsin and which is used in medicine and in the drinks industry.

CARUM CARVI

CARAWAY

Umbelliferae

| 47 | Eur, C+N+W Asia
N Am |

CARYA ILLINOENSIS

PECAN

Juglandaceae

| 48 | E−N Am, E Asia
Temperate Zones |

CASTANEA VULGARIS

SWEET CHESTNUT

Fagaceae

| 49 | Medit, SW Asia
Temperate Zones |

CERATONIA SILIQUA

CAROB

Bignoniaceae

| 50 | Medit, SW Asia
Warm Temperate Zones |

Annual or biennial 2 ft (60 cm)

The plant takes its name from Caria in Asia Minor where it grows about rocky outcrops in full exposure of the sun, which is necessary for its seeds to ripen. It is grown commercially in all but the most northerly countries of Europe and Asia. The plant requires a long season to ripen its seeds and is usually grown as a biennial, sowing one year and fruiting the next. The plant has hollow stems and bi-pinnate leaves which have the same pungent scent as the seeds. The roots also have the same smell. They grow as large as parsnips. The white flowers are borne early in summer and are followed by the seeds which are oblong and curved, like the boats of ancient Egypt where the best seed is grown. It is used to flavor the liqueur Kummel. In early times, the seeds were roasted with apples to which they impart a "warm" aromatic scent.

Tree To 100 ft (30 m)

They are members of the walnut family (Juglans). C. illinoensis, the pecan, is deciduous and is one of the hickories which are used in furniture making. The trees grow on the banks of rivers and in woodlands, the bark being deeply grooved like the oak, the large compound leaves divided into numerous pairs of opposite leaflets, with a terminal leaflet. Like those of the walnut tree, the leaves emit an aromatic smell when handled. The catkins appear early in spring, the females producing oval nuts, pointed at one end and which are about 2 in. (5 cm) long. The nuts ripen in autumn when they fall and are collected. The kernel which is sweet and nutritious is easily removed from the shell which is thin. C. laciniosa is the big shell-bark hickory, distinguished by its more deeply toothed leaves and larger nuts which are enclosed in a round hull divided into 4 compartments. The flavor is superior to all other hickory nuts.

Tree 60−80 ft (16−22 m)

Native only of S. Europe and Asia Minor, it was introduced to Europe by the Romans who appreciated the food value of its nuts. Of all nuts it is the most farinaceous and least oily, hence it is easily digested. It makes a large erect tree with deeply grooved bark, and its long serrated leaves which turn brilliant gold in autumn, distinguish it from all forest trees. It is deciduous and long living, many trees being over 1000 years old. The flowers are borne in long catkins and the fruits or nuts are enclosed in 4 spiney valves. They hang in clusters, the green burs being covered with sharp spines which turn brown as they ripen and fall to the ground. When the valves open, the nuts are seen to be bedded in a soft felt-like case from which they are easily removed. The nuts are covered in a hard mahogany skin and are rounded on one side, flat on the other.

Tree 25−30 ft (7−8 m)

A spreading evergreen tree, indigenous to the E. Mediterranean where the sweet, mucilaginous pods when ripe are enjoyed as food both by man and animals. From the seeds, which were once used as standards of weight, the term "carat" which denotes weight of gold and diamonds was introduced into commerce. The shiny, pinnate leaves are like those of the ash, the small yellow flowers appearing solitary or in clusters on the previous year's wood. They are replaced by long flat pods, often 10 in. (25 cm) in length and 1 in. (2.5 cm) wide, containing pea-like seeds embedded in mucilaginous pulp, which is like thick syrup when fully ripe and very sweet. In the Near East, they are enjoyed as a delicacy. The trees grow on rocky outcrops and afford shade from the heat of the sun with their spreading branches.

CHENOPODIUM
BONUS-HENRICUS

GOOD—KING—HENRY

Chenopodiaceae

51 Eur, W Asia
Temperate Zones

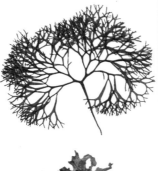

**Annual or perennial
4 in.—2 ft (10—60 cm)**

C. bonus-henricus was so named because it was thought to have as many virtues as Henry IV of France. It is perennial, to be found on wasteland and sand dunes. The genus includes the beet and spinach, the latter of which C. bonus-henricus so much resembles. The plant grows 12—20 in. (30—50 cm) tall with broad triangular leaves, tinted with red, and it bears its tiny flowers in leaf-less spikes throughout summer. It forms large quantities of basal leaves. They are equally rich in salts of iron and potassium and are free of much of the oxalicacid content of spinach. White goosefoot, C. album, an upright annual growing 1—3 ft (30—90 cm) tall, is so named because its wedgeshaped leaves resemble a goose's webbed foot. C. ambrosioides or wormseed is an annual, native of Mexico and S. America. The plant grows to 20 in. (50 cm) tall with toothed leaves covered with scent glands.

Perennial Prostrate

It is not a moss but a seaweed. Its much-branched fan-shaped fronds vary in color from green to brownish-purple but fade with exposure to air, so that, thrown up on the sea shore by heavy seas, it may be almost white. It is found in deep water and also grows in shallow rock pools on the sea shore. It is plentiful on both sides of the North Atlantic but especially on the West Coast of Ireland where its nourishing qualities have been appreciated since ear-liest times. Washed, soaked and boiled, its mucilage dis-solves to a thick paste or jelly which is wholesome and nourishing. It contains neither sugar nor starch but a large amount of gelatinous material and acts as an excellent demulcent. It is a valuable food for diabetics and to suf-ferers from pulmonary com-plaints.

**Perennial or annual 1—4 ft
(30—100 cm)**

Important commercial edible plants of a small genus indigenous to Europe and the Near East where they have been appreciated since ear-liest times. Cichorium is an ancient Egyptian word and its country name, succory, is from the Latin *succurrere*, to run under, for like the dan-delion, it forms a long tap root. Chicory is perennial with branched stems and clasping leaves. The bright blue flowers are borne in sessile heads. It is a plant of grass-lands, dying back late in autumn when the roots, as thick as a man's wrist, are carefully dug up, trimmed of all side growths and forced in

the dark, in a cellar or shed. C. endivia, the salad endive, grows like a crinkled lettuce. When the head has formed, the leaves are lightly tied together to blanch the hearts which are crisp and crunchy in autumn salads. It has an important vitamin A content.

CINNAMOMUM CASSIA	CITRULLUS VULGARIS	CITRUS LIMON
CASSIA	WATER MELON	LEMON
Lauraceae	Cucurbitaceae	Rutaceae

 54 S Asia / *S Am*

 55 NE Af, Trop Asia, Medit / *Warm Temperate Zones*

 56 SE Asia, China / *Warm Temperate Zones*

Tree or shrub 6−20 ft (2− 6 m)

A genus of 12 species, native of S. China and S. E. Asia but cultivated in warm places everywhere. The lime forms a small prickly tree with ovate leaves and bears small white flowers followed by yellowishgreen fruits about half the size of lemons. C. limon, the lemon, contains more vitamin C than any fruit and the skin contains the sunshine vitamin D. In the wild the tree grows on rocky ground and makes a small twiggy tree with spines, grey bark and ovate evergreen leaves. The pinkish-white flowers are borne in the leaf axils all the year and are followed by oval fruits, about 3 in. (7.5 cm) long with a nipple-shaped end. The fruits are green, ripening to bright yellow, and are rich in citric acid which gives them their sharp taste. C. medica is the citron, native of S. China and which reached N. India and Persia early in history. It makes a small tree with elliptical leaves and large purple-white flowers often 4 in. (10 cm) across. The fruits are twice as large as lemons and ripen to deep golden-green. The pulp is green and sour like lemons. C. paradisi (syn. C. maxima), the grapefruit, bears a globular fruit almost as large, and flattened at one end. It ripens to bright yellow and has a smooth skin. It grows 6−9 ft (2−3 m) tall with

Tree 10−30 ft (3−8 m)

These evergreen trees grow on rocky outcrops. Cassia or bastard cinnamon grows 10−12 ft (3−3.5 m) tall with broad reddish-green leaves, deeply grooved and broadly lanceolate and bearing small white flowers in terminal sprays. The undeveloped pea-size fruits are collected and dried and sold as ''cassie buds,'' somewhat like cloves, with a similar smell. Tree growth continues to arise from the rootstock over many years, but the finest bark is removed from 10−12 year old trees. It is grey and of the thickness of parchment, curling up as it dries in the sun. The pieces are about 4 in. (10 cm) by 10 in. (25 cm) and are tied in bundles. C. zeylonicum is a more vigorous tree with pale green leaves and bears pinkish flowers in loose panicles. The pronounced aromatic smell of its bark is due to eugenol.

Annual climbing or trailing to 20 ft (6 m)

A genus of 2 species native of Africa, tropical Asia and the Mediterranean and closely allied to Cucumis. It has been grown throughout S. Asia and in Egypt and Palestine since earliest times, being a staple food of the people. The fruit has a smooth skin (rind) and grows oval in shape, attaining a length of up to 20 in. (50 cm) and about 14 in. (35 cm) across. They may weigh up to 30 lb. (14 kg) and have reddish flesh and black seeds. The Nile delta provided the ancient Egyptians with large crops of watermelons, while the fruit was also grown along the Nile banks, in Jordan and India on the banks of the Ganges, for nowhere do they grow better than in the alluvial deposits left by flooding and where water is freely available. Watermelons reached S. Europe at an early date and were used by French and Italian cooks in fricassees and for baking.

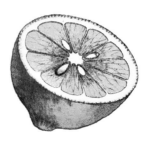

large glossy leaves and bears small white flowers. C. sinensis, the sweetorange, which is cultivated in Palestine as the Jaffa orange and around the Mediterranean, was first brought from China early in the 16th century by the Portugese traveller, Juan de Castro. The fruits are globular or oval with a thick rough skin or rind covered on the inside with white pith. The flesh is sweet and juicy and divided into segments each of which has a thin transparent skin which is edible. C. aurantium, the Seville orange, was introduced into Spain by the Moors in the 10th century. It grows 20 ft (6 m) tall with green shoots and elliptic leaves with a winged stalk and thorns. The scented white flowers are followed by orange fruits of the size of a tennis ball.

COCHLEARIA OFFICINALIS	COCOS NUCIFERA	COFFEA ARABICA	COLA ACUMINATA
SCURVY GRASS	COCONUT PALM	COFFEE	COLA
Cruciferae	Palmae	Rubiaceae	Sterculiaceae
57 C+N Eur, Asia, NE−N Am *Temperate Zones*	**58** Tropical + Subtropical Zones	**59** E Af, Arabia *Torrid Zones*	**60** C Af *S Am, Jamaica*

Annual or perennial 8−12 in. (20−30 cm)

Widespread by the coast, usually on cliffs and sand-dunes, C. officinalis is a hair-less perennial with long stalked spoon-shaped leaves, dark green and fleshy, and bears white or purple flowers in short racemes throughout summer. The fresh leaves included in salads are anti-scorbutic and contain large amounts of iron and pot-assium salts. Early in history, the plant was taken on long voyages by navigators, for it provided all that citrus fruits provide today. At one time the plant was used in the making of beer, and the juice mixed with that of oranges to make what was known as "spring drinks." The annual and almost prostrate form, C. danica, found on the coast of N. Europe, about sand-dunes and on rocks and cliffs, has heart-shaped leaves and is equally beneficial included in salads and to make blood purifying drinks.

Tree 80−100 ft (25−30 m)

Believed to be native of Poly-nesia, it grows close to the sea and forms an un-branched slightly curving trunk with the scars of fallen leaves all the way up the stem. At the apex is the head of large pinnate leaves each about 6 ft (nearly 2 m) long, the bud or cabbage at the top making a delicious vegetable. The flowers are borne in a dense infloresence and are followed by a large fruit with a hard shell enclosed in a fibrous pericarp. At the base of the shell are 3 circular marks, and inside, the shell is lined to a thickness of about half an inch (1 cm) with white edible flesh. Inside the flesh, the nut is filled with "milk", that from the unripe fruits being highly nutritious. Much of the world's vegetable fats which are made into mar-garines are obtained from the tree.

Tree 20−30 ft (6−8 m)

A genus of 25 species, mostly native of tropical Africa with C. arabica native of Abyssinia (Ethiopea) and introduced into S. Arabia early in the 15th century. The plant takes its name from Caffa, a province of Abyssinia where it was dis-covered and from which the alkoloid caffeine, contained in the seeds, is also named. The Dutch introduced the plant into the East Indies in the 17th century from where it reached Brazil. In 1652, the first coffee house opened in London, in George Yard, Lombard Street. C. arabica grows best in the shade of other trees, hence its great commercial value. It has smooth, glossy dark green leaves (which are also rich in caffeine) 6 in. (15 cm) long and bears its white scented flowers in clusters in the axils of the leaves. They are followed by fleshy red berries each containing two seeds, flat on one side, with a furrowed longitudinal line; the other side is convex.

Tree 30−40 ft (10−12 m)

A genus of 125 species, native of tropical Africa, chiefly Sierra Leone and the Congo. C. acuminata makes a broad-topped tree with leaves 7−8 in. (17−20 cm) long, pointed at each end. The yellow flowers spotted with purple are borne in short inflorescences and are fol-lowed by large seeds con-taining fleshy endosperm. The cola is closely related to the cocoa tree, the seeds or nuts yielding theobromin. The nuts are stripped of their shell and when exposed to the air become reddish-brown. They vary in size from 1 to 2 in. (2.5−5 cm) long and are juicy and succulent so that they can be cut into small pieces for chewing which the natives do while working in the forests. C. vera is a smaller tree and is found in more open places.

COLOCASIA ESCULENTA

DALO

Araceae

 61 SE Asia, Polynesia
Warm Temperate Zones

CORIANDRUM SATIVUM

CORIANDER

Umbelliferae

 62 S Eur, Asia, N Af
Temperate Zones

CORYLUS AVELLANA

HAZEL

Betulaceae

 63 C+S Eur, SW Asia
Temperate Zones

Perennial 18—20 in. (45—50 cm)

A genus of only 8 species, native of S.E. Asia and Polynesia where the species and their many varieties form an important part of the diet of the people and are cultivated on a large scale. They are herbaceous plants with a tuberous rhizome from which arise the arrow-headed leaves with waved edges, held at the end of thin black stems about 20 in. (50 cm) long. In the wild, the plants grow in marshland and on river banks, the leaves dying down late in the year to be replaced by new leaves in spring. Only one leaf is taken from each plant so as not to deprive the tubers of nourishment, and they are cooked in two waters, like the tubers, to remove any poisonous properties. C. esculenta is closely related to Caladium, an ornamental house plant with its red and green leaves, and to Cyrtosperma edule, which has smaller leaves than the dalo.

Annual 1—2 ft (30—60 cm)

A genus of only one species, native of the Mediterranean regions and named by Pliny from the Greek *koros,* a bug, for the seeds when unripe have an unpleasant fetid smell of bugs but when ripe have a sweet orange scent which they impart to junkets and blancmange. Pliny said the best seed came from Egypt and it does today. In the wild, the plant grows on wasteland and by the side of fields. It has rigid stems and dark green deeply divided leaves and bears its white flowers in umbels in late summer. They are followed by round pale yellow fruits which should not be harvested until ripe and they require long hours of sunlight to achieve this. Even so, the seeds are best kept for 6 months before using them for the longer they are kept, the better the flavor will be.

Tree or shrub 10—16 ft (3—5 m)

One of a genus of 8 species, closely related to the alder and birch. C. avellana forms a small twiggy tree or shrub and is present in hedgerows and woodlands, reproducing itself by suckers to form dense thickets. Its young branches are covered in reddish hairs and its leaves are heart-shaped with irregular edges. They are also covered in short hairs. Early in spring, the unstalked female flowers show crimsontipped pistils and are fertilized by the crooping catkins, produced at the ends of the previous year's shoots. After fertilization, the female flowers begin to grow away from the branch to form a new one, at the end of which the nuts are borne. The name filbert is derived from feuille, a leaf and bard, a beard, denoting the leafy involucre (the husk) which projects beyond the nut. In this way it is distinguished from the hazel or cob nut in which the husk is shorter than the nut. The nuts ripen in autumn when they change from green to yellow, then brown. Allow them to stay on the trees until fully ripe, for if gathered green they soon become moldy when stored. They have a high vitamin B1 (Thiamine) content which is needed to strengthen the heart and builds up the muscles of the body. Nuts also provide the body with choline and inositol which, together, lower cholesterol levels in the blood stream and prevent fats accumulating in the liver. Hazels grow well in partial shade and as the flowers are fertilized by wind, they crop better in drier parts. The plants provide the forked twigs used by water diviners to find underground supplies.

CRAMBE MARITIMA	CRATAEGUS MONOGYNA	CRITHMUM MARITIMUM
SEAKALE	HAWTHORN	SAMPHIRE
Cruciferae	Rosaceae	Umbelliferae

64 Eur, N Af, W Asia
Temperate Zones

65 N Am, Eur, Asia
North Temperate Zones

66 W Eur, Medit
Temperate Zones

Tree 20 ft (6 m)

The tree usually grows on rocky outcrops and in hedge-rows. It was long used to divide areas of land as it quickly formed an inpenetrable hedge. The stems are thorny, the small leaves being 3–5 lobed. The creamy white flowers, fishy scented due to the presence of trimethyle-mine, appear in May in large clusters and have only a single style so that the fruits are 1-seeded. They are small round and crimson when ripe in autumn. They are known as pixie pears and are a valuable source of vitamin C.
C. azarolus is the Azarole of W. Asia and the Near East with leaves that are wedge-shaped at the base and bearing large edible orange fruits; and C. aronia also bears large fleshy fruits which are crimson and used to make preserves.

Perennial 1–2 ft (30–60 cm)

This hairless perennial of coastal areas makes a large cabbage-like plant with thick fleshy leaves, grey-green and crinkled and in June and July bears large white flower heads followed by small round seedpods. It is the thong-like roots that are used for forcing and it is the lower part of the stem that is eaten when blanched. Those living close to the seashore, where the plant is mostly found, lift the roots in autumn as the plant dies down and after removing the foliage. The smaller thongs are removed with a sharp knife and in spring are re-planted in beds of well drained soil, with the top of each thong 1 in. (2.5 cm) below soil level and 16 in. (40 cm) apart. Plants in the wild can be forced where they grow by covering them in spring with a deep box as soon as growth begins.

Perennial 8–12 in. (20–30 cm)

It grows on cliffs and rocky outcrops in sight of the sea, often in the most inaccessible places, which makes its gathering a dangerous occupation, to which Shakespeare alludes in King Lear. The plant's name is a corruption of Saint Peter, patron saint of fishermen. Samphire is a pale green, succulent, much-branched herb, the smooth fleshy leaves divided into numerous narrow leaflets. The plant has woody stems at the base. During summer it bears its tiny green flowers in umbels and they are followed by small oval fruits which, like the leaves, are gathered fresh and boiled with malt or tarragon vinegar and spices to make a delicious aromatic pickle. The whole plant is pleasantly aromatic. At one time it was sold from barrows in the streets of London for pickling.

CROCUS SATIVUS

SAFFRON

Iridaceae

67   S Eur, W Asia
Warm Temperate Zones

CUCUMIS SATIVUS

CUCUMBER

Cucurbitaceae

68   Af, S+C Asia
Temperate Zones

Corm-bearing perennial
3–4 in. (7.5–10 cm)

It ranks with maize and flax as one of nature's oldest plants still in commercial use, being employed to color and flavor food for which purpose the dried stigma has been used since pre-Christian times. It requires the stigmas of more than 4000 flowers to make an ounce of saffron and they are collected soon after the flowers open. The plants can be grown commercially only where they receive long hours of sunshine to ripen the corms, otherwise they produce few flowers. They must also be grown in areas of low rainfall, for once the flower opens, it will not close up again, not even in dull, wet weather or at night. The plant forms a round, rather than a flat, corm like other crocus species from which arise 10 or 12 narrow grey-green leaves a month before the flower appears, both leaves and flower being protected by scale or sheathing leaves at the base. The dried grains of the stigma are bright yellow and are used to add flavor and color to bread and cakes. Henry VIII's tunic at the Field of the Cloth of Gold was dyed with saffron. It was also used for the gold of mediaeval manuscripts.

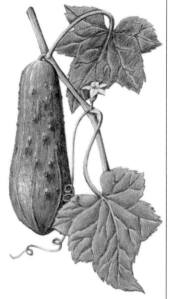

Annual climbing or trailing to 10 ft (3 m)

A genus of 25 species native of Africa, with C.sativus of S.W. Asia but possibly introduced from N. Africa. The common cucumber climbs by tendrils but is often grown on the flat where in Palestine and Egypt it has been grown as a field crop for thousands of years. In these parts the plant has been an important item of food since earliest times. C.sativus has fleshy stems covered in short hairs and long-stalked palmately-lobed leaves. From the nodes is formed a leaf, single flower and a tendril on the upper side of the leaf base. A branch or extension shoot is also formed. The fruits grow to 16 in. (40 cm) long and become straight and pointed at one end. They may be 4 in. (10 cm) in diameter. They are dark green with soft pale green flesh and covered with a hard rough rind with blunt spines. The soft white seeds, pointed at both ends, are enclosed in the flesh. The skin of young fruits is edible but is removed from older fruits before use. Ridge cucumbers are the hardiest and can be grown outdoors in N. Europe. C. chate is the round cucumber, with melon-like flesh and curved fruits. All parts of the plant are covered in soft downy hairs. C. melo is the melon, a native of S.W. Asia and Africa where, like the cucumber, it has been an important item of food since earliest times. In the wild it grows in sandy soil on waste ground and in hedgerows climbing up other plants by its tendrils. It has large palmately-lobed leaves and bears male and female flowers on the same plant. The common melon is also the musk melon. The fruit may be of grapefruit size or as big as a human head and round, the yellow skin or rind being too hard to eat. It is filled with juicy orange flesh which encloses the mass of seeds at the center and which are removed before the fruits are eaten.

C. cantalupensis is the cantaloup, named after the Italian town to where it was introduced in the 16th century and where it was first grown in Europe. It is native of Persia and the Caucasus and is the richest of all fruits in its vitamin A and next to the citrus fruits in its vitamin C content. C. dudaim is also native of Persia and is the dudaim or pocket melon which produces a small globular fruit with an orange rind spotted with green. Its pale green flesh has a musky flavor.

CUCURBITA PEPO

SQUASH

Cucurbitaceae

69 C Af, S Asia
Torrid + Warm Temperate Zones

A genus of 15 species indigenous to tropical S. America and the warmer parts of N. America, C. maxima, the winter squash, is native of tropical Africa and C. moschata, the crookneck squash, of S. Asia. They come in all sizes and shapes. Italian zucchini marrows or courgettes can be the size of small cucumbers, and banana and pearshaped squashes and pumpkins may attain a weight of 80 lb. (36 kg) or more. There are marrows that grow large and cylindrical, reaching 20 in. (50 cm) long and 16 in. (40 cm) in circumference. The plants have large triangular leaves and climb or trail by tendrils making rapid growth. The large bell-shaped flowers are bright yellow, and male and female appear on the same plant. Squashes are used as a vegetable when ripe, cutting away the hard skin and cutting the flesh into strips.

CUMINUM CYMINUM

CUMIN

Umbelliferae

70 S Eur, W Asia, N Af
Warm Temperate Zones

Annual 1−2 ft (30−60 cm)

It is native of the E. Mediterranean, E. Africa and the Black Sea region and has been grown commercially in Egypt, Ethiopia and Palestine since earliest times, the seeds being mixed with flour to bake into bread and cakes. Elsewhere, caraway is now more popular and the use of cumin in Europe has diminished over the years though it is an important ingredient in curry powders and to make chutney. In its native lands, the plant grows on waste ground and by the wayside, usually in an open situation and in sandy soil. The plant branches from the base and has finely divided leaves, like those of fennel but smaller. It bears umbels of tiny reddish-white flowers followed by aromatic seeds which resemble caraway in taste and appearance but are straight and lighter in color.

CURCUMA LONGA

TURMERIC

Zingiberaceae

71 S Asia
Torrid Zones

Perennial 3−4 ft (1 m)

A genus of 7 species with tuberous roots from which arise long sheath-stemmed elliptical leaves reaching a height of 1 m above the roots, which resemble those of ginger. They are yellow, the plant taking its name from the Arabic *karkum,* saffron, the stigma being of similar color. The flowers are also yellow and appear soon after the leaves early in the season. C. longa is found on rocky hillsides. The rhizomes are cylindrical and vary in size from 1 to 4 in. (2−10 cm). They are pale yellow, tapering at one end with a rough appearance. Pieces are planted on the top of ridges. The seeds are also dried and ground and have the same smell. The roots of old plants become hard and woody and push themselves out of the ground.

CYDONIA OBLONGA

QUINCE

Rosaceae

72 W Asia, Eur, N Am
North Temperate Zones

Tree 12−16 ft (3−4 m)

Native of Cydonia, a city of ancient Crete, it makes a small twisted tree and is usually found growing in heavy clay soils, in hedgerows and open woodlands. The trees are completely hardy and grow to a great age. But although the fruit makes excellent preserves, it needs plenty of sun to ripen well and in gardens there are better fruits to grow against a sunny wall. The quince is now grown commercially as a rootstock for pears rather than for its fruit but it needs no pruning and suffers neither from pest nor disease. The quince bears large solitary pinkish-white flowers and is self-fertile. It is propagated from suckers which grow from the base around the trunk. It begins to fruit when 5 years old, the pear-shaped fruits being gathered late in autumn when turning yellow.

CYNARA SCOLYMUS	DAHLIA OFFICINALIS	DAUCUS CAROTA	DILLENIA INDICA
GLOBE ARTICHOKE	DAHLIA	CARROT	KALINGA
Compositae	Compositae	Umbelliferae	Dilleniaceae
73 S Eur *Warm Temperate Zones*	**74** C Am *Warm Temperate Zones*	**75** Eur, SW+N Asia, N Af *Temperate Zones*	**76** SE Asia, N Aus, Polynesia *Tropical Zones*

Annual or biennial 16—30 in. (40—75 cm)

A small genus present in hedgerows and on waste ground usually of a chalky nature. It has stiff stems and 3-pinnate fern-like leaves. In mid-summer it bears flat heads of dingy white flowers followed by flattened oval fruits with hooked spines which attach themselves to browsing animals. In early times, the roots with their sweet aromatic taste were used to boil as a vegetable to accompany meats but it was not until it became a cultivated plant that the red roots increased in size and eating qualities. Carrot is the chief source of vitamin A (carotene).

Native of S. Europe and N. Africa where the Romans found it growing along the coast near Carthage; they may have introduced it to Gaul and Britain. It is closely related to the cardoon which some botanists place in the same family (C. cardunculus). The globe artichoke has handsome spiny leaves and in early spring forms a large globe-like head or flower bud, as big as a man's clenched fist, composed of spiny purple-green scales which overlap to enclose and protect the flower bud. The plants grow in sand dunes in an open, sunny position and are propagated from suckers which spring up around the plants. The heads (globes) are cut before they become too large and tough. The cardoon is native of the sandy soils and coastal regions of Spain and Portugal.

Perennial 12 in.—5 ft (30—150 cm)

After two centuries of hybridization, it is now one of the most beautiful of garden plants. Far greater enjoyment is to be had from the brilliantly colored flowers than by eating the tubers, but to the Aztecs of Mexico, nutritious dahlia roots were their staple diet. The plant, which grows wild in the sandy meadows about 5000 ft (1500 m) above sea level, makes a large root composed of several thick tubers which may be 2—6 in. (5—15 cm) long and up to 4 in. (10 cm) in circumference. From the roots arises the stem (or stems) at the end of which is borne a single red or orange flower. At the end of summer the plant dies back and it is then that the tubers are most nutritious. They contain inulin, present also in dandelion and chicory roots, and yield pure laevulose or diabetic sugar.

Tree 30—40 ft (10—12 m)

A genus of 60 species of erect trees or shrubs, with D. indica indigenous to E. India, Burma and Malaysia and the East Indies. It has spreading branches and makes a rounded head of bright green leaves which grow in tufts at the ends of the branches. The lance-shaped leaves are 10—12 in. (25—30 cm) long, pointed at the end and with toothed margins. The nerves run parallel to the toothed edges to give the leaves a fluted appearance. The large handsome single white flowers appear at the end of the branches and are 4—6 in. (10—15 cm) across with a central boss of stamens forming a golden crown. They are followed by hard green fruits often as large as a grapefruit and filled with sweet glutinous pulp, but it is the large sepals of the calyx enclosing the fruit that are used. They have the sour but refreshing taste of a cooking apple.

DIOSCOREA VILLOSA

YAM

Dioscoreaceae
 77 Trop Am, Trop Asia
Tropical Zones

DIOSPYROS VIRGINIANA

PERSIMMON

Ebenaceae
 78 Trop S+C Am
Tropical Zones

ELEOCHARIS TUBEROSA

WATER CHESTNUT

Cyperaceae
 79 SE Asia, S China
Warm Temperate Zones

ELETTARIA CARDAMOMUM

CARDAMOM

Zingiberaceae
 80 SE Asia
India, Ceylon, Guatemala

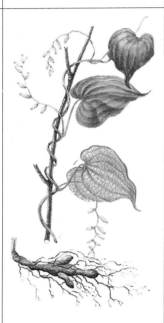

Perennial 2–3 ft (60–90 cm)

One of a genus of more than 200 species of sedge, native of S.E.Asia, especially S.China and the East Indies, where it is known as the Chinese water chestnut. E.tuberosa is widespread by the side of lakes and ponds, growing in shallow water, and it is also present in marshlands, increasing by horizontal underground runners or rhizomes. They root at the nodes, from which arise the tubular rush-like leaves which grow erect and into large clumps. At the base of the leaf stems is formed a round flattish tuber, like a gladiolus corm, about 2 in. (5 cm) in diameter.

Perennial Climbing to 20 ft (6 m)

A family of plants closely allied to liliaceae and consisting of 8 genera and more than 600 species. All are climbing plants with annual twining stems which arise from an underground tuberous root, a structure designed to store up food to ensure the rapid growth of the shoots. The roots of D.batatas, known as yams, resemble those of the dahlia, a new root-tuber being formed each year until they often reach a considerable size. As the shoots die back, the nourishment returns to the roots which contain large amounts of starch and are highly nutritious. The plant has stalked alternate entire net-veined leaves, aerial tubers being formed in the leaf axils. The inconspicuous flowers are bell-shaped, borne singly or in pairs, the fruit a 3-angled capsule.

Tree 30–40 ft (10 m)

The ebonies are of the tropical and sub-tropical regions of the Old and New Worlds, D.ebenum of Ceylon yielding the finest wood. D.ebenaster and D.lotus are known as the date plum. Natives of sub-tropical Asia, it is also used by cabinet makers. The fruits when dried are eaten as sweetmeats, while the fruit of D.virginiana, native of the southern United States, yields the sugar plum or persimmon. It makes a small tree with black bark and with leaves 2–3 in. (5–7.5 cm) long, terminating to a point. The fruit is round like a hard skinned plum and is green at first, turning orange when ripe. Like the medlar, it must be frosted for several weeks before it becomes soft and falls to the ground. It is the sweet and sticky pulp that is used, after it has been removed from the hard skin and allowed to dry and harden.

Perennial 3–4 ft (1 m)

It is native of S.India and Ceylon where it grows in the rain forests, up to 5000 ft (1500 m) above sea level. It forms fleshy rhizomes which carry the scars of the leaf stems. These grow to 4 ft (1 m), the dark green lanceolate leaves being up to 2 ft (60 cm) long. They are covered with silky hairs on the underside. The flowering stems appear separately in April and May and are only a few inches tall, often growing horizontally and close to the ground. The flowers are yellow with purple veins and are replaced by oblong slightly curved fruits containing, in each of the 3 cells, a double row of small, dark brown seeds. They are harvested just before the pods open and the seeds are kept in the pods as long as possible, to retain their aromatic taste.

EPILOBIUM ANGUSTIFOLIUM

WILLOW HERB

Onagraceae

N Eur, Asia
Temperate Zones

Perennial 4–7 ft (1–2 m)

A small family, most of which are indigenous to temperate N. America. E. angustifolium is a showy plant with narrow lanceolate leaves like those of the willow tree and bearing its tall tapering spikes of rosy-purple flowers from June until September. It is present on waste ground, mountain slopes and moist open woodlands. In the USA, it often appears after forest fires, hence its name fireweed. In USSR and Siberia, the dried leaves are used as a substitute for tea. The leaves of E. birsutum, the Hairy Willow herb are also used and the juice of the stems boiled and made into ale. The young shoots before the leaves unfold in spring, are cut when 6 in. (15 cm) tall and are boiled and eaten like asparagus. The plant contains mucilage and is both astringent and a tonic.

ERUCA SATIVA

ROCKET

Cruciferae

82
S Eur, W Asia, N Af
Temperate Zones

Perennial 26–30 in. (65–75 cm)

One of a small genus of edible plants native to the Mediterranean regions and extending into Afghanistan and N. India, where an oil is prepared from the seeds which is used for making pickles. The plant grows on rocky wasteland and takes the place of those cruciferae of more northerly regions as a supplier of vitamin C to guard against scurvy. The basal leaves grow to 4 in. (10 cm) long, becoming smaller near the top of the stem. The cross-like flowers are pale yellow with brownish-purple veins which give them a dingy appearance. The leaves also have purple veins and stems. They have serrated edges and the blade folds over to give a cylindrical effect. The leaves are rich in mineral salts, which give them an appetizing bitterness, but should not be used too liberally.

ERYNGIUM MARITIMUM

SEA HOLLY

Compositae

83
S Eur, SW Asia
Temperate Zones

Perennial 2–3 ft (60–90 cm)

One of nature's most interesting plants, it has since early times been included in herbaceous borders in many gardens. It has spiny blue-green leaves with white veins. In mid-summer, it bears 20–30 blue flowers to a stem and they have blue bracts covered in short bristles. It is the roots known as eringoes which are used. They are brittle and rhizomatous, extending deep into the earth, but should not be lifted until the plant is 2–3 years old for until then they will not have made good size. In the 17th century, Robert Burton, a confectioner of Colchester, England, sold the candied roots which he exported to the Continent and made a small fortune. They are said to act as an aphrodisiac and the demand was enormous. Water distilled from the roots is restorative.

FAGUS SYLVATICA

BEECH

Fagaceae

84
Eur, Asia
North Temperate Zones

Tree up to 100 ft (30 m)

The common beech is present throughout the N. temperate regions where it grows solitary and in deciduous woodlands and often forms a homogeneous forest, especially in calcareous soils. The thick trunk is smooth and greyish, and the hard wood is used for cooking utensils and to make parquet floors, chairs and tool handles. The ovate leaves are slightly toothed and are of palest green when unfolding, the beech being one of the earliest trees to come into leaf in spring. The tree takes its name from the Greek "to eat" and the nuts or mast as they are called are appetizing. The nuts are triangular and encased in a brown husk covered in short bristles. The flowers appear with the leaves as a green tassle, the males being stalked, the females unstalked. The trees do not flower every year.

	FICUS CARICA	FOENICULUM VULGARE	FRAGARIA VESCA

FICUS CARICA

FIG

Moraceae

85   S Eur, SW Asia
Warm Temperate Zones

FOENICULUM VULGARE

FENNEL

Umbelliferae

86   S+E Eur, N Af, W Asia
Temperate Zones

FRAGARIA VESCA

STRAWBERRY

Rosaceae

87   Eur, Asia, NW–N Am
Temperate Zones

Tree 12–20 ft (3–6 m)

Native of Palestine, Asia Minor and Persia, the fig has been a staple food of the peoples of the Near East from earliest times. It had reached Malta, Athens and S. Italy long before the time of Christ. Pliny described 29 varieties (more than we know today), those from Caria in Asia Minor being best of all; the cultivated fig was named in its honor. It makes a tall bush or small tree and grows well against a sunny wall. It has large, deeply lobed leaves and its fruit is a hollow, fleshy pear-shaped receptacle which conceals the flowers. It is borne in the leaf axils and is continually in fruit, next season's fruits having formed on the new seasons shoots before those of the previous year have ripened. The plant lives to a great age and grows well in a chalky soil and in sight of the sea.

Perennial 1–4 ft (30–100 cm)

A small genus, native of S. Europe and N. Africa and named foeniculum by the Romans because of its hay-like scent when growing. F. vulgare is an erect perennial growing 4 ft (about 1 m) tall, its 3–4 pinnate leaves divided into numerous hair-like segments. In mid-summer it bears small yellow flowers in terminal umbels. They are followed by narrow fruits with 8 longitudinal ribs, and when dry, also have the scent of aniseed. It is found on wasteland and in hedgerows but in open situations and often in sight of the sea. It is the Florence fennel, F. dulce, the sweet fennel native of Italy, that is most grown for its "roots." Also known as finocchio it grows only 12 in. (30 cm) tall, the leaves, borne on broad stalks, folding over at the base to form a ball-like head which sits on top of the soil.

Perennial 4–6 in. (10–15 cm)

A genus of 15 species, they grow in hedgerows and open woodlands. From several of the wild species the garden strawberry was raised. New varieties are continually being raised which, with those fruiting in autumn, now give 8 months of fruit. F. vesca, the wild strawberry of the woodlands of Europe and the British Isles, is a hairy perennial, rooting and increasing by runners or string-like growths which root at the leaf nodes. The trefoil leaves have pointed leaflets and give off a musky scent as they die back in autumn. The white flowers with 5 overlapping petals are borne in clusters on upright stems. The small many-seeded fruits are red or white, garden varieties being many times larger, and have orange flesh which is fragrant, sweet and juicy. The plant was first illustrated in the Mainz Herbal of 1454. F. elatior is another European strawberry, known as the Hautbois or Framboise. It is F. moschata, so named on account of its musky perfume. F. viridis, with its greenish-white fruit is also European. It is a plant of alpine meadows and is tolerant of limestone soils where as other species prefer slightly acid soils. F. virginiana, which grows in profusion on the Blue Ridge Mountains of Virginia, was introduced into Europe early in the 17th century by John Tradescant and was first recorded in 1624 by Jean Robin, botanist to Louis XIII. It was this strawberry when crossed with F. chiloensis, native of Chile and the islands of Juan Fernandez, in France late in the 18th century which gave rise to the first large fruiting varieties. Other American species such as F. californica and F. cuneifolia, to be found along the west coast from California to British Columbia and as far north as Alaska, later came to be used by breeders such as Michael Keens and Thomas Knight, Englishmen working with French-bred plants. Keen's Seedling, the first large fruiting variety, appeared in 1821, and since then the strawberry has remained the most popular of summer fruits. The plant was given its name because straw was placed around the plants to prevent the fruit being splashed by soil during heavy rain.

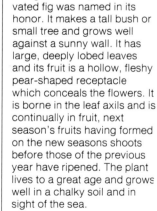

FRAXINUS EXCELSIOR	FREYCINETIA BANKSII	GARCINIA MANGOSTANA	GAULTHERIA PROCUMBENS
COMMON ASH	KIE-KIE	MANGOSTEEN	CHECKERBERRY
Oleaceae	Pandanaceae	Guttiferae	Ericaceae
88 N+C Eur *Temperate Zones*	**89** SE Asia, NZ, Polynesia *Warm Temperate Zones*	**90** SE Asia, S Af *Tropical Zones*	**91** E–N Am *Temperate Zones*

Tree to 80 ft (25 m)

Closely related to the olive, there are about 70 species of ash, mostly growing in limestone soil. F. ornus, the Manna ash, grows 20–50 ft (6–15 m) tall with pinnate leaves composed of 3 or 4 pairs of lanceolate leaflets. The flowers are borne with the leaves and appear in panicles in the leaf axils. The fruits are winged "keys." From the bark an edible exudation occurs when cuts are made in the trunk in summer. This solidifies and the gum is collected from the trees in autumn. Known as flake manna, it has a sweet aromatic taste. F. excelsior, the common ash of N. Europe, has smooth grey bark and opposite pinnate leaves up to 10 in. (25 cm) long, with dark green lanceolate leaflets. The fruits are about 2 in. (5 cm) long with a narrow wing on one side and they hang from the trees like bunches of keys.

Perennial 30–40 ft (9–12 m)

A member of the screw-pine family, it is a climbing shrub, native of the tropical rain forests of the Old World. Of the 3 genera which make up the family, Pandanus, the screw-pine, is the most widely distributed. It is a tall palm-like tree with a twisting trunk supported by large aerial roots. Freycinetia, discovered in New Zealand by Sir Joseph Banks on Captain James Cook's first expedition, is called kie-kie by the maoris. The fruit, an upright green spadix, about 4 in. (10 cm) long and sausage-shaped, has a rough outer skin but is soft and edible. The inside consists of a sweet, juicy pulp filled with numerous small seeds. The plant has leaves 2 ft (60 cm) long which are finely toothed, and sheathing at the base, while the flowers are borne in terminal spikes 4 in. (10 cm) long, surrounded by white fleshy bracts.

Tree 20–30 ft (6–8 m)

A genus of more than 400 species native of tropical America and the West Indies, many of which are plants of economic importance. The Mangosteen is now cultivated throughout the tropics. It has simple opposite elliptic leaves which are leathery and evergreen and it bears its flowers in a cymose inflorescence. They are followed by large round edible fruits of the size of an orange and with a thick brown skin when ripe. The fleshy aril which envelops the seeds is sweet and juicy with a melon-like flavor and may be removed from the fruit with a spoon. The aril is divided into 5 or 6 divisions, like an orange and its juice is milky-white. The closely related Mannea americana, the West Indian apple, makes a smaller tree.

Perennial 1–4 ft (30–100 cm)

A genus of about 100 species of low growing woody shrubs of the heath family increasing by underground stems and found on mountainous slopes, usually in peaty soils and in the shade of trees. Several species are valuable plants for the wild garden if provided with a peaty soil, for they give valuable ground cover. G. procumbens is the creeping wintergreen of N. USA and Canada, an evergreen whith small glossy oval leaves which, when pressed, release the penetrating smell of wintergreen in the manufacture of which its essential oil is used. The waxy white urn-shaped flowers, borne on red stems, are also aromatic. They are followed by large edible crimson fruits which persist through winter and make a sauce with a pleasantly "sharp" acid taste.

Perennial 1—10 ft (30 cm—3 m)

A genus of about 50 species indigenous to N. and S. America, usually growing in boggy land and in open woodlands. They increase by suckers which arise from around the plant and are often found in dense colonies. The glossy oval leaves, resinous on the underside, are alternate, the stems reddish-brown. The bell-shaped flowers are pinkish-white and are borne in drooping racemes. They are followed by small shiny black-skinned fruits containing 10 hard seeds. There are summer and winter varieties, the one flowering in spring and ripening its fruit in mid-summer; the other blooms in July and fruits late autumn so that there is a succession of fruit from early July until late October. The pea-sized fruits are sweet and juicy.

Annual or perennial 4 in.—4 ft (10—100 cm)

A genus of 400 or so species, chiefly native of the N. temperate regions of Europe and Asia with G. lutea, the stately yellow gentian, present in the Alpine regions of C. Europe, extending from Switzerland to the Balkans. It is also found in the Pyrenese and on the islands of Corsica and Sardinia, usually grows at 3000—4000 ft (900—1200 m). For centuries the roots have been collected, dried and exported to N. European countries to make a tonic drink known as "gentian bitters". Before the introduction of hops, the roots were used in brewing. They are a valuable restorative for those suffering from debilitating illness. The roots are yellow when freshly lifted but turn pale brown as they dry. From old plants, the roots measure 10—12 in. (25—30 cm) long and 1 in. (2.5 cm) in diameter but often are much larger. They have an unpleasant smell when lifted and a bitter taste. The leaves are pale green, oblong and pointed, the upper leaves stem-clasping. The large orange-yellow flowers are borne in whorls to make this one of the most handsome of wild flowers and worthy of a place in the garden. G. campestris, an annual, native of N. Europe and in the British Isles and Scandinavia has for long been employed to brew tonic beers. It was widely used in the brewing industry before hops. It is a plant of pastures and often found close to the sea. It is a low much-branched plant and bears purple trumpet-like flowers in July and August.

Tree 60—80 ft (20—25 m)

A genus of a single species which has remained unchanged for some 200 million years, according to fossilised specimens. Usually grouped with the conifers, it is a slender, slow growing deciduous tree. It is completely hardy and grows well in all soils everywhere. Of conical habit, the leaves are fern-like, fanning out at the ends. They resemble the maidenhair fern (Adiantum) and each leaf is divided by a notch from which it takes its name biloba, two-lobed. The leaves unfold in spring from curious knobs formed along the branches which are clothed in pale grey bark. The tree is either male or female, the former catkin-bearing; the latter fruit-bearing, though it is rare for it to do so in northerly climes. The fruits (cones) are like small yellow plums and are borne in twos and threes at the end of twiggy stems.

GLYCINE LISPIDA

SOYA BEAN

Leguminosae

95 Asia
Tropical Zones

GLYCYRRHIZA GLABRA

LIQUORICE

Fabaceae

96 SE Eur, SW Asia
SW Eur, N Af, C Am

HELIANTHUS ANNUUS

SUNFLOWER

Compositae

97 Mexico, Peru
Temperate Zones

HELIANTHUS TUBEROSUS

JERUSALEM ARTICHOKE

Compositae

98 N Am
Temperate Zones

Perennial 6–7 ft (2 m)

The sunflower, Helianthus annuus, is annual, native of Mexico and Peru, the seed being rich in oil which is almost tasteless and more nearly resembles olive oil than any other vegetable oil. It was extracted and used by the Aztec Indians and later by their Spanish conquerors who introduced the plant into Europe where it is grown commercially to mix in health margarines which are low in cholesterol. Each seed contains 30 mg of vitamin E per 100 g of seed and this is the vitamin which protects the polyunsaturates from oxidation. The seeds also contain 7 mg per 100 g of iron and quantities of zinc and magnesium.

Annual 1–2 ft (30–60 cm)

A small genus of edible plants, indigenous to the tropics and sub-tropics of Africa and Asia, one of which, the soya bean, has for long been cultivated in the Far East for it is rich in protein and the oil has many uses in the food industry. The plant is found on wasteland and by the side of fields, growing in sandy soil. It has trifoliate leaves with oval leaflets and serrate edges. The pale mauve pea-like flowers, borne in the leaf axils, are followed by pods about 1 in. (2.5 cm) long each containing 2 or 3 seeds. From the ripe seeds, an oil is obtained which is more widely used in cooking over most of Asia and Africa than all others. The seed contains as much as 20% oil and is one of the highest of all plant foods in protein. Soya beans are a fine vegetable or, put through a grinder, can be served as a breakfast cereal.

Perennial 3–4 ft (1 m)

A genus of 18 species, one of which, G. glabra, is native of S. Europe and the Near East and is present in W. Asia. Dioscorides named the plant from the Greek *glucos,* sweet, and *rhiza,* a root, and it is often known as sweetroot. The plant has pinnate foliage and from the leaf axils are borne pale blue flowers followed by smooth pea-like pods. But it is the underground part of the stem and roots, which may grow 3–6 ft (1–2 m) long in a rich soil, that are used. But not until the plant is 4 years old. Plants are lifted in autumn, the soil washed off and the roots cut into small pieces. The yellowish-brown roots are used fresh, being crushed to a pulp before being transferred to boilers for distilling. The thick tar-like mass is then removed and rolled into sticks 6 in. (15 cm) long. It contains salts of calcium and potassium and is low in calories.

Annual 6–7 ft (2 m)

Its name Jerusalem is a corruption of an Italian word *girasole* which means turning towards the sun, like the sunflower to which it is closely related. The plant is found in open places by the wayside and grows best in a light, well drained soil but one enriched with compost to retain moisture in summer. The tubers were highly prized by North American Indians from earliest times and by the early settlers in Virginia, but it was the French who introduced it into Europe, from Canada. Parkinson, botanist to Charles I of England, called it the Potato of Canada. A valuable garden crop, the white knobby tubers are ready to use in autumn and until the year end, being lifted as required. The plant is like a small sunflower in that the flowers, borne late in summer, measure 2 in. (5 cm) across, whereas those of the sunflower measure up to 6 in. (15 cm).

HELICHRYSUM ANGUSTIFOLIUM	HEMEROCALLIS LUTEA	HIBISCUS ESCULENTUS	HIPPOPHAE RHAMNOIDES
CURRY PLANT	DAY LILY	OKRA	SEA BUCKTHORN
Compositae	Liliaceae	Malvaceae	Elaeagnaceae
99 Medit *Warm Temperate Zones*	**100** C Eur, E Asia *Temperate Zones*	**101** Trop Af *Tropical Zones*	**102** Eur, Asia

Tree; shrub 6−7 ft (2 m)

A genus of 2 species closely related to Rhamnaceae. H. rhamnoides is usually found on the coast, growing in sandy soil and is a valuable wind-resistant tree for maritime planting. The small trees are attractive with their narrow, silvery leaves. The branches are thorny with brown stems and all the way up are borne tiny green flowers, followed on the female plants, by small orange berries which remain through winter untouched by birds on account of their acidity. They are gathered when ripe in early autumn and are a valuable source of vitamins A and C.

Perennial 18−20 ft (45−50 cm)

One of a large genus, the curry plant is present about rocky outcrops of S. Europe and the Near East where it makes a shrubby bush-like plant with handsome silver-grey foliage which, when pressed, releases ''hot'' curry-like smell. The fresh or dried leaves are used to flavor soups and stews and to include in stuffings. To dry the leaves for winter use, remove them in late summer and spread out on a shelf in an airy room, turning them daily until crisp. Late in summer, the plant bears small yellow flowers in umbels and they can be cut and dried for indoor decoration. Propagation is by cuttings of the new wood removed in summer and rooted in a sandy compost. Move to small pots when rooted and if in a cold climate, give glass protection during winter.

Perennial 2−3 ft (60−90 cm)

The day lily is so called because its flowers last only for a day but open in long succession throughout summer. It is indigenous to the temperate regions of Europe, Asia and the Japanese islands. Many new hybrids raised in recent years make this one of the most handsome of border plants, for its lily-like flowers are so freely produced. Not all the buds need be allowed to open. If some are picked when just showing color, they may be included in salads; pickled like capers; or simmered and served with sauce to accompany meat and game. The thick roots are also delicious when cooked until tender. The plant has pale green straplike leaves which die back in winter. The 6-petalled flowers are like small lilies, the petals recurving attractively.

Annual 4−5 ft (1−2 m)

It is closely related to the mallows. The plants grow on wasteland and in sandy soil and require warmth and a high rainfall to fruit. In northerly climes, okra needs the protection and humidity of a warm greenhouse where the plants are grown in large pots. The plant has 5-lobed leaves and its fruit is a capsule or pod which resembles a small cucumber, being about 2 in. (5 cm) in diameter and 8 in. (20 cm) long, dark green and terminating to a point. Like a cucumber, it is covered in blunt spines. H. sabdariffa is Indian sorrel, so called because the calyces of the flowers and its leaves taste like sorrel, having a refreshing bitterness. The plant has 5-lobed leaves with long stems, the flowers being borne in the axils.

HORDEUM VULGARE	HUMULUS LUPULUS	HYSSOPUS ARISTATUS	ILEX PARAGUARIENSIS
BARLEY	HOP	HYSSOP	PARAGUAY TEA
Cramineae	Cannabidaceae	Labiatae	Aquifoliaceae
103 C Asia *Temperate Zones*	**104** Eur, N Am, Asia *Temperate Zones*	**105** Medit *Temperate Eur, Asia*	**106** C–S Am

Annual or perennial 3–4 ft (1 m)

A genus of 20 species of corn-bearing plants which is believed to have its natural home between the Tigris and Euphrates rivers, extending north to the Caspian Sea. Barley was the corn of poor people and in the Bible there is constant reference to "barley cakes" and "barley loaves". It was considered inferior to wheat as in Revelation where "a measure of wheat" is given for a penny but "three measures of barley". Today, barley is grown in all parts of the temperate world and from the grain, malt is extracted by steeping and drying to develop an enzyme which transforms the starch into sugar during fermentation. The plant forms an unbranched stem with each spikelet terminating in stiff awns 1 in. (2.5 cm) or more in length. H. vulgare has its spikelets arranged in 6 rows.

Perennial 18 ft (5 m)

One of a small genus of climbing herbs. Though hops were used by the Romans 2,000 years ago for brewing ale, they were not used in Britain until the 16th century. The hop is a hairy climbing plant, its dark green 3–5 lobed leaves with serrated edges being held on a long petiole. The flowers are yellowish-green, the males borne in a catkin-like inflorescence; the females in the leaf axils to form a cylindrical spike or cone. The bracteoles have glandular hairs which when ripe produce lupulin, which is the important ingredient in brewing beer. Lupulin is a bitter principle with tonic properties. The plant grows in hedgerows and in open woodlands, climbing up other plants to a height of 18 ft. (5 m).

Perennial 12–14 in. (30–35 cm)

A genus of 15 species of hardy evergreen plants native of C. and S. Europe and taking their name from the Hebrew *azob,* a Holy herb for it is so often mentioned in the Bible. H. aristatus is a bushy, woody plant found on rocky ground across C. and S. Europe to the Near East. It often grows on old walls and is now naturalized in various parts of N. Europe around monastic foundations. It has small dark green linear leaves and bears its pink or purple flowers from June until September. They are much visited by bees and butterflies. The plant has many uses and as it withstands clipping it was once widely planted to make a low hedge to surround small beds of herbs or flowering plants. It requires a well drained soil and an open sunny situation.

Perennial 6–8 ft (2 m)

A small genus distributed throughout the warm temperate regions with Ilex aquifolium, the holly, native also of the cooler parts. Most of the genus are native of S. America, including I. paraguariensis, indigenous to Paraguay, Brazil and Argentina where it is found on banks of rivers and streams but has for long been cultivated commercially, for an infusion of its leaves and smally twiggy branches provides a pleasant drink known as Paraguay tea or mate tea. It makes a dense, broad shrub with large toothed lanceolate leaves and bears small white flowers in the axils. The flowers are followed by red drupes. The people of S. America, who consume the tea in large quantities, call it yerbs which signifies its excellence, and its name mate is from the pot in which it is made, lemon juice being added before drinking.

IPOMOEA BATATAS	JUGLANS REGIA	JUNIPERUS COMMUNIS	KLEINHOVIA HOSPITA
SWEET POTATO	WALNUT	JUNIPER	BITANG
Convolvulaceae	Juglandaceae	Cupressaceae	Sterculiaceae
107 Trop Am, SE Asia *Tropical + Warm Zones*	**108** SE Eur, SW Asia *Temperate Zones*	**109** Eur, NW Af, Asia, N Am *Temperate Zones*	**110** Trop Asia *Tropical Zones*

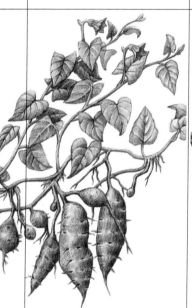

Perennial tuber 2–3 ft (60–90 cm)

More than 400 species comprise the genus which are native of the tropics and warm temperate regions, especially S. America, many being climbing plants with several having edible roots. I. batatas since earliest times has been one of the staple foods of S. American Indians and was introduced into Europe by the Spaniards in the 16th century. The tubers, which are really tuberous lateral shoots, contain large amounts of starch and sugar and are nutritious and sustaining. The haulm or top growth falls around the plant as it grows from a tuber of the size of a hen's egg which in the garden is planted 4 in. (10 cm) deep. If the foliage is earthed up when 8 in. (20 cm) tall, the shoots take root and bear more and more tubers and by late autumn, a single plant may produce 1000 or more. Lift in autumn when the haulm dies down.

Tree 70–80 ft (25 m)

The common walnut is among the most handsome of deciduous trees. Its name Juglans means Jove's nut or nut of the gods. The trees have a large trunk covered in smooth silver-grey bark and grey-green pinnate leaves tinted with red. They release a resinous scent when pressed. The male flowers are borne in drooping catkins; the females in erect terminal spikes. The fruit or drupe is covered with a thick green husk like a large plum. It stains the fingers black when the husk is removed to reveal a wrinkled bony shell containing the nut. The shell is opened by two valves to reveal a lobed nut covered in a brown tunic. J. nigra, the black walnut, is so-called because its grooved bark is dark brown while its pinnate leaves are pale green. The nuts are smaller than those of J. regia but of similar flavor.

Tree 10–30 ft (3–8 m)

A genus of 60 species, J. communis, the most widely distributed, being found up to 5000 ft (1500 m) above sea level. The plant is usually present on chalky outcrops and is tolerant of shallow stoney soils and intense cold. An evergreen, its needle-like leaves are arranged in whorls of three while the pale brown bark peels from the trunk. The female flowers appear early in summer and are greenish-yellow. They are followed by green berries (really cones) which turn purple-blue in their second year. They are the size of blueberries, and when dried, emit the unique resinous smell of the entire plant. The berries are collected in early autumn and dried in a temperature of 80° F (27° C), for in higher temperatures the essential oil that gives the berries their balsamic perfume will be lost.

Tree 30–40 ft (10–12 m)

A genus of a single species, the tree grows tall with a spreading head, and as it sprouts again from the main stem when the branches are cut (like the willow), trees in the wild often have a gnarled appearance. In the decaying cavities are found snakes and lizards, ferns and fungi which make their home there, hence it was named hospita by Linnaeus, as giving hospitality to many creatures. It is named for the physician Christian Kleynhoff. Its large heart-shaped leaves have 3–7 deep veins which grow out fanwise from the base. The small rose-pink flowers grow in large inflated 5-celled capsules containing seeds marked with small tubercles. Yellow at first, the capsules turn brown before they fall.

LACTARIUS PIPERATAS

MILK CAP

Fungus

111 Eur, Asia

LACTUCA VIROSA

WILD LETTUCE

Compositae

112 N+C Eur, Asia
Temperate Zones

LAMIUM AMPLEXICAULE

HENBIT

Labiatae

113 N Eur, W+N Asia
North Temperate Zones

LAURUS NOBILIS

BAY LAUREL

Lauraceae

114 S Eur, NW Af, SW Asia

The milk cap, Lactarius piperatas, so named because all parts are milky white and it exudes a milk-like liquid when cut, is also found in woodlands across northern Europe and Asia. As it ages, the cap becomes concave. It has a peppery taste and is often dried and cut into small pieces to use in soups and stews to which it imparts a sharp "hot" taste. L. deliciosus, the saffron milk cap, is common in pine woods. It has an orange yellow cap which turns grey with age and it exudes a greenish-yellow liquid when cut. It has a sharp, aromatic smell and taste and is usually included in soups and stews rather than eaten on its own. Pleurotus osteratus is the oyster mushroom which requires a host plant for its nourishment and is found on dead or dying trees, appearing in tiers, the cap being fan-shaped like the shell of an oyster and creamy brown. Only the caps are edible.

Annual 3 in.—6 ft
(7.5 cm—2 m)

A genus of more than 100 species of annual or biennial plants and taking its name from the Latin, lactis denoting the milky juice that plant contains. The plant is also called the greater prickly lettuce to distinguish it from the prickly lettuce, L. serriola. L. virosa grows 6 ft (2 m) tall and has stiff purple-brown stems and pale green alternate leaves, the lower of which are stem clasping. The leaves have weak spines on the margins which have disappeared entirely from the garden lettuce (which was evolved from L. virosa). It was a food plant of ancient Egypt and from it the Cos lettuce with its narrow crinkly leaves was evolved. It was appreciated by the ancient Greeks, and then the Romans, who may have introduced it to N. Europe and Britain where it is still known as the Roman or romaine lettuce. Garden lettuce is an annual and grows less than 6 in. (15 cm) tall.

Perennial 4—12 in.
(10—30 cm)

Of the same family as the lavender and mints, the dead nettles are so called because although their leaves resemble those of the nettle, they are without the "sting" when touched. They are present throughout the north temperate regions where they grow in hedgerows and on wasteland. They have been used for food by the Scandinavian people for centuries. L. amplexicaule, a perennial with bluntly toothed rounded leaves, bears purple flowers in whorls all the way up the stems throughout summer. L. album, which bears white flowers, is also perennial but L. purpureum is a downy annual. Its heart-shaped leaves are pointed at the tips and its flowers are pale mauve. It grows only half the height of the other dead nettles. The dead nettles are much visited by bees and are a valuable source of nectar in early summer.

Tree 60 ft (about 20 m)

Native of S. Europe, it was named by the Romans from the Latin *laudis,* praise, for it was esteemed above all plants. The Romans crowned their poets and warriors with chaplets and wreaths made from the leaves, which are always green and sweet smelling. The much-branched trees or shrubs have lanceolate leaves with smooth, wavy margins. New leaves are pale green but later turn darkest green. They are glossy and when handled give off a warm aromatic scent. The small yellow flowers appear in May and June and grow in clusters. They are followed by fleshy black, ovoid aromatic berries. The wood too is scented. A green volatile oil is distilled from the leaves and berries and contains geraniol and eugenol as in cloves. Propagation is from cuttings of the half-ripened wood, taken with a "heel" (piece of the main stem attached) and rooted in a sandy compost.

LENS ESCULENTA

LENTIL

Leguminosae

115 SW Asia, Medit
Warm Temperate Zones

LEPIDIUM CAMPESTRE

FIELD CRESS

Cruciferae

116 Eur, SW Asia
North Temperate Zones

LEPTOSPERMUM SCOPARIUM

TEA TREE

Myrtaceae

117 S Asia, Aus, NZ
Warm Temperate Zones

LEVISTICUM OFFICINALE

LOVAGE

Umbelliferae

118 SW Asia
Temperate Zones

Annual 1−2 ft (30−60 cm)

Native of the Near East, its culture extends into Egypt and along the N. African coast, also to S. Europe and W. Asia where it has been grown as a staple food since earliest times. It is mentioned in Genesis when the starving Esau sells Jacob his birthright for "some bread and a pottage of lentils." The seeds are orange-red and round, about ½ cm across and lens-shaped (hence their name), being convex on both sides. L. esculenta is an erect annual with slender stems and compound, tendril-bearing leaves. It bears white, violet-veined flowers which give way to short flat pods which are dried in the sun and threshed to remove the seeds exactly as they were 4,000 years ago. The crop can be grown in poor sandy soil.

Annual 2−30 in. (5−65 cm)

The cresses are of the temperate regions of the world and like many plants of the Order are among the most health-giving of all plants, being rich in vitamins A, B_2, B_6 and C, also in mineral salts. The field cress is a stiff, hoary plant with lanceolate toothed leaves. The upper leaves clasp the stem, while the tiny white flowers produced throughout summer are followed by small narrow seed pods. The leaves, gathered when young, make a welcome addition to a salad and have the same pleasant bitterness of lady's smock and watercress. L. ruderale is the narrow-leaf pepperweed which grows to only half the height but has the same bitter cress-like taste and has the same culinary uses. The plants are common in pastures and on wasteland. L. sativum is the garden cress, usually grown with white mustard to improve the flavor.

Tree 20−30 ft (6−8 m)

A genus of 50 species indigenous to Australia and New Zealand, being mostly small trees or shrubs with alternate narrow leathery leaves teminating to a point. L. scoparium, snow-in-summer, is the most abundant of New Zealand shrubs, taking the place of the European gorse and at Christmas, large areas of the countryside are white with its blossoms. The small flowers are scentless, with the petals splashed with crimson. It flowers from early November until late March and seedling plants begin to bloom when only a few inches tall. The aromatic wood is used for canoe paddles and to make fences, while the leaves are also highly scented and when dried make an excellent "tea," to be enjoyed either hot or cold, hence its name of tea-tree or tea-plant. L. ericoides, the Heath Manuka, grows taller and has heath-like leaves which are also aromatic.

Perennial 3−4 ft (1 m)

L. officinale, present in hedgerows and on wasteland, resembles angelica (and also contains angelic acid which gives it a "warm" taste). The stems are candied like those of angelica and are used in confectionery. The glossy dark green pinnate leaves are divided into narrow segments like those of celery, which they resemble in taste and smell. The aromatic seeds which are pale brown and elliptical are used for flavoring and for pickling mushrooms and gherkins. They are harvested late in summer. Whereas the flowers of L. officinale are yellow and appear in June and July, those of L. scoticum are white, while its leaves are broader and of a brighter green. The plant is found only in Scotland and grows to about half the height of L. officinale. Propagate by root division or from seed.

LITCHI CHINENSIS

LITCHEE

Sapindaceae

119	E Asia, China *Warm Temperate Zones*

LOTUS TETROGONOLOBUS

ASPARAGUS PEA

Leguminosae

120	Medit, Asia *Temperate Zones*

LYCOPERSICUM ESCULENTUM

TOMATO

Solanaceae

121	C+S Am *Temperate Zones*

Tree 30–40 ft (10–12 m)

A genus of a single species, native of central and S. China where it grows in open woodlands. It is cultivated for its fruits in which a single seed is enclosed with sweet and juicy fleshy aril contained inside a rough brittle case covered all over with small tuber-like structures. The fruits are round, about 2 in. (5 cm) in diameter, and are borne singly at the end of long drooping stalks. Litchi "nuts" are the dried fruits which resemble plums or prunes, while the fresh fruit has a juicy white flesh inside the woody skin or outer covering which is readily peeled away. The flesh has the taste and flavor of muscat grapes. It is an evergreen tree, with opposite bright green elliptic leaves, about 8 in. (20 cm) long and 3 in. (7.5 cm) broad with prominent veins.

Annual 18–20 in. (45–50 cm)

A large genus, native of the warmer parts of Europe and Asia, chiefly Mediterranean, several of its species are used as fodder for cattle. Lotus tetrogonolobus has trifoliate leaves, like those of clover and trefoil, and in early summer bears reddish-purple flowers like those of the everlasting pea. The plant grows as broad as it grows tall and is found in hedgerows and on wasteland, usually close to the sea and growing in sandy soil. The flowers are followed in late summer by small deeply grooved rectangular pods containing small round seeds, which when boiled, have the taste of asparagus. The pods are gathered when little more than 1 in. (about 4 cm) long, before the seeds become large, for it is the pods (with the seeds inside) that are cooked until tender. The plants are of easy culture but require a warm climate to produce heavy crops.

Annual 3–4 ft (1 m)

Native of Pacific S. America, L. esculentum was introduced into Europe early in the 17th century by the Spaniards. Though at first eaten only by the wealthy, it soon became, with the potato, the most popular of all nature's foods. In its native land, the plant grows in sandy soil on wasteland often close to the sea where it grows 3–4 ft (1 m) tall. Under greenhouse culture, where in cooler climes large quantities are grown each year, the plants reach twice that height. The plant forms a branching stem with large pinnate leaves, divided into 2–4 pairs of opposite leaflets. The white flowers are produced in panicles of up to 20 or more from the axils of the leaves and are replaced by round juicy fruits (berries) of 3–4 in. (15–20 cm) circumference. They are green, turning yellow, then red as they ripen, a soft but firm glossy skin enclosing pink flesh in which are distributed many flat yellow seeds. In Europe the fruit was first named Pomi dei Mori, for it was originally grown by the Moors and the unripe fruit resembled green apples. The name was corrupted by the French to pommes d'amour and in English to love apples.

MAHONIA AQUIFOLIA

OREGON GRAPE

Berberidaceae

122 W—N Am, N Eur, Asia
North Temperate Zones

MALUS SYLVESTRIS

CRAB APPLE

Rosaceae

123 N Eur, Asia
North Temperate Zones

MANGIFERA INDICA

MANGO

Anacardiaceae

124 S Asia
Tropical Zones

Perennial 2—4 ft (60—100 cm)

One of a genus of 70 species, indigenous to W. Asia and Japan and N. America, especially the Pacific West where it grows in open woodlands. As it is evergreen and grows well in shade, it has been widely planted all over the British Isles and N. Europe, to act as game cover and for shelter-belts. The stems are thornless, the glossy leaves pinnate and hollylike, usually taking on red tints in winter. The golden yellow flowers are borne in dense racemes early in spring, often before the end of February, and are followed by decorative round, blue-black berries which are covered in purple-grey "bloom"-like grapes. The fruits ripen late in summer and make delicious tarts, flans, and preserves and they freeze well but should not be gathered until fully ripe. The Oregon grape is a handsome plant for a garden shrubbery or for planting beneath tall trees.

Tree 6—12 ft (2—4 m)

This small, smooth barked deciduous tree is one of 35 species and is believed to be a parent of M. domestica, the garden or cultivated apple, the most widely grown of all fruits. M. sylvestris is present in open woodlands and hedgerows in those parts enjoying a cool climate. It is slow growing and makes a much-branched tree with ovate short-stalked leaves and bears pinkish-white flowers in large clusters. Their conspicuous golden anthers add to their beauty. The flowers are followed by small yellow fruits (apples) which turn red as they ripen and which are juicy but sour. The John Downie variety, widely planted in gardens, bears conical orange-red fruits. M. coronaria and the closely related prairie crab, M. ioensis, are wild apples of the E. USA with downy stems and leaves and bearing fragrant pink blossom.

Tree 30—40 ft (10—12 m)

A small genus of smooth barked evergreen trees. M. indica, native of India, Malaysia and S.E. Asia, has long elliptic leaves, and early in spring, bears large terminal panicles of tiny pinkish-white flowers followed by a large 1-seeded drupe or fruit, of the color and size of a peach with a delicious juicy mesocarp. There are many varieties grown throughout the tropics, for the fruit was first planted in E. India on a commercial scale as long ago as the 14th century. The mango is a plant of the woodlands, often present on hillsides, and fruits from May until September. The fruits have a smooth yellow skin and flesh, are virtually free of fiber and have something of the flavor of melons. A writer of a century ago described it as being "superior to any fruit the earth can produce." The fruits are eaten raw as dessert but can be made into pies or flans and also preserves. They freeze and can well. The unripe fruits make the best Indian chutney and have a high vitamin C content. Propagation is by budding or grafting and the trees need heavy cropping and a deep, well-nourished soil to be long-lived.

MANIHOT UTILISSIMA	MARANTA ARUNDINACEA	MEDICAGO SATIVA	MELISSA OFFICINALIS
CASSAVA	ARROWROOT	ALFALFA	BALM
Euphorbiaceae	Marantaceae	Papilionaceae	Labiatae
125 Trop Am	**126** Trop Am	**127** S+E Eur, Asia *Temperate Zones*	**128** SE Eur, SW Asia *Temperate Zones*

Perennial 6−9 ft (2−3 m)

M. utilissima, one of more than 150 species, is a shrubby plant, its large palmate leaves divided into 6 elliptical leaflets 3−4 in. (7.5−10 cm) long. The small greenish-yellow flowers are borne at the end of pale green succulent stems like those of the dahlia, and the plant forms large tuberous roots of similar size and texture to those of the dahlia. When lifted at the end of summer, the roots may weigh 30 lbs (14 kg) and are full of starch and a poisonous juice containing hydrocyanic acid which is removed before the roots are edible as Brazilian arrowroot. After boiling, the juice also loses its poisonous properties. The thick mass of the roots is ground into a flour to make tapioca, which is exported and used for milk puddings.

Perennial 6−7 ft (2 m)

It is an herbaceous plant with cylindrical tuberous roots and bears creamy white flowers at the end of long upright stems. The sheaths of the ovate leaves enclose the stem. From the young roots after washing, starch is extracted. The roots are pounded in vats of water and the milk-like fluid allowed to settle into a jelly-like mass which is then spread out on clean linen sheets to dry before being finely ground. It is readily digested and is given to invalids and to those suffering from diarrhea and stomach disorders. It is both nutritious and sustaining and one can survive on it for a considerable time without any other food. Brazilian arrowroot, also known as tapioca, is obtained from the dahlia-like roots of Manihot utilissima, and Tahitan arrowroot is from the roots of Tacca oceanica. Both are demulcents and highly nourishing.

Perennial 1−2 ft (30−60 cm)

A deep-rooting perennial with clover-like leaves and bearing purple pea-like flowers, it is present on grassy alpine slopes. It is a valuable fodder crop, staying green throughout the year and yielding two crops. It greatly increases the milk yield of cattle. The sprouting seeds have been appreciated by the Mediterranean people for centuries and more recently by Americans who have called it the "miracle" or "wonder" food. Photosynthesis releases the high amount of protein it contains as well as vitamins and mineral salts. It contains salts of sodium, phosphorus, potassium and magnesium, while its vitamin B_2 and C content will increase by more than 1000% within 6−7 days of the seeds sprouting, when a teacupful of the sprouts will contain as much vitamin C as 10 glasses of pure orange juice.

Perennial 3−4 ft (1 m)

Balm makes a bushy, leafy plant and is hardy everywhere, dying down in winter and coming early into growth in spring. It is known as lemon balm for the leaves, when pressed, emit a refreshing lemon scent while its botanical name is from the Greek, melissa, honey for its flowers provide bees with large amounts of nectar. The plant is believed to have been taken to N. Europe and Britain by the Romans, for it has many uses. The bright green heart-shaped leaves are deeply wrinkled and the small white flowers are borne in short axillary whorls in late summer. Balm was the chief ingredient (with angelica root) of Carmelite Water, made at the Abbey of St. Juste in the 14th century and which was used in the toilet of most cultured people of Europe, to rub on the body after washing and also to take internally "to renew youth."

MENTHA VIRIDIS	MENYANTHES TRIFOLIATA	MESPILUS GERMANICA
SPEARMINT	BOGBEAN	MEDLAR
Labiatae	Gentianaceae	Rosaceae

129 N Eur, N Asia
North Temperate Zones

130 Eur, Asia, N Am
Temperate Zones

131 SE Eur, SW Asia
Temperate Zones

Tree 10—16 ft (3—4 m)

It is native of S.E. Europe and W. Asia but reached N. Europe in prehistoric times The common medlar makes a small twisted tree and lives to a great age. It is as colorful in blossom as the cherry and the large leaves of the Dutch or broad-leaf variety cast excellent shade. In the wild, the branches frequently carry spines, whilst the leaves are long and elliptic. The flowers appear solitary early in summer and are about 1 in. (2.5 cm) across. They are pinkish-white and are followed by brown globular fruits on which the leafy flower sepals persist around the deep depression at the apex. At this stage the fruit is too hard to eat and must be allowed to hang for as long as possible, until frosted, which encourages its ripening. "You'll be rotten ere you be half ripe, and thats the right virtue of a medlar", said Rosalind in Shakespeare's *As You Like It*. It was believed a medlar should be rotten before it was ripe to eat, though it should not necessarily have decayed. After the fruit is frosted, gather and place eye downwards on cotton wool in a warm room and leave them for about 3 weeks when they will be soft and juicy.

Perennial 1—2 ft (30—60 cm)

A genus of 25 species, which takes its name from Mintha, daughter of Cocytus, who was believed to be metamorphosed into the plant by Proserpine because of Pluto's love for her. M. viridis, the best known species, is a plant of hedgerows and damp woodlands, the mints enjoying semi-shade and a moist soil. M. viridis is a hairless perennial, increasing by underground stolons from which arise upright stems clothed with brilliant green lanceolate leaves. Late in summer it bears lilac flowers in a spire-like inflorescence, its early name being spiremint. M. longifolia, possibly a variety of M. spicata, has longer and narrower leaves and is also known as the horse mint. M. piperita is a natural hybrid of M. aquatica (the water mint) and M. viridis.

Perennial 20 in. (50 cm)

The only species of the genus, it grows in bogs and by stagnant ponds, its large fleshy leaves, composed of 3 leaflets like those of the broad bean, overtopping the water. It has a creeping rootstock and stem covered by the leaf sheaths. The flowers are rose-pink with red stamens and cluster together on a tall spike. They appear early in summer. The leaves contain vitamin C and are anti-scorbutic. (Its German name, Schorbock, comes from the latin, scorbutus.) They act as a tonic and purify the blood and should be included in summer salads; also in cream cheese sandwiches to which they impart a pleasant bitterness. The root contains the chemical glucocide, menyanthin, which (when taken with liquorice) is antiscorbutic and acts as a tonic. The roots were at one time boiled in honey to make a kind of mead.

MONARDA DIDYMA	MORCHELLA CONICA	MORUS NIGRA	MUCUNA PRURIENS
BERGAMOT	MOREL	BLACK MULBERRY	COWAGE
Labiatae	Fungus	Moraceae	Leguminosae
132 E–N Am *Temperate Zones*	**133** Temperate Eur, Asia	**134** Temperate N+S Am, SW Asia, Japan *Temperate Zones*	**135** Trop Am *Tropical+Subtropical Zones*

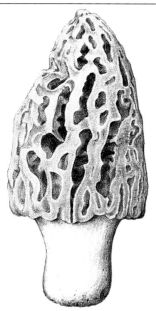

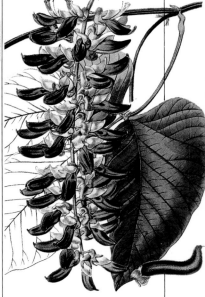

Perennial 2–3 ft (60–90 cm)

The plant was introduced into Europe in 1774 and named in honor of Dr. Nicholas Monardes of Seville, who published the first authentic herbal on the flora of America in 1569. It received its name bergamot because the leaves when pressed release the delicious scent of the bergamot orange. Monarda is one of the most attractive plants of the herb garden, and like most N. American perennials, is tolerant of intense cold and of a heavy soil. It increases by underground stems, like mint to which it is closely related. It has deeply grooved square stems and pointed lance-shaped leaves, slightly hairy on both surfaces. The shaggy flowers are borne in whorls at the ends of the stems and appear in July and August. They are red, pink, purple or white green bracts.

Morels appear in the spring in wood clearings, hedges and gardens, especially on chalky soils. They also have a curious liking for burnt places, and there were many records of colonies springing up on bomb sites in the war. They are best recognized by their fleshy consistency and the pitted head on a stalk. Morels have not been grown commercially with success. Mushroom growers would have a large market for these fungi if a method could be found to produce them commercially. Morchellus conica is one of the most useful of fungi for culinary purposes for its tall conical cap is hollow. The stem grows right up to the top and when removed, the cap which is pitted like a honeycomb, can be stuffed before cooking but always steep them first for several hours in salted water which is poured away.

Tree 30–40 ft (10 m)

The Black Mulberry is a deciduous stiffly branched tree, native of Persia though it has been grown throughout Palestine since early times. The tree bears edible fruits. The greenish flower spikes are followed by dark red fruits in late summer. The fruits should not be gathered until fully ripe. To prevent squashing them in the fingers, the best way is to spread a large cloth beneath the branches and to shake them to release the fruits. After removing the core, use them for preserves or for dessert, after sprinkling with claret. The White Mulberry, Morus alba, is native of China and on its leaves silkworm feed. The trees afford pleasant shade in summer with their large lobed leaves, and live to a great age. In Lebanon, mulberries are as plentiful as the palm is in Egypt. Mulberries also make delicious pies and tarts.

Perennial 15–20 ft (4–6 m)

A plant native to the tropics and sub-tropics of both the Old and New Worlds, especially the East and West Indies, India and Brazil. It climbs by tendrils, pulling itself up trees and shrubs which grow on wasteland, and its presence is noted by the stinging hairs which cover the pods and attach themselves to those who pass by or are blown by the wind, causing irritation of the skin. A slender plant with lance-shaped leaves up to 10 in. (25 cm) long and held on hairy petioles. The flowers are white with a purple corolla and are followed by thick hairy pods 4 in. (10 cm) long which contain up to 6 dark brown pea-like seeds also covered in short hairs. When young and tender, the pods make a popular dish with the people of India. The seeds when ripe are said to be aphrodisiac. The hairs are taken with syrup to expel intestinal worms.

MURRAYA EXOTICA	MUSA SAPIENTUM	MYRISTICA FRAGRANS
CURRY LEAF TREE	BANANA	NUTMEG, MACE
Rutaceae	Musae	Myristiceae
136 S Asia *Tropical Zones*	**137** Tropical Zones	**138** SE Asia *Tropical + Warm Zones*

Tree 20—40 ft (6—12 m)

A single genus of about 80 species, the most important being M. fragrans. It is a woody evergreen, flat-topped tree with smooth grey bark and simple entire pointed leaves which are glossy and covered in oil glands. From the leaf axils are produced small yellow flowers in clusters of 3—6, held on long footstalks and resembling flowers of lily of the valley. The single seeded fruit is like a small peach, being yellow with a suture line and a fleshy outer covering, the aril or mace, which encloses a branching red cage-like covering of the seed. The seed, which is the nutmeg of commerce, is covered by a pale greyish brown shell like a small walnut. The trees grow in volcanic ash, in dense shady plantations in intense heat and where the rainfall is heaviest. They begin to fruit when 8 or 9 years old. An established female tree when 15 years old will yield up to 2,000 nuts each year and remain productive for 100 years. The trees bear all the year but most plentifully in the last 3—4 months. The aril (mace) and the seed (nutmeg) are then dried in special drying houses, which takes about 4 months.

Tree or shrub 4—20 ft (1—6 m)

A genus of 12 species closely related to the orange. M. exotica makes a small twiggy tree 10 ft (3 m) tall with small dark green glossy leaves like those of the box, hence its name of the Chinese box tree. The small white flowers are borne in terminal corymbs and are strongly scented. They are followed by shining red fruits like small cherries with resinous glands as on the skin of an orange. M. koenigii, native of S.E. Asia, grows to a similar height. All parts of the bark, roots and red fruits have the same "hot" spicy smell and taste of the small dark green leaves. M. paniculata, native of Indonesia, makes a taller, more spreading tree with larger leaves, its white flowers borne in terminal and axillary panicles followed by cherry-like fruits.

Tree 6—30 ft (2—8 m)

A genus of about 60 species, native of the tropics of the old world, especially W. Africa. The plants, with their stems composed of overlapping leaf stalks, inhabit the rain forests where they grow to a considerable height, though the dwarf or Cavendish banana reaches to only 6—8 ft (2 m). They are characterized by their large spirally arranged leaves which are used for plaiting into mats. When the last leaf has formed, the flower bud which forms at the base of the plant grows up inside the stem and droops down from the top. The female flowers appear on the lower part of the inflorescence; the males on the upper part. Each cluster forms a "hand" or bunch of 20 or more fingers, each developing into a bunch of bananas. A single stalk may contain 300—400 berries (the fruits), about 6—10 in. (15—25 cm) long. Green bananas or plantains are a staple food of the tribes of tropical Africa.

MYRRHIS ODORATA

SWEET CICELY

Umbelliferae

139 Eur, Asia
Temperate Zones

NASTURTIUM OFFICINALE

WATERCRESS

Cruciferae

140 Temperate Zones

NIGELLA SATIVA

NUTMEG PLANT

Ranunculaceae

141 Medit
Warm Temperate Zones

Perennial 4–5 ft (1.5 m)

The plant is indigenous to the mountain pastures and hedgerows of Europe and W. Asia, extending from the Pyrenese to the Caucasus, the whole plant having a myrrh-like smell while the leaves taste as if they have been steeped in sugar. In earlier times, the dry seeds were crushed and the powder rubbed onto oak furniture to which it imparted a high gloss and myrrh-like smell. It is an erect pubescent plant with hollow stems and pale green fern-like leaves which are included in salads and used to flavor stews. The small white flowers are borne early in summer in terminal corymbs and are followed by dark brown fruits which are ridged and smell slightly of cloves. The plants die back in winter. Plants readily seed themselves in the countryside and garden.

Perennial 4–10 in. (10–25 cm)

It grows in running water in most parts of the temperate regions, increasing by under-ground stems. The pinnate shiny leaves are green all the year. The green stems are hollow and the small white flowers borne at the end of the stems are replaced by cylindrical seed pods. The form sterilis is that planted by the commercial growers. It does not set seed and its leaves are tinted with brown or purple. It is planted in specially made beds, the rooted cuttings being set 4 in. (10 cm) apart and with 4 in. (10 cm) of soil over the roots. It requires a mild winter climate to produce its green shoots in winter. It is readily distinguished from fool's cress which also grows in water and has toothed and pointed leaves.

Annual 12–16 in. (30–40 cm)

A genus of 20 species native of the Mediterranean regions and W. Asia, where it grows by the side of cornfields and on wasteland. The plants have finely divided leaves and hairy stems. It bears its pale blue flowers during the latter weeks of summer, when the plant takes on a misty appearance from a distance. The small black seeds have an aromatic scent and were at one time put in muslin bags to place among clothes and linen. In France and Italy, the seeds are baked into bread and cakes and included in cheese. Apothecaries extracted an oil from the seeds which was used as a substitute for expensive spikenard oil. The seeds are ground to use a condiment and to season egg dishes. They stimulate the appetite and increase the flow of gastric juices but should not be used too often. In early days the ground seeds were rubbed into the hair to remove lice and large quantities were consumed by the women of ancient Egypt as they believed the seeds gave plumpness to the breasts. N. damscena is the love-in-a-mist of gardens. It has larger flowers which are star-like and bluish-white with green veins.

NYMPHAEA LOTUS	OCIMUM BASILICUM	OENOTHERA BIENNIS	OLEA EUROPAEA
LOTUS LILY	BASIL	EVENING PRIMROSE	OLIVE
Nymphaeaceae	Labiateae	Onagraceae	Oleaceae
142 Trop Af, SE Asia	**143** C+S Asia *Warm Temperate Zones*	**144** N Am *Temperate Zones*	**145** S Eur, N Af, SW Asia *S Af, W–N Am, Aus*

Annual 6–16 in. (15–40 cm)

The sweet basil, O. basilicum, is believed to take its name from basileum which denotes its connection with royalty, for it was an ingredient of a costly unguent used in royal households. The plants grow on wasteland, in sandy soil, where they seed themselves freely. O. basilicum grows 16 in. (40 cm) tall and bushy with dark green lance-shaped leaves tinted with red and covered in pellucid dots which release a "warm" aromatic scent when pressed. O. minimum, the bush basil, grows to only half the height but has similar properties.

Tree 12–24 ft (4–7 m)

The olive is native of the Mediterranean regions and of W. Asia. In the Holy Land in ancient times and in all those countries bordering the Mediterranean olive groves were to be found everywhere. In the wild it is a small twisted evergreen tree with pale green bark and thorny twigs. The lanceolate leaves are about 2 in. (5 cm) long, dark green above, grey on the underside. Since earliest times it has been revered for this highly edible oil, the finest of all the vegetable kingdom and it was used by the people of the Mediterranean regions to massage into the body to prevent the skin drying in the sun. The fruit of O. europaea

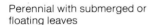

Perennial with submerged or floating leaves

A genus of 32 species, native of warm and temperate regions of the world. N. lotus is the lotus lily of ancient Egypt and may have been the pattern for the ornamentation of Solomon's temple. In the Song of Solomon, there is reference to "feeding amongst the lilies" which would seem to refer to the lotus lily, as its seeds and roots have been articles of food in the East since earliest times. They are also ground to make flour and are eaten roasted. As many as 30,000 seeds are present in a single fruit of the lotus. The flowers, about 8 in. (20 cm) across, are self-pollinating and open only at night, when they float on the water like a white rose. The floating leaves are twice as large and arise from a horizontal rhizome. The fruit is a berry which ripens under water and is removed before the seeds are released and float to the surface.

Biennial 3–4 ft (1 m)

The plant is in no way connected with the primrose and cowslip, being of the same family as the fuchsia, clarkia and godetia, plants of the temperate regions of the New World, especially of the Pacific west. The evening primrose, so called because its flowers open only in the coolness of evening, was brought to Europe in the 16th century and has become naturalized in most parts. It is usually found in open situations, on wasteland, railway sidings and river banks. The leaves, which are covered in short hairs, are 4–5 in. (10–12.5 cm) long and pointed; the chalice-like flowers which appear in June being of primrose yellow with a delicious perfume at night. They appear in succession throughout summer. The French and Italians make use of the young leaves in salads and boil the long taproots to serve with sauces.

OPUNTIA FICUS-INDICA

PRICKLY PEAR

Cactaceae

146 C+S Am, Medit
Warm Temperate Zones

ORCHIS MASCULA

SALOP

Orchidaceae

147 N+C Eur, SW Asia
Temperate Zones

is a small purple drupe with a thick bony stone surrounded by the fleshy part which is full of oil. The best olives are now grown commercially in Italy, Spain and Greece where more than 4 million acres are under cultivation. Oil is extracted from the ripe fruits by pressure. It is pale yellow, almost tasteless and nourishing. It is used to make salad dressings and is the best oil for cooking. The trees begin to bear when 2 years old and continue for centuries, sometimes growing gnarled and mis shapen, many with hollow trunks. Being evergreen, they provide valuable shade from the heat of the sun.

Perennial 10—20 ft (3—5 m)

The opuntias occupy desertlands and barren mountainous slopes, exposed to full sunlight and often to many degrees of frost. The plants are found as bushes or of tree-like proportions, the stems being composed of a number of flat oval pads joined together and with a few short bristle-like spines on the areoles where the yellow flowers are borne singly. The fruit is pearshaped, about 3 in. (7.5 cm) long, and ripens to deep red but there are several other varieties cultivated for their fruit. Alba bears large white fruits; lutea, yellow; pyriformis is also yellow but smaller, and serotina, yellow streaked with red. The pulp is of the same color as the skin. The plants bloom and ripen their fruits, which have the taste of ripe figs, over a long season and hence are much appreciated by the peoples of the New World.

Perennial 8—12 in. (20—30 cm)

The 3 chief orchids from which the nourishing drink salop is made (from the Arabian sahlep) are native to the British Isles, Europe, Asia and the near east where, in the Levant especially, the food is prepared from the tubers of plants collected in the wild. The roots of these orchids contain a starch-like substance, bassorin which actually replaces starch in the tuber and has a sweet pleasant taste taken hot when it is a nourishing beverage and is soothing to the lining of the stomach. In Europe, many wild orchids are now protected by Government Order and salop is manufactured

mostly in India and the Near East. The plants are lifted at the end of summer and are washed and dried in the sun before being ground to a yellow powder. The tubers can be stored for as long as 2 years.

O. mascula, the early purple orchid is found in open woodlands. It has broad leaves and bears its long spurred flowers in a loose spike during April and May. O morio, the green orchid blooms at the same time. It has scented purple flowers veined with green and inhabits damp meadows. O. maculata is the spotted orchid of heaths and moorlands. It bears pinkish mauve flowers spotted with crimson in a cylindrical spike and blooms May—July.

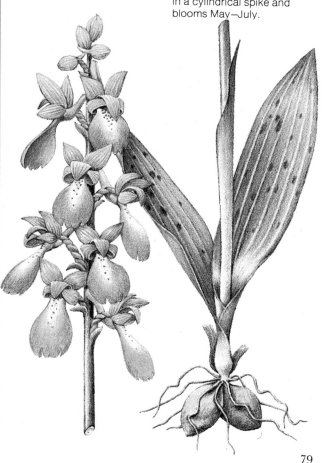

ORIGANUM MAJORANA	ORNITHOGALUM UMBELLATUM	ORYZA SATIVA	OXYCOCCUS PALUSTRIS
MARJORAM	STAR-OF-BETHLEHEM	RICE	CRANBERRY
Labiatae	Liliaceae	Gramineae	Ericaceae
148 S Eur, W Asia, N Af *Warm Temperate Zones*	**149** S+C Eur, Near East	**150** SE Asia, China *Tropical Zones*	**151** N+C Am *Temperate Zones*

Annual 2–8 ft (60 cm–2 m)

O. sativa is a marshland plant. The stem is woody, the leaves forming a long open sheath and narrow blade. The spikelet is single flowered. The lower part of the stem floats on the water, rooting at the nodes.

Rice is planted in shallow water, in rows 12 in. (30 cm) apart, and there are almost 100 varieties suited to different depths of water. Rice fields are mostly situated by the side of rivers whose flood waters submerge low lying land. During the growing season, the plants are flooded for 80 or 90 days. When they are almost ripe, the water is drained away before harvesting.

Perennial 12 in. (30 cm)

O. marjorana is native of S. Europe and found on hilly pastures. It has small shortly-stalked, ovate leaves and bears its tiny rose-red flowers with purple bracts in terminal cymes June–September. There is also a handsome golden leaf form, aureum. It is also known as Sweet Marjoram for in a warm climate it secretes a sweet-smelling essential oil from its stems and leaves. Origanum is an important plant of a bouquet garni used to flavor soups and stews. Origanum will survive a severe winter only in a sheltered garden and in a well drained sandy soil. O. vulgare is native of the British Isles. and most of Europe and W. Asia, taking its name from the Greek oros, a mountain, and ganos, joy, for it allegedly brought joy to all who saw it.

Perennial 6 in.–3 ft (15–90 cm)

O. umbellatum grows abundantly about the hilly terrain of Syria and Jordan so that from a distance, its small starry white flowers resemble bits of dove's dung on the rocks, and this was the name it was given in the Bible. It grows 6–8 in. (15–20 cm) tall, its narrow root leaves having a central white stripe, while the flowers appear in umbels on a leafless stem, the back of each petal having a green stripe. It blooms in early summer. In S. Italy and the Near East including Arabia, the bulbs have for centuries been used as food. Dioscorides said that they were dried by roasting and ground into meal to mix with wheat flour for bread. But they must first be either boiled or roasted otherwise they act as a mild poison. The bulbs were roasted and taken on the pilgrim caravans to Mecca.

Perennial 8–12 in. (20–30 cm)

A small genus indigenous to the N. temperate regions of Europe, Asia and America. They are prostrate, evergreen, shrubby plants with wiry stems which trail over the ground for several feet. The tiny ovate leaves are silver beneath and the nodding pink flowers with recurving petals appear early in summer. They are followed by white fruits which turn red when ripe and are about the size of red currants. They are rich in vitamin C and contain citric and benzoic acids. The fruits are picked in autumn and freeze well. The plant requires to have its roots in moisture – the bilberry is happy in drier soils. O. macrocarpus is confined to E. N. America. It is of prostrate habit with slender creeping stems and oval leaves, glaucous beneath.

OXYDENDRUM ARBOREUM

SORREL TREE

Ericaceae

152   N Am

PANAX GINSENG

GINSENG

Araliaceae

153   S Asia, E—N Am

PAPAVER RHOEAS

RED POPPY

Papaveraceae

154   C+S Asia
Temperate Zones

PASSIFLORA EDULIS

PASSION FRUIT

Passifloraceae

155   Trop+Warm Am,
West Indies
*Warm Temperate Zones
of New World*

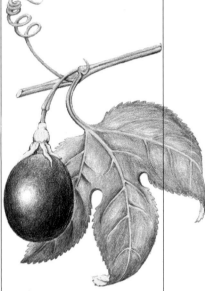

Annual 2 ft (60 cm)

A genus of about 100 species, the red poppy being a colorful weed of corn fields and found on waste ground everywhere. It is called red poppy to distinguish it from the white or opium poppy which has white flowers with a purple blotch at the base and white seeds. The scarlet petals are about 2 in. (5 cm) across with a black patch at the base and with blue-black stamens. The flowers are fleeting and are replaced by large globular seed heads and contain numerous small black round seeds. The seeds are highly nutritious and from them a cooking oil is obtained.

Perennial 6—10 ft (2—3 m)

The only species of the genus, it makes a tall twiggy shrub or small tree and is native only of the E. USA and Canada, where it flourishes in sunshine or shade and in a lime-free soil. The dark green lanceolate leaves turn to brilliant crimson, orange and yellow in autumn before they fall, and in mid-summer it bears drooping clusters of pure white bell-shaped flowers at the tips of the shoots. The plant is found in bogs and in damp open woodlands, where cranberries also grow, and it was introduced to Europe during the mid-18th century. The leaves, when young, possess a refreshing acid taste and are used to make summer drinks, also to flavor soups and stews. They are dried to use in winter stuffings to accompany pork and goose, for the slight acidity counteracts the greasiness.

Perennial 2 ft (60 cm)

A small genus of low growing shrubby plants native of E. Asia and N. America, closely related to the ivy. Ginseng is said to have been appreciated as a food noted for its tonic qualities in China, Korea and Tibet as long ago as 3000 BC. It grows in the valleys but mostly on hillsides beneath trees in a well drained loamy soil for it is intolerant of excess moisture about its roots. It also requires shade. The stems, which arise from the crown just below soil level, have 5 terminal leaflets, about 2 in. (5 cm) long and pointed. The plant is slow growing, the seed taking 2 years to germinate and the roots another 10 years before they are large enough to harvest. They grow 12 in. (30 cm) or more in length and are yellow on the outside, white inside, and have a pleasant bitter sweet taste.

Climbing perennial 20—30 ft (6—8 m)

Forest plants, these species climb by axillary tendrils while the flowers are borne in the same axils. An evergreen, P. edulis has large 3-lobed grey-green leaves with serrated edges. It was named passion flower by the Spaniards in South America because of its representation of Christ on the Cross. The sweetly scented flowers are colored blue, purple and yellow, the center corona representing the Crown of Thorns; the 3 stigmas the nails; the 5 anthers, the wounds; the 10 petals, the 10 apostles. They are of the size of apricots and ripen to deep golden-yellow, hence another name for it is the apricot vine. The skin is thick and the pulp is released with a popping sound. The juice is thirst quenching. In the USA, it is known as maypop and the pulp is delicious when made into preserves. The fruit of P. quadrongularis is larger than that of P. edulis and has purple flesh.

PASTINACA SATIVA	PAULLINIA CUPANA	PERSEA AMERICANA	PETROSELINUM CRISPUM
WILD PARSNIP	GUARANA	AVOCADO PEAR	PARSLEY
Umbelliferae	Sapindaceae	Lauraceae	Umbelliferae

Annual or biennial 2–3 ft (60–90 cm)

It is present as a hedgerow plant throughout N. and Central Europe and Asia including the British Isles and Scandinavia and since earliest times its root has been used as a winter vegetable. In a deep loamy soil, the roots may reach 2 ft (60 cm) in length and being hardy, can be left in the ground until required to use in winter. P. sativa is a hairy plant with pinnate leaves and broad leaflets, the small yellow flowers which appear in July and August being followed by flat oval fruits. The plant is widespread especially on chalkland. The whole plant, including the root, has an unusual aromatic smell much of which is lost when roots are boiled or braised, when they take on a flavor similar to that of roast chestnuts.

Climbing perennial 30 ft (10 m)

Native of the forests of Brazil and Uruguay, the plant climbs by means of axilliary tendrils and may reach a considerable height. It has compound leaves and bears large yellow flowers in panicles. They are followed by pear-like fruits, divided into 3 cells, each of which contains a large seed enclosed in fleshy aril. Guarana is made only by the Guaranis Indians of S. America, who remove the outer case, then roast the nuts for 6 hours. They are then shaken in sacks to remove the shells before pounding them. The powder is mixed with water to make a thick paste which is rolled into 6 in. (15 cm) long squills and dried hard in the sun. It resembles cinnamon, being dark brown and with a bitter taste. Guaran sticks, as they are called, are carried by travellers who chew them or dissolve them in hot water to drink, hot or cold.

Tree 20–40 ft (6–12 m)

A genus of about 150 species, native of the tropics of the new world, the avocado pear provides a delicious pear-shaped fruit (a drupe) containing a single seed or stone enclosed by aromatic flesh. The plant is distributed throughout tropical America where it grows in swamplands, hence its name the alligator pear. It is not a pear but is a member of the bay tree of Laurel family and makes a handsome tree like the bay with glossy laurel-like leaves about 6 in. (15 cm) long and 2 in. (5 cm) broad. The small flowers are borne in a large terminal inflorescence and open twice. The first time only the female part, the pistil, is functional. The next day, the flower opens again when the male parts, the stamens, are functional. Thus the flowers cannot fertilize themselves. They are followed by large pear-shaped fruits covered with a smooth thin green skin, with soft butter-like flesh. The fruits contain large amounts of vitamin E.

Perennial or biennial 6–8 in. (15–20 cm)

A handsome plant present on rocky ground and taking its name from the Latin *petra,* a rock. It is usually found in sight of the sea. All parts of the plant have a strong aromatic smell and all parts have their uses. The Greeks held the plant to be sacred and crowned the victors at the games with its leaves, which better retain their freshness than any other plant. It is a bright green glabrous plant, the tri-pinnate leaves being crisped and crimped to give it a fern-like appearance. If the plants are not allowed to flower, they will be more permanent. For good germination it is important to sow fresh seed. The variety radicosum, also known as Hamburg parsley, forms a large bulbous root which is lifted in winter and grated raw into salads or boiled and served with sauce a vegetable.

PHASEOLUS COCCINEUS

POLE BEAN

Leguminosae

160 Warm N+S Am
Warm Temperate Zones

PHOENIX DACTYLIFERA

DATE PALM

Palmae

161 Warm Af, Asia

PHYSALIS EDULIS

CAPE GOOSEBERRY

Solanaceae

162 Warm N+S Am
Warm Temperate Zones

Annual climber 6–12 ft
(2–4 m)

P. coccineus, also called the
scarlet runner, is native of
Mexico where it is found in
hedgerows and open wood-
lands, climbing by tendrils to
a height of 10–12 ft (4 m).
The leaves are trifoliolate,
each leaflet being about 2 in.
(5 cm) long and 1 in. (2.5 cm)
wide. They are borne all the
way along the thin wire-like
stems terminating in a tendril
which twines up supporting
plants (or canes when grown
in the garden) in an anti-
clockwise manner. The
scarlet flowers appear in twos
and threes from beneath the
leaf nodes and are replaced
by bright green pods 6–12 in.
(15–30 cm) long and about
½ in. (1 cm) wide containing
up to 10 kidney shaped seeds
which are reddish-purple and
about 1 in. (2.5 cm) long.
P. vulgaris is the French or
dwarf bean for it grows only
12 in. (30 cm) tall. P. luneus is
the lima or haricot bean.

Tree 70–80 ft (about 25 m)

The date palm is the most
important source of food for
the people who frequent hot,
arid regions. It also provides
oil and timber for shelter. The
Arabs have a saying that the
palm tree has as many uses
as there are days in the year.
The trees often grow in
groves, giving shade from the
sun, the branchless trunks
rising to a height of 80 ft
(about 25 m) or more, and at
the top is a cluster of leaves,
each one up to 10 ft (3 m)
long. Baskets and food containers are made from them.
The fruits appear among the
leaves in large drooping clusters. They are the staple food
of the desert people. Date
palms are grown extensively
along the N. African coast
where the exportation of the
fruit to all parts of the western
world provides a large part of
the income of the people.
From earliest times, dates
were imported into many
countries. They gave Phoe-
nicia its name, for nowhere
did the date palm grow in
greater abundance. Dates are
today eaten chiefly as dessert
but in earlier times were
baked in pies and used to
make jams and chutneys.
They are nourishing and sustaining and have a high sugar
content. They are also easily
digested.

Perennial 20 in. (50 cm)

Native of the warm temperate
regions, especially
S. America. P. alkekengi, the
winter cherry, is native of
Europe and Asia. Long naturalized in S. Africa, P. edulis
takes its name from Cape
Province where it grows wild
in sandy soil. It increases by
fleshy underground roots like
mint and sends up its fruiting
stems at regular intervals. It
quickly covers a large area.
The deeply veined leaves are
broad at the base, terminating
to a point and having purple
flowers, borne in the leaf
axils. The fruits, which
resemble cherries, are
enclosed in the inflated calyx,
like small balloons, hence its
name of Chinese lantern.
They turn yellow when ripe
late in summer as do the fruits
inside. The fruit is then at its
best. Later, the pods will turn
red. The fruits are sweet and
juicy with the flavor of goose-
berries. The stems die down
in winter and reappear in
spring.

PHYTOLACCA AMERICANA

POKEWEED

Phytolaccaceae

163 SE–N Am
Warm Temperate Zones

PIMENTA OFFICINALIS

ALLSPICE

Myrtaceae

164 S Am, West Indies
Tropical Zones of New World

PIMPINELLA ANISUM

ANISE

Umbelliferae

165 SW Asia, N Af
Warm Temperate Zones

Annual 18–20 in.
(45–50 cm)

It is native of S. Europe, N. Africa and the Near East and takes its name Pimpinella from di-pinella, twicepinnate, from the formation of its leaves. The tiny white flowers, borne in large heads, open star-like and are followed by round seeds. It is mentioned in St. Matthew's gospel for it was one of the tithes of Mosaic law. During mediaeval times, its culture spread all over S. Europe, the seeds being sent to all parts of the continent for they had many uses. The plant is found on wasteland, in full sun and in a sandy soil for it needs long hours of sunshine to ripen its seeds. During Roman times, mustacae was a spiced cake served at the end of a rich meal to prevent indigestion and aniseed "tea," made by pouring half a liter of boiling water onto a teaspoonful of seed and when cool, taking a wineglassfull, will in the same way cure acute fatulence. In Italy and Germany, aniseed is a popular ingredient for imparting its special flavor to cakes and bread and in France and Spain the seed is used to flavor liqueurs. It will also impart its unique flavor to soups and stews, while the young leaves are included in salads. Seeds were at one time popular with confectioners, who made them into aniseed "balls" coated with hard sugar for children to suck. The best seed is produced in Italy and Spain, at Alicante where the seeds are dried on trays and exported to all parts of the world. The seeds are greyish-brown with a sweet, spicy taste. Pimpinella saxifraga is the burnet saxifrage, so called because its tiny leaves, divided into 6 or more pairs of leaflets, resemble the leaves of the

Perennial 10–12 in.
(25–30 cm)

A genus of some 35 species, most being native of subtropical and warmer regions, especially of the New World, with P. americana present as far north as Canada where it is as well known as the dandelion and found about farm buildings and the side of fields. The root is large and fleshy and in spring, the young shoots appear above ground with the leaves tightly folded about the hollow stem. As they unfold, the leaves are lance-shaped and deeply veined. But it is the young shoots that are most wanted and which are cut away at soil level when 6 in. (15 cm) high and steamed like asparagus. The greenish-white flowers are borne in sprays and are followed by red berries which are fed to pigeons and poultry but which are poisonous to humans. An excess, however, causes the meat to take on a purgative action when the birds are eaten.

Tree 30–60 ft (10–18 m)

An evergreen tree, it grows about rocky outcrops, mostly near the sea. It comes into bearing when 3–4 years old and forms a spreading top. It has smooth greyish-green bark and large, glossy oval leaves which smell like those of bay laurel. The small white flowers are borne in terminal clusters and are replaced by the fruits, which resemble green pea-like berries. They are gathered when fully mature, but just before they begin to ripen when they lose much of the essential oil and hence their value. They are sweet and aromatic, the plant being named allspice because the berries smell like cloves (thanks to the presence of eugenol) and juniper and also have peppery undertones, hence the name pimento used by the natives, from the Portugese *pimenta*, pepper.

salad burnet. It is perennial and an Umbellifer, found on hillsides or dry meadows throughout Europe and W. Asia. It grows 2 ft (60 cm) tall. The leaves to use are those which form in a basal rosette. They are included in salads to which they impart a sharp, spicy taste and make a pleasant "green" sauce to serve with fish or cold meat.

PINUS PINEA	PIPER CUBEBA	PIPER METHYSTICUM	PISTACIA VERA
PINE-NUT	CUBEB	KAVA	PISTACHIO
Pinaceae	Piperaceae	Piperaceae	Pistaciaceae
166 N+C Eur, Asia, Am *Temperate Zones*	**167** SE Asia *Tropical Zones*	**168** SE Asia	**169** S Eur, W Asia *Warm Temperate Zones*

Tree 40—60 ft (12—18 m)

It may be the fruit of the "green fir tree" of the Book of Hosea, for the stone pine, so called because it grows about rocky outcrops in the Holy Land and Near East, has since earliest times been appreciated for its edible nuts. The tree usually has a twisted naked trunk and wide spreading top, its upper branches formed horizontally and it bears its stiff narrow leaves in twos. They are 4 in. (10 cm) long. The cones, or apples as the old herbalists called them, are borne solitary or in pairs at the ends of the branches, the seeds being sweet and nutty, like small almonds and with a similar taste. They are used as dessert and grated over cakes and into bread. The pines take their name from the Latin *pinus,* pitch or resin, which is obtained from the tree by tapping.

Perennial 9—12 ft (3—4 m)

The Cubeb, P. cubeba, native of Java and Sumatra, has narrower pointed leaves than other species and the brown berries are borne in short cylindrical clusters. They are larger than those of the black pepper and wrinkled with long, thin stalks attached. The dried fruits have a camphor-like smell and taste and are used in curries and many eastern dishes. P. niger is the black pepper, the finest product coming from the Malabar coast of eastern India. It grows best in rich soil close to the sea is and is now cultivated all over the tropics. The berries are formed in drooping cylindrical spikes 4 in. (10 cm) long and are gathered 2 or 3 times a year while still black and before they redden. White pepper is obtained from the white seeds of the ripe fruit. Ground pepper is used as a condiment and to impart its sharp, acrid taste to flavor soups, sauces and stews.

Perennial 9—12 ft (3—4 m)

A large genus of more than 2,000 species of perennial plants, indigenous to the tropics of the Old and New Worlds, especially Indonesia and Polynesia, and providing numerous items of food value. They are mostly climbing plants with alternate simple leaves, the stems with conspicuous scars and swellings of the nodes and leaves which in P. methysticum are heartshaped, about 6 in. (15 cm) long and 4 in. (10 cm) wide and dark purplish-green. The plants climb by aerial roots. The stems are black and are used in Polynesia to make the popular and nourishing beverage yaquona but it is the thickened underground part of the stem that is mostly used. The drink is taken hot and is similar to arrowroot. It is demulcent but used in quantity, has a stupefying effect.

Tree 20—30 ft (6—8 m)

In the Bible, the trees of this small genus are often mentioned as supplying gum resins, incense and food. The nuts mentioned in Genesis would most likely be those of P. vera, a deciduous tree with leathery, odd-pinnate leaves. It makes a large spreading top, providing valuable shade for man and animals. It is said that Batnam, near Aleppo, took its name from the large number of trees which grew there, *batam* being Arabic for nuts; the Hebrew is *botnim.* The nut has a light brown shell and the kernel is yellow-green, Pistachio-green now being a recognized color. P. terebinthus, which grows with it, yields a fragrant resin, the Cyprus-turpentine of commerce, hence its name "turpentine" tree. P. lentiscus yields a gummy exudation known as mastic which is employed in the drinks trade and which children of the Near East chew as a sweetmeat.

PISUM SATIVUM	PODOPHYLLUM PELTATUM	POLYGONATUM MULTIFLORUM
PEA	MAY APPLE	SOLOMON'S SEAL
Leguminosae	Podophyllaceae	Liliaceae
170 Medit, C Asia *Warm Temperate Zones*	**171** E–N Am *NE Asia*	**172** N Eur, Asia *North Temperate Zones*

Annual climbing to 6 ft (2 m)

A genus of 6 species, from which the garden pea is derived. It is a plant which grows up to 6–7 ft (2 m) high, climbing by tendrils which replace the leaflets at the end of the rachis. The leaves are alternate and compound; the flowers purplish-white; the fruit a pod or legume which opens by a suture line and contains up to 12 or more seeds. Like the vetch, with which it grows on sand dunes and on barren ground round the Mediterranean, pulling itself up nearby plants, its early history is lost in obscurity. With the broad bean it was in early man's staple diet for it could be harvested in summer and dried in the sun to use through winter. It was used for making pottage, a thick soup as an alternative to lentils, and not as a vegetable as it is today. The pea was first grown as a garden plant at Roncesvaux in France, and early in the 16th century, the Runcival pea as it came to be called was well established in England and Germany. It was Thomas Knight, a Hereford squire, who took up its improvement and it was he who introduced the wrinkled or marrowfat pea.

Perennial 2–3 ft (60–90 cm)

Species of this small genus are mostly native of the Himalayas and E. Asia, with one, the may apple, a familiar woodland plant of E. North America. From the rhizome-like root arises a shoot bearing two large peltate leaves measuring more than 1 ft (30 cm) across and which droop down when young like half-closed umbrellas. The leaves are deeply lobed and are held up at the center by long sturdy stems. From the intersection of the two leaf stems, a white flower appears in May, hence its name May apple, which has the scent of a lily. It is about 1 in. (2.5 cm) across and is followed by a heavy lemon-like fruit which ripens in August. The fruits, which are usually found in large groups, are green at first, ripening to golden yellow. All other parts of the plant are poisonous.

Perennial 20–24 in. (50–60 cm)

A small genus present in open woodlands and hedgerows. It increases by underground rhizomatous roots which are knotted together, while the stems of P. odoratum, the scented Solomon's seal, are angular and thus gave the plant its botanical name. The common Solomon's seal has round, arching stems and alternate, elliptical leaves which are ribbed and from the axils of which appear greenish-white bell-shaped flowers which hang in drooping clusters. They are unscented but those of P. odoratum have a lily-like scent. They appear later than those of the common Solomon's seal, which blooms in May and June, and are followed by blue-black berries. The round marks on the roots resemble the mark of a seal and are like a 6-pointed star.

POLYGONUM BISTORTA

BISTORT

Polygonaceae

173	N Eur, Asia *Temperate Zones*

PORPHYRA LACINIATA

LAVER

Algae

174	Seas, Coasts *Temperate Zones*

PORTULACA OLERACEA

PURSLANE

Portulacae

175	S Asia *Warm Temperate Zones*

POTERIUM SANGUISORBA

BURNET

Rosaceae

176	N Eur, N Asia *Temperate Zones*

Perennial 16 in. (40 cm)

It takes its name from the twice (bis) twisted root formation, for which reason it is also called snakeweed. It grows in damp meadows and pastures and has black roots, red inside, which contain tannic acid. The blue-green leaves are arrow-shaped and arise directly from the rootstock, while the flesh-colored flowers are borne in June and July in a cylindrical spike. In times of food scarcity, the roots are boiled and used with other available foods or, after steeping in water and roasted, are ground to make into flour which can be baked into nourishing bread and cakes. The young shoots, with those of nettles and a small quantity of barley, can be boiled in a cloth bag to make "pudding". The young shoots can be simmered to serve with meats and the water, with its valuable mineral salts, included in soups and stews. The dried leaves make a useful addition to stuffings.

Annual Prostrate

Taking its name from a Greek word meaning "purple," this annual seaweed is present in coastal areas, growing on rocks in shallow salt water and also in river estuaries. The fronds grow long and narrow, like ribbons, and are much cut and divided with waved margins. For many years, at the Reform Club in London, laver and lemon was served from a silver saucepan to accompany roast leg of mutton. Lemon juice is used as an alternative to vinegar. As a preventative of scurvy, and as it can be kept in boxes for some months without deterioration, laver was taken on long sea voyages until the introduction of citrus fruits. Not as rich in food value, but used in a similar way, is the green laver, Ulva latissima. It is often found growing with the purple laver, from which it is distinguished by its pale green coloring.

It has now become established on wasteland in most parts of the world as a garden escape. It forms a spreading, bushy plant with thick succulent leaves which are oval and about 1 in. (2.5 cm) long. They are usually in groups of five and like the stems, are tinted with purple or crimson. The flowers are small and brightest yellow. The leaves have a slightly salty taste and should be used when young. They contain vitamins A and C and are rich in mineral salts. The leaves are valuable spring tonic and can be eaten with a vinegar dressing, while the older leaves and shoots are included in soups and stews. The French include it, with sorrel, in their famous Soup Bonne-Femme. The Sea purslane is Atriplex partulacoides, a plant of salt marshes and the seashore.

Perennial 16—24 in. (40—60 cm)

The burnets are plants of downlands, usually growing in a chalky subsoil. Shakespeare associated them with good husbandry and sheep love to graze on them. P. sanguisorba, the lesser or salad burnet, grows 16 in. (40 cm) tall and has small pinnate, finely toothed leaves which Turner in his *Herbal* likened to the "spreading wings of little birds." In summer it bears small globular heads of greenish-brown petal-less flowers. When crushed, the leaves and stems smell of cucumber and bring their unique flavor to salads. Remove the leaves from the stems before including them in salads. The plant was named from the Greek *poterion*, a drinking cup, and sanguisorba because of its ability to heal wounds. The greater burnet, P. officinalis (syn. Sanguisorba officinalis), grows 2 ft (60 cm) tall with larger, less deeply toothed leaves which appear on branched stems.

PRIMULA VERIS

COWSLIP

Primulaceae

177 C Eur
Temperate Zones

PRUNUS ARMENIACA

APRICOT

Rosaceae

178 S Eur, C Asia
Warm Temperate Zones

PRUNUS CERASIFERA

WILD CHERRY

Rosaceae

179 N Eur, Asia
North Temperate Zones

Perennial 6–8 in. (15–20 cm)

One of a large genus of decorative plants, P. veris is present in the British Isles and N. Europe where it inhabits hilly pastures and open meadows. One of the loveliest of wild flowers, it blooms in May, after the primrose. Both plants die back in winter and produce new basal leaves in spring. The leaves are obovate and deeply grooved, to enable every drop of moisture to be channelled to the roots before evaporation. The leaves are hairy on the underside, while the golden yellow flowers with their inflated bell-shaped calyx are borne in umbels of 6–8 on short downy peduncles. The flowers are included in early salads, also the leaves which purify the blood and act as a tonic. The primrose (from the Latin *primus,* first) is one of the earliest of the year's flowers. They are pale yellow and appear on short peduncles, as if growing singly from the crown of the plant. The leaves are similar to those of the cowslip but are larger. It enjoys shade, being found in open woodlands and hedgerows. Propagation, as far the cowslips, is by root division or from seed.

Tree 6–12 ft (2–4 m)

The genus includes the almond and peach, edible plants and highly decorative. The apricot makes a small twiggy tree with rounded leaves, pointed at the apex, and bears white flowers tinted with red. They open early in spring; the plant takes its name from the latin *traecox,* early. The trees are found in hedgerows and on barren hillsides in their native lands. The fruit is a drupe with a downy golden yellow skin, tinted red and with yellow flesh surrounding the kernel, which is edible and similar to the bitter almond. The essential oil is used in confectionery while the fruit, used fresh or dried, contains, like all fruits and vegetables with yellow skins, large amounts of carotene (vitamin A). It also has liberal amounts of the B vitamins as well as being rich in salts of iron and calcium.

Tree 10–30 ft (3–8 m)

A genus of mostly deciduous trees or shrubs with simple undivided leaves and white or pink flowers arranged in showy racemes. The genus includes almond, peach, plum and cherry. The wild cherry is native of the Balkans and Near East and is one of the parents of the cultivated or sweet cherries. The cherry takes its botanical name from Kerasons, a city of Asia Minor where the fruit once grew in abundance. It has pale green leaves and blooms early in spring, the flowers being followed by yellowish-red fruits. P. avium is also a wild cherry and known as the gean. It is distributed throughout Europe and W. Asia and makes a tall tree with smooth bark which peels horizontally. The white flowers are borne in dense clusters and are followed by small red fruits.

PRUNUS COMMUNIS

WILD PLUM

Rosaceae

180 N Eur, Asia
North Temperate Zones

PRUNUS PERSICA

PEACH

Rosaceae

181 Medit, C Asia, China
Warm Temperate Zones

Tree 6–30 ft (2–8 m)

The wild plum, P. communis, is probably a natural hybrid and is present in hedgerows and open woodlands. A deciduous tree reaching 30 ft (8 m) in height, it has smooth bark and elliptic leaves about 4 in. (10 cm) long and 1 in. (2.5 cm) wide. The white flowers arise from lateral spurs, usually in twos. They appear early in spring with or before the leaves and are often damaged by frost. They are followed by round or oval fruits about 4 in. (10 cm) in diameter and which vary in color from yellow to crimson and purple. A shining outer skin encloses the thick golden flesh which is sweet and juicy and which in turn encloses a large stone. Garden varieties developed from P. communis are grown commercially all over the temperate world for dessert and for canning and bottling. They also freeze well. When dried, they are called prunes and keep for a year or longer. They are eaten after soaking in water. The green-gage is a round yellowish-green plum of exceptional flavor. Possibly a derivative of P. communis, they are believed to have originated in Armenia and reached France about the year 1500. Named Reine Claude in honor of Francis I's Queen, they were introduced into Britain by Sir William Gage and called greengages in that country. The damson is P. institia, a small oval purple plum which is native of the Near East. It takes its name from the town of Damascus where it abounds but is now natu-ralized over most parts of Europe and Asia. The Bullace is closely related to the damson but bears oval fruits. The plant is native of the British Isles and N. Europe and possesses extreme hardiness. The sloe or black-thorn is a wide shrub, the twigs being covered in black down, the small purple-black fruits being covered, like all plums, in grey "bloom" as on grapes. They are used when ripe to make sloe gin and for preserves.

Tree 6–12 ft (3–4 m)

Small twisted trees which are native of W. China and Persia. Prunus davidiana has nar-rower leaves than P. persica and bears white flowers, present in N. China, where it is a common plant. It may be a parent of the cultivated peach now grown commer-cially. P. persica, believed to have originated in W. China and Persia, has oval leaves and bears bright pink flowers which appear before the leaves. Peach blossom is fre-quently mentioned in the Chinese Book of Odes, and as the trees grow to a great age, the peach is recognized as the symbol of longevity. The Chinese god of longevity, Shou Hsing, is usually depicted arising out of a peach fruit. The peach reached Europe early in history by way of the silk route from China. A peach will begin to crop when only 3 years old and will bear heavily for several hundred years though only in a climate where the winter is cold and dry, followed by a warm dry summer. However, moisture at the roots is essential if the fruit is to set well. It crops well in a soil with a high lime content. The orange-yellow fruits, flushed with crimson or pink, ripen in late summer. The fruit is a drupe, about tennis ball size, with a delicate outer skin and golden orange flesh which encloses a large rough stone or kernel. Down one side of the fruit is a furrow or suture line, as with apricots and plums. When served as dessert, the stone is the only part removed after cutting in half. The fruits can also be bottled in syrup and canned. In USA and Australia where peaches are plentiful, they are cooked in pies as apples are in colder climes.

PSALLIOTA CAMPESTRIS

FIELD MUSHROOM

Fungus

182 Temperate Zones

PSIDIUM GUAYAVA

GUAVA

Myrtaceae

183 Trop Am
Tropical Zones of New World

PUNICA GRANATUM

POMEGRANATE

Lythraceae

184 Medit, SW+S+E Asia
Warm Temperate Zones of Old World

The field mushroom has been prized for its good eating qualities through the centuries. Its growth depends upon organic matter obtainable from material either dead or alive. P. campestris is only one of hundreds of edible fungi, but many are extremely poisonous. This fungus is found in meadows and grows in decayed animal manure. It appears in early autumn, often in fairy rings. It has a white (or brown) cap which expands about 1 in. (2.5 cm) every 24 hours until it reaches 6 in. (15 cm) across. The gills beneath the cap from which the reproductive spores are released, are at first flesh-pink becoming blackish-brown with age. Its faint aromatic (mushroomy) smell is well known. Attached to the cap is the stalk which arises from the ground to about 4 in. (10 cm) long. All parts are edible. The Horse mushroom, P. arvensis, grows in clumps in meadows and parks. It has an egg-shaped cap of yellowish-brown which with age cracks open. The gills are greyish-pink turning black with age when the spores are released. It has the smell of aniseed but is slightly bitter and its appearance is not as pleasing as the field mushroom. P. augusta, a delicacy of pine woods, has a nutty almond-like taste. The semi-globular cap has pale brown scales but the flesh is firm and white though turns yellow with age. Also present in deciduous and coniferous forests is the chanterelle, a favorite food of the French and Italians. Cantharellus cibarius has a white funnel-shaped cap 2–3 in. (5–7.5 cm) across and white gills and spores, the stems being short and thin. The flesh is white with the smell of ripe apricots and it makes excellent eating. It usually grows in circles about moss and dead leaves.

Tree or shrub 6–12 ft (2–4 m)

One of a genus of 140 species native of tropical America and the West Indies where P. guayava is grown commercially for its sweet and juicy yellow fruits. The trees come into bearing when 5–6 years old and have opposite elliptic leaves leathery to touch and are evergreen. The white flowers are borne singly in the leaf axils and are followed by round yellow-skinned fruits like small oranges. The flesh inside is pink, with a delicious taste and aroma. It makes a decorative house or garden room plant and will fruit indoors in 3 years. Rarely exceeding 3–4 ft (1 m) tall, it grows bushy and is tolerant of the dry atmosphere of a house which has central heating. In the wild, the plants grow on rocky ground but in rich alluvial soil and they flourish in semi-shade.

Tree 18–20 ft (5–6 m)

A small much-branched tree or shrub, since earliest times ilt has been appreciated for its deliciously flavored globular fruits the size of apples. The branches of the tree carry thorns and the lanceolate leaves are dark green; the cup-shaped flowers being of rich crimson. In their native land, N. Africa, they appear almost the whole year round. Testimony to its beauty is borne out by its selection for one of the ornaments on the ark of the Tabernacle. The fruit when ripe has a hard skin or rind of yellowish-red and is crowned by the lobes of the calyx which persist on the ripe fruits. The word *granata* means full of grains or seeds, which are present in the fruits, enclosed in chambers of yellow pith. The seeds are soft and can be consumed with the red pulp, which is full of juice and thirst quenching.

PYRUS COMMUNIS

PEAR

Rosaceae

 185 S Eur, W+C Asia
Temperate Zones

QUERCUS ROBUR

ENGLISH OAK

Fagaceae

186 Eur
Temperate Zones

RAPHANUS SATIVUS

RADISH

Cruciferae

187 C Eur, C Asia, Medit
Temperate Zones

Tree 6–18 ft (2–6 m)

A genus of 30 species, native of the Mediterranean regions and S.W. Asia, the pear being of warmer parts, the apple of more northerly climes. P. pyrifolia makes a small deciduous tree with rounded leaves which are dark green and glossy above and with yellowish stems. The white flowers, borne in clusters, are followed by small pear-shaped brownish-yellow fruits. The tree is native of W. Asia, Persia and the E. Mediterranean while P. communis is also present in France and Italy. It is now naturalized in the British Isles and may have come with the Romans or with the Normans, for it is often found close to old castles and monastic buildings. Its oval leaves are held on long yellowish stalks; the flowers are dingy white with purple anthers; the fruits greenish brown. From these two wild pears have been raised the large delicious fruits which, when eaten at their peak of perfection, have no equal as a dessert, with their melting juicy flesh and an aroma like that of fragrant red roses. Wall paintings at Pompeii show the tree and its fruit and Virgil tells of having received three kinds as a gift from Cato, one being the Volemus, so called because it would entirely fill the hand with its broad rounded base, the hallmark of a well grown pear, the upper part tapering almost to a point. From the juice of ripe pears, a wine known as perry is obtained and which aids the digestion and stimulates the appetite. Pears do not store as long as apples which can be kept for 6 months and require a temperature of 50° F (10° C) to maintain them in condition. They keep for about 4–6 weeks.

Tree 50–60 ft (about 15 m)

A genus of more than 450 species of widely distributed majestic evergreen or deciduous trees, the nuts or acorns of several species being used to make flour for bread in times of famine. Houses and ships have for centuries been built from the timber, for it is one of the most durable of woods. Q. robur with its deeply furrowed brown bark is native of Europe and W. Asia. Q. aegilops, distributed throughout Palestine and the near east, bears the largest acorns of all the species. Acorns are partly enclosed in scaly cups which hold them to the branches by a strong stem 2 in. (5 cm) long. The acorns are oval, tapering to a point, and are green at first, the shell turning brown as they ripen. The nut is released when the shell is cracked open.

Annual 10–12 in. 25–30 cm)

Native of temperate Asia, N. Africa, China and Japan, it was grown in ancient Egypt and fed to those who built the Pyramids, for the roots are sustaining and, with their slightly bitter juice, quench the thirst. They are rich in mineral salts and contain more iodine than any plant. The Roman armies consumed the radish in large quantities and so did the Saxons, who named it *raedic,* from its thin red skin which hides the succulent white flesh. Its roots grown round and sit on top of the soil, or are long and cylindrical, like the little finger, and grow down into the soil. They are occasionally found in cultivated fields and by the sea shore but are mostly grown in the vegetable garden. The winter black and China white are winter radishes, forming knobby roots as large as a clenched fist.

RHEUM RAPONTICUM	RHODYMENIA PALMATA	RHUS GLABRA	RIBES GROSSULARIA
RHUBARB	DULSE	STAGHORN	GOOSEBERRY
Polygonaceae	Algae	Anacardiaceae	Grossulariaceae

Perennial 2–3 ft (60–90 cm)

Perennial Prostrate

Tree 6–60 ft (2–16 m)

Perennial 3–4 ft (1 m)

Its name is derived from Rha, the ancient name for the River Volga on whose banks it grows wild, as it also does across Siberia and N. Asia. Seed reached Britain and N. Europe about 2 centuries ago. The plant produces its fruity stems early in spring. They measure up to 2 ft (60 cm) long and more than 1 in. (2.5 cm) across. They are deeply grooved and greenish-red and at the end is the lobed leaf which may measure 2 ft (60 cm) in length and the same across. Like most of the family which includes sorrel and dock, the stems contain potassium oxalate and malic acid. The leaves should not be used either fresh or cooked as to some, they act as a mild poison. Rhubarb roots soon grow into large clumps, each producing numerous stems during the spring and summer, at the end of which they die back.

It is found in shallow pools and often attached to the rocks. The fronds are smooth and wide apart, like an open hand, hence its maritime name of drowned men's fingers, although it has been greatly prized as a food since earliest times. It is a purple seaweed which can be eaten fresh after washing to clean it of sand; or it is cooked. After gathering and washing dulse is spread out to dry, when it becomes covered with a white powder which has a pleasant sweet taste. This powder is known as ''mannite'' and is present on many seaweeds. Pepper dulse (Laurencia pinnatifida) is a small brown seaweed which is highly nutritious, but as it has a ''hot'' taste, is best used with purple dulse at a rate of one part to two.

A large genus, native of subtropical and the warmer regions of the world. R. vernicifera is the lacquer-tree of Japan, and R. trilobata, the lemonade tree of the USA, where it is found in open woodlands and clearings. There are several poisonous species but they are readily distinguished for their flowers are borne in axilliary panicles and the fruit is smooth. With the edible sumachs, the fruit is covered in crimson hairs. The leaves and bark of many sumachs are used in the tanning industry, but R. glabra and other species produce berries which yield a lemon tasting juice from which summer drinks are made and also preserves. The plant grows in thickets and produces its berries in large clusters. They are green at first, turning to reddish-orange when ripe, at which stage the upright stem on which they are held will begin to droop.

A genus of 150 species native of the N. temperate regions of the world, several providing edible fruits of universal popularity. Red and black currants take their name ''currants'' from Carinth in Greece, from where small dried grapes were exported in large quantities. Later, wild red currants of the Epirus were harvested and dried in the same way and retained the original name. R. rubrum, the red currant (and its white form, alba) is widely dispersed and is present in open woodlands and hedgerows. Like all members of the family, it makes a woody plant 3–4 ft (1 m) tall. Its 3–5 lobed leaves are bluntly toothed, and its small green flowers, borne in drooping clusters, are followed by small green berries which turn red when ripe.
They are found in profusion in the Alpine regions of Europe and are made into cooling drinks and preserves. The fruits contain malic acid and vitamin C and they have a

ROSA CANINA

WILD ROSE

Rosaceae

192 Eur, NW Af, C+W Asia
N Am

"sharp" taste so that the preserve is suitable to serve with cold meats. R. nigrum, the black currant, grows 4 ft (just over 1 m) tall and is present in damp soils. It is a plant of extreme hardiness, fruiting well in Siberia. Unlike the red currant and gooseberry, it forms a thicket of shoots which arise from underground stem buds. The leaves are aromatic and infused in boiling water make a pleasant "tea." The berries ripen to purple-black in late summer. They are richer in vitamin C than any other fruit and so make a health-giving drink for children and invalids. The fruits are also used for dessert and in pies and are the base of the French liqueur de cassis.

R. grossularia, the gooseberry, is also rich in vitamin C and contains important mineral salts. It prefers more shade than the currants and makes a small muchbranched deciduous bush covered in short spines. It has 3−5 lobed leaves and bears small drooping reddish green flowers followed by round or oval fruits, often hairy. They ripen in early summer and are green, yellow or crimson when mature. They are the size of small cherries but when cultivated often reach a much larger size. They are sour in the wild but often treacle-sweet when cultivated and are used as dessert and for pies. They make delicious preserves and freeze and bottle well, remaining whole with their firm skins.

Perennial 4−8 ft (1−2 m)

A genus of 250 or more species, native of the N. temperate regions of the world, their stems covered with large hooked thorns, those of R. canina being shaped like a dog's tooth, hence its common name. The leaves have 2−4 pairs of serrate leaflets and are hairy at the veins. The pinkish-white flowers measure 2 in. (5 cm) across and are sweetly scented. They appear early in summer, their beauty being enhanced by the numerous golden stamens. The fruit (hips) consist of a number of achenes enclosed in a fleshy receptacle. They ripen to bright red and are harvested in late summer. Hips have been collected from plants growing in the hedgerows of every northern an central European country since earliest times. In Britain, rose hip seeds were found in the skeleton of a Neolithic woman of 2,000 BC. The hips contain malic acid and are rich in vitamin C.

Perennial 6−7 ft (2 m)

A genus of a single species, native of S. Europe and the Mediterranean islands of Corsica and Sardinia and one nature's most useful plants. It is a shrubby evergreen with small linear leaves and in spring bears pale blue flowers in short axillary racemes. In its natural habitat it grows about rocky ground usually in sight of the sea, hence its name Ros marinus, "dew of the sea." The entire plant is highly resinous, its essential oil contained in microscopic goblet-shaped cells deeply embedded in the leaves; hence it retains its scent for a long time when the stems are cut. Because of this it was used at weddings and at burials. Though native of the Mediterranean, the plant will withstand many degrees of frost but in N. Europe is best grown against a sunny wall to give winter protection. One sprig or shoot will impart its balsamic scent to roast meats better than any other herb, while the flowers, which are so much visited by bees in spring, lend interest to a salad. Rosemary is used to make Eau de Cologne which Napoleon, a native of Corsica, used to refresh himself and perhaps remind him of his beloved Corsica where it grows in profusion.

RUBUS FRUTICOSUS	RUMEX ACETOSA	RUTA GRAVEOLENS

BLACKBERRY

Rosaceae

194 Eur, N Af, Asia, N Am
Temperate Zones

COMMON SORREL

Polygonaceae

195 Eur, Asia
Temperate Zones

RUE

Rutaceae

196 SE Eur
Warm Temperate Zones

Perennial 3–10 ft (2–3 m)

A large genus of more than 250 species distributed throughout the N. temperate regions of the world. R. fruticosus, the blackberry, is a plant of sprawling stems, forming dense impenetrable thickets, with their large thorns, the stems often growing 12 ft (4 m) long and rooting at the tips where they touch the soil. The pinnate leaves have 3–5 toothed leaflets and are also prickly. The pinkish-white flowers in summer are followed by green fruits (drupes) which turn red, then black when ripe in autumn. They have a unique aroma and are sweet and juicy. They are found in hedgerows everywhere. R. idaeus is the raspberry, a plant of open woodlands. The canes or stems grow upright ans 3–4 ft (1 m) tall from underground runners and are covered with small prickles. The pinnate leaves have 3–7 toothed leaflets. The white flowers, borne in drooping clusters, are followed by red fruits when ripe. They have an aromatic perfume and are sweet and juicy.

R. chamoemorus is the cloudberry, a creeping plant of moorlands and mountains slopes and increasing by underground stems. Its palmate leaves terminate as a single flower which is replaced by an orange fruit used for preserves. The stone bramble, R. saxatilis, is present in similar country. It has slender stems with trifoliate leaves and bears greenish-white flowers followed by red berries. R. alleghiensis is the Alleghenny blackberry of the E. USA, a familiar plant of the Alleghenny Mountains. The plants produce thick woody stems covered in sharp spines, the palmate leaves usually divided into 5 leaflets. The white flowers with yellow stamens are borne in clusters throughout summer and are followed by jet black berries in autumn. R. occidentalis is the black raspberry or thimbleberry, a plant of hedgerows and open woodlands of the E. USA and Canada, from Quebec to Georgia. It has brown upright stems covered in large hooked prickles and it bears pink flowers in generous clusters. They are followed by green fruits which turn red, then purple and black. They part from the core like all raspberries, leaving a hole, like a thimble in size and appearance. They are used for dessert and for preserves and have a sharper taste than blackberries.

Perennial 6 in.–2 ft (15–60 cm)

A cosmopolitan genus which includes the docks, distributed throughout the N. temperate regions of the world. The common sorrel, R. acetosa, is widespread on grassy hillsides and by the side of fields. It has long stalked arrow-shaped leaves 4–6 in. (10–15 cm) long which are dark green, tinted with crimson, and in June bears whorled spikes of reddish-green flowers on red stems. The young leaves are rich in potassium salts and are restorative. They also contain large amounts of vitamins A and C but as they have a high oxalic acid content, they should be cooked in two waters. R. scutatus is the French sorrel. The leaves are larger than those of R. acetosa and less acid. With its sharpness, sorrel sauce is the ideal complement for fish, goose and duck.

Perennial 20–24 in. (50–60 cm)

A shrubby evergreen, native of S. Europe and the Near East and taking its name from the Greek *reuo,* to set free, for it was thought to be able to free the body of all ills. Because of its extreme bitterness, it was the herb of repentance or Herb O'Grace. It was also considered to have magical powers and to guard the wearer against witchcraft. It is one of the bluest-green of nature's plants, the variety jackman's blue having leaves that are more blue than green. It is also one of nature's most beautiful plants, the leaves being divided into numerous oblong segments. The yellow flowers with toothed petals are borne during mid-summer. Rue has tonic qualities and is rich in mineral salts. It grows on rocky ground in well drained soil and exposed to the full heat of the sun.

SACCHARUM OFFICINARUM	SAGITTARIA SAGITTIFOLIA	SALSOLA SODA	SALVIA OFFICINALIS
SUGAR CANE	ARROWHEAD	SEA SPINACH	SAGE
Gramineae	Alismaceae	Chenopodiaceae	Labiateae
197 Trop E Asia *Tropical Zones*	**198** Eur, W Asia	**199** N Eur, Asia, Am *Temperate Zones*	**200** S Eur *Temperate Zones*

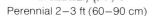

Perennial 10–15 ft (3–4 m)

A genus of 5 species native of the tropics and subtropics with S. officinarum perhaps of S.E. Asia. It is now cultivated in all the warmer parts of the world, but is believed to be absent from the wild except as a local escape from sugar plantations. The plant forms a rhizamatous root from which arises new shoots each year. They are about 2 in. (5 cm) across and topped by a woolly inflorescence covered in long hairs. Each year young shoots containing a bud are removed and reset to form a new plantation, which remains productive for about 4 years. It needs a rich, well irrigated soil. At the end of the growing season before they flower, the stems are cut with a machete just above ground level and the juice extracted by crushing the stems between rollers. They yield about 15% sugar.

Perennial 2–3 ft (60–90 cm)

A plant of the waterside, of rivers and lakes, its roots are much prized by country folk as a valuable item of food. The plant forms a swollen stem or tuber at the base, about the size of a walnut. The plant has long stalks which are triangular and glossy leaves shaped like an arrow head which arise above the water, the stems varying in length with the depth of water. The flowers appear in spring in whorls of 3 or more and on leafless stems which arise from the base. They are white with a purple mark on the base of each petal and appear late in summer. The species S. chinensis (Is-ze-kn), found in most parts of China, forms a similar edible root. The plants increase by creeping stolons. Established plantations provide large numbers of tubers which are lifted from the mud all year.

Annual 1–4 in. (2.5–10 cm)

There are about 150 species of the saltworts distributed throughout the temperate world, but confined to the coast where they grow in sandy soil in salt marshes and often in almost pure sand by the seashore. They are mostly prostrate or low growing plants with short thick grey-green leaves ending in a spine. The leaves are fleshy, and Dr. Fernie, physician of Brighton, England, writing in the late 19th century, said that it was the best of all wild vegetables for the table, its fleshy cylindrical leaves when boiled and served with white sauce making delicious eating. The leaves can also be included in salads. The tiny green flowers are borne at the base cf the leaves in mid-summer. The saltworts are antiscorbutic and are rich in mineral salts.

Perennial 18–20 in. (45–50 cm)

It takes its name from *salvere,* to be saved, for, as an Anglo-Saxon manuscript says, "Why should man die where sage grows in his garden?" It had so many culinary and medicinal uses that it was one of the most important of all herbs. Salvia officinalis is a shrubby plant with square stems and narrow opposite leaves which are grey-green and wrinkled. There are golden and purple leaf forms. The small purple flowers are borne in whorls in the axils of the leaves. The plant is native of S. Europe, especially Dalmatia, where it grows on rocky ground fully exposed to the sun's rays and these are the conditions it enjoys in the garden. Propagation is by seed or from cuttings.

SAMBUCUS NIGRA

ELDERBERRY

Sambucaceae

 201 Eur
W Asia, N Am

SASSAFRAS OFFICINALE

SASSAFRAS

Lauraceae

202 E–N Am

SATUREIA MONTANA

SAVORY

Labiatae

203 S Eur
Warm Temperate Zones

Tree or shrub 6–20 ft
(2–6 m)

A genus of 40 species, taking its name from the Saxon *aeld*, fire, for the hollow stems with the pith removed were blown through to kindle fires.
S. nigra is deciduous with furrowed bark an dark green pinnate leaves. Both the bark and leaves release a fetid smell when touched, but the flowers, borne in large flat umbels in early summer, have a pleasant muscatel scent and are used to impart this to pears in store, for the flowers retain their fragrance when dry. The flowers are replaced by small green fruits, purple-black when ripe, and large numbers make up the truss. A narcotic wine is made from the berries which is usually taken hot before bedtime in winter. The juice, thickened with honey or sugar and taken hot, is known as a ''rob'' (syrup) and will ease a tight chest brought on by a cold. Damsons or sloes are usually included and also when making elderberry wine. Elder fruits, with crab apples or wild pears, make delicious pies and tarts; also jams and preserves; and with wild ginger (snakeroot) and spices make chutneys and ketchups. An infusion of elder flowers in boiling water and allowed to cool makes an effective after-shave lotion.

Tree 30–40 ft (10–12 m)

A genus of only 2 species, one (S. officinale) native of the eastern United States and Canada; the other to China and Formosa. S. officinale is believed to have been introduced into Europe by the Spaniards in the 16th century and was named by the botanist Nicolas Monardes from the Spanish for saxifrage though it bears no resemblance to that plant. It is a smooth, brown-barked deciduous tree with slender branches and with glossy oval laurel-like leaves about 4 in. (10 cm) long and 2 in. (5 cm) broad. The leaves are dried and finely ground and used in the S. United States as an aromatic condiment and in curry powders, while from the young shoots in spring, a tonic beer is brewed. All parts of the tree have commercial uses. From the spongy roots and the bark, also from the red berries, an oil is distilled and used in medicine and perfumes.

Annual or perennial 6–10 in.
(15–25 cm)

A genus of more than 200 species present especially in the Mediterranean. The plants were believed to have had connections with the Satyrs, hence their botanical name. They are low-growing woody herbs like the thymes.
S. montana, the winter savory, is found on cliffs and rocky hillsides, and is especially prevalent in S. Italy and Greece. As it retains its foliage all the year it is a valuable plant to use fresh or dried in stuffings and to make savory butter to serve with grilled meats and fish. Winter savory is a hardy plant with small oblong linear leaves and

in late summer its pinkish-purple flowers, borne in racemes from the axils of the leaves, are a valuable source of nectar. S. hortensis is the summer savory. It is a half hardy annual, widely used in the 16th century to make stuffings to have with veal and venison because of its "hot" pungent flavor. The plant grows 8 in. (20 cm) tall, with branched hairy stems and leaves which are downy on the underside. The pinkish-mauve flowers are borne in small clusters from the leaf axils in late summer. It is readily raised from seed sown early in spring.

Perennial 3–4 ft (1 m)

This small genus of edible thistle-like plants, of a widely dispersed order, is prevalent around the Mediterranean. Closely related are the globe artichoke and sea holly, parts of which are edible. They are plants with prickly or spiny leaves and compound flower heads with blue or purple disc florets. The plants are usually found growing in sandy soil close to the sea. The young white shoots of S. hispanica and also of S. maculatus appear early in spring and are removed when about 8 in. (20 cm) tall. Plants are readily raised from seed sown in spring and grown on in a light well drained soil which was manured for a previous crop. The young shoots can be used the following spring and the roots in winter, lifting them when required.

Perennial 2–3 ft (60–90 cm)

It is one of more than 150 species native of C. and S. Europe and C. Asia but is most common in the Iberian Peninsular where it grows on waste ground of a sandy nature, often close to the sea. In Spain it is called viper's grass, for it was believed that the juice of the roots could cure snake bite. But it had other properties apart from the delicious flavor of its roots which are steamed or fried in butter to serve with meats. For one thing, they relieved flatulence and indigestion so effectively that Louis XIV ordered his head gardener to grow scorzonera in large quantities to have as a vegetable all the year round. The roots keep well without shrivelling and without losing flavour. They have black skins but are white inside. They "bleed" and lose flavor if peeled, so should be cooked first and peeled after. For the same reason, lift the roots carefully so as not to cut or break them. At one time they were cooked, peeled and candied to eat as a sweetmeat like eringoes. If the roots are left down for another year, the flower buds can be eaten in early summer and have much the same flavor as the roots. Lightly cook them before mixing into beaten eggs to make into omelettes. The cooked buds are also included in salads.

SECHIUM EDULE

CHOCHO

Cucurbitaceae

206 Trop Am

Annual, climbing or trailing to 20 ft (6 m)

A genus of a single species native only of tropical S. America where it grows on the banks of the Amazon, though it is cultivated in the tropics of the Old and New Worlds. It climbs by tendrils and has large 6-sided leaves terminating to a point and with conspicuous veins. From the stem nodes a leaf is formed, together with male and female flowers, and on the underside a branched tendril. The female flower is replaced by a large, single-seeded oval fruit with thick melon-like flesh which is sweet and juicy. It is used for dessert and for making into preserves.

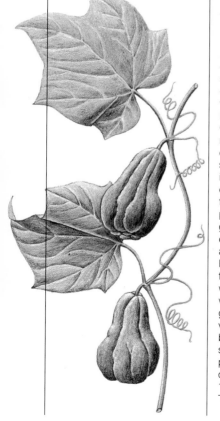

SEDUM TELEPHIUM

ORPINE

Crassulaceae

207 N+C Eur
North Temperate Zones

Perennial 2 ft (60 cm)

The plant is one of the largest species of the large sedum family which are distributed about the temperate and colder parts of the N. Hemisphere of the Old World. The orpine is widespread in open woodlands throughout the British Isles and N. and C. Europe, usually growing on mountainous slopes for it desires a well-drained, sunny situation. As its name implies, it is happy among stony outcrops, and because its large fleshy roots, almost tuberous, penetrate deeply into the ground making the plant difficult to eradicate, it is known as Long Life. The thick, fleshy leaves are blue-green and toothed, the upper leaves without footstalks, the lower wedge-shaped. They are glossy as if they have been varnished. The flowers are borne in compact heads late summer and are brightest pink though often may be crimson or purple. They have 10 stamens and red anthers. The plant takes its name from Telepheus, son of Hercules who appreciated its properties. The leaves were included in salads before lettuce became better known. They are nourishing and slightly astringent. Another species, S. reflexum, present on rocks and dry walls throughout N. and C. Europe, grows less than 12 in. (30 cm) tall, its slender pink stems clothed with small reflexed leaves which, together with the young shoots in spring, are also used in salads. The bright yellow flowers are borne in terminal cymes during July and August.

SESAMUM INDICUM

SESAME

Pedaliaceae

208 S Asia, C Af
Tropical Zones of Old World

Perennial 6—7 ft (2 m)

A genus of 30 species, mostly native of tropical Africa, with S. indicum also present in S. India where it is cultivated for its aromatic seeds. When pressed, they yield a pale yellow oil which is the equal of olive oil for salad dressing and for cooking. It is also used in confectionery and in the cosmetics industry. The husks which are winnowed from the seeds are nutritious and readily digestible. S. indicum has opposite leaves spirally arranged along the upright stems. They are about 6 in. (15 cm) long and 1 in. (2.5 cm) broad, ending in a point. In the axil of each leaf is borne a pinkish-white tubular flower followed by a 4-chambered capsule containing about 50 small seeds which are sprinkled over bread and cakes and baked into bread as caraway seeds are in Europe. The seeds are also used for sweet making.

SINAPSIS NIGRA	SIUM SISARUM	SMYRNIUM OLUSATRUM	SOLANUM MELONGENA
BLACK MUSTARD	SKIRRET	ALEXANDERS	EGGPLANT (AUBERGINE)
Cruciferae	Umbelliferae	Umbelliferae	Solanaceae
209 S Eur, N Af, W Asia *Temperate Zones*	**210** SE Eur, W+C Asia *Temperate Zones*	**211** Medit *Temperate Zones*	**212** Tropical+Temperate Am

Annual 8–20 in. (20–50 cm)

S. nigra is the black mustard of commerce, a plant long naturalized in the New World. Each pod contains 8–10 black seeds. Ground down, they make a yellow powder which is used the world over as a condiment. The slender 3 ft (90 cm) tall stems of the plant are topped by flowers of brilliant yellow. They are followed by seed pods less than 1 in. (about 2 cm) long which are harvested and threshed when ripe, late in summer. S. alba is the white mustard, used for salads and for garnishing. It is marketed when only 3 in. (7.5 cm) high but in the wild grows to 12 in. (30 cm). It has divided leaves and yellow flowers followed by short seed pods in silky white hairs. S. arvensis is known as charlock. It has less divided leaves and hairless seed-pods. It is a troublesome weed of cornfields but its young leaves make a nourishing vegetable.

Perennial 3–4 ft (1 m)

The plant is said to be native of W. China and reached Europe and later Britain during the 16th century when it was first mentioned by garden writers. It resembles S. latifolium of N. Europe, a plant known as the water parsnip, and in Scotland where S. sisarum is a naturalized garden escape, it is called crummcocks. The plants grow in ditches and on wet, low lying ground and take their name from the Celtic *siu,* water, the lower leaves usually being submerged in water. It has hollow stems and its upper leaves are divided into 5 pairs of leaflets. The white flowers are borne in a long stalked umbel from June until August. It is the roots that are used as food and writers of old describe them as the most delicious of all root crops. The long narrow roots grow 4–6 in. (10–15 cm) long and have the aroma of parsnips.

Perennial 3–4 ft (1 m)

Native of S. Europe and the E. Mediterranean and so named because it once grew in profusion around the Egyptian port of Alexandria. It may have been introduced into N. Europe and the British Isles (where it is now naturalized) by the Romans. It is present in hedgerows and on waste ground, usually growing in calcareous soils and in sight of the sea. It has hollow, smooth and furrowed stems and its yellowish-green leaves are deeply toothed. The flowers are borne early in summer and are followed by broad black seeds which when dry omit a spicy smell. The large fern-like ternate leaves have broad leaflets and resemble those of sweet cicely, with the same myrrh-like smell and taste.

Annual 2–3 ft (60–90 cm)

More than 1000 species are included in the genus Solanum, including many poisonous plants and several that are among the most important of the world's food crops, including the potato, tomato and eggplant. Most species are native of S. America and the southern USA and reached Europe in the 17th century. Eggplants grow by the side of woods and on waste ground, usually in sandy soil but under cultivation, outdoors in S. Europe and those parts enjoying a long warm summer; indoors in northerly parts, they require a rich soil to produce an abundance of fruit. They may be long and cylindrical, like sausages, or egg-shaped with highly polished purple skins; or white or yellow, like yellow plums. The plants have wrinkled dark green leaves and bear large purple flowers in the leaf axils.

SOLANUM QUITOENSE

NARANJILLA

Solanaceae

213 Trop S Am
Tropical Zones of New World

Perennial 4—6 ft (1—2 m)

Known as the golden fruit of the Andes, it grows in well drained fertile soil but is rarely found in low lying ground. It makes a dense, shrubby bush growing as wide as it grows tall. Its large entire leaves are hairy on the underside. In areas of high rainfall, the plant grows rapidly and begins to fruit when 6—8 months old. It continues to bear without a rest for 2—3 years, then virus and fungal diseases may cause the plants to lose vigor and shorten their cropping, new plantings being made regularly on clean land. The golden-yellow fruits are of the size of oranges and are sold all the year from the wild and from plantations in the native markets, the juicy fruits having the flavor of strawberries when ripe. They are used to make jams and preserves and a greenish-yellow thirst-quenching drink or sorbet.

SOLANUM TUBEROSUM

POTATO

Solanaceae

214 S Am
Temperate Zones

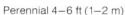

Perennial 2 ft (60 cm)

A genus of more than 1700 species, many being poisonous plants and native to tropical and temperate regions with S.tuberosum native of S. America, mostly Chile and Peru where it grows near the coast. The stalks, leaves and fruits possess narcotic and poisonous qualities of many of the genus, but the tuberous roots are part of the staple diet of western people. It was introduced into Europe by the Spaniards early in the 16th century and into England by way of Ireland, about 50 years later, by Sir Walter Raleigh upon his return from colonizing that part of America he called Virginia. The plant forms numbers of edible tubers which are produced at the end of underground stems and grow large. The tubers contain ''eyes'' from which arise further stems, and in the wild, the plants form dense thickets.

SORBUS AUCUPARIA

ROWAN

Rosaceae

215 N+C Eur, W Asia
North Temperate Zones

Tree 20—40 ft (6—12 m)

A genus of 100 species, native of N. temperate regions, especially Europe and Asia, and tolerant of acid soils and bleak sparse conditions, often being found about rocky outcrops, exposed to strong winds. The handsome pinnate leaves have 11—19 toothed leaflets which give them a fern-like appearance. It bears its small creamy-white flowers in large corymbs. They are followed by glossy scarlet (or yellow) fruits (berries) in autumn, which when ripe contain generous amounts of citric and malic acid which gives them a sweet-sour taste. The juice has a high vitamin A and C content and contains pectin and tannin so that it is astringent (and so is the bark) and makes an effective gargle for a sore throat. It has many culinary uses. After pressing the juice from the berries, it is made into a jelly to serve with meat and game as an alternative to red currant or cranberry jelly; or it may be used as a jam, after adding a few cloves and lemon rind to the preserving pan. The variety S.edulis, a natural hybrid, has larger leaves and broader leaflets, less deeply toothed. The fruits are larger and carried in bigger bunches. It is a better garden tree than the type.

SORGHUM VULGARE	SPINACIA OLERACEA	STACHYS PALUSTRIS	STACHYS TUBERIFERA
MILLET	SPINACH	WOUNDWORT	CHINESE ARTICHOKE
Gramineae	Chenopodiaceae	Labiatae	Labiatae

 216 S Asia
Temperate Zones

 217 C Asia, Medit
Temperate Zones

218 Tropics+Subtropics, except Australasia

219 S Asia, China
Warm Temperate Zones

Annual 5–10 ft (2–3 ft)

A genus of 60 species, native of the sub-tropics and warmer areas of the world, with S. vulgare native of the E. Mediterranean and Near East, where it has been grown since earliest times as a valuable item of food. In river valleys the plant may attain a height of 18 ft (6 m), the ears of corn often large enough to provide a meal for a family. The stem may be 2 in. (5 cm) thick and the leaves more than 1 in. (2.5 cm) across, with the flowers borne in dense terminal panicles like a bush. The corn ripens in late summer when the grains are large enough for roasting to serve as a vegetable; or they are ground to make a coarse flour for bread and cakes. The variety S. durra is today that grown in Egypt, the Near East and also on the arid plains of C. India.

Annual 2 ft (60 cm)

A genus of only 3 species, native of the E. Mediterranean and C. Asia, where since early times the leaves have been appreciated for their health-giving qualities. The plant contains large amounts of chlorophyll. It is rich in salts of iron and potassium and in vitamin A, and also contains vitamin E and vitamin K, which regulates coagulation of the blood and prevents hemorrhages. The leaves also have a high oxalic acid content which may cause loss of calcium in the blood. It is oxalic acid which gives spinach its peculiar "earthy" flavor when cooked. In the wild, the plant is present about hedgerows and on waste ground, usually growing in a moisture-laden soil.

Perennial 2–3 ft (60–90 cm)

A hairy aromatic plant, one of a genus of more than 300 species present throughout the temperate regions of the world except Australasia. The plant is common by the side of ponds and in ditches and marshy ground and has hollow quadrangular unbranched stems and toothed lanceolate leaves, stem-clasping at the base. The flowers appear late in summer and are rosy-mauve, borne in whorled spikes. The plant increases by its creeping rootstock which is white and tuberous and forms a nutritious and pleasant vegetable. The young roots which arise from the rootstock in early summer are equally nourishing. Stachys betonica is the wood betony, a hairy perennial growing 20 in. (50 cm) tall with crenate leaves and bearing rosy-purple flowers in terminal spikes. It is present in damp woodlands in most parts of Europe and Asia.

Perennial 2 ft (60 cm)

It is a plant of extreme hardiness, native of the woodlands of N. China and Siberia and growing best in moist soils. It is in no way connected with other artichokes and is now cultivated in China and Japan for the nutritious value of its tuberous roots which are boiled or fried in butter. In France, the white finger-like tubers are known as crosnes and are a much-appreciated item of food for autumn and winter use. The plants require a humus-laden soil to retain summer moisture or the tubers will not grow plump. If dry in the ground or in storage, the tubers shrivel and are of no value. In the garden they are planted in spring, in drills 4 in. (10 cm) deep and 8 in. (20 cm) apart, in a warm, sunny position and kept well watered. Begin lifting in mid-autumn, when the foliage begins to die down but leave the tubers in the ground until just before required. They shrivel if too long out of the ground.

STELLARIA MEDIA	TAMARINDUS INDICA	TAMARIX MANNIFERA	TANACETUM BALSAMITA
CHICKWEED	TAMARIND	TAMARISK	COSTMARY
Caryophyllaceae	Leguminosae	Tamaricaceae	Compositae

220 Temperate Zones

221 Trop Af, Asia *Tropical Zones of Old World*

222 Medit, C Asia *Warm Temperate Zones*

223 S+C Eur, Asia *Temperate Zones*

Annual 2 in. (5 cm)

Tree 30–40 ft (10–12 m)

Tree or shrub 6–18 ft (2–5 m)

Perennial 2–3 ft (60–90 cm)

It is, with the dandelion, distributed over the entire north temperate regions and into the Arctic Circle and it is equally valuable as food. It is present in hedgerows and woodlands and on waste ground. It is a plant of trailing habit and has small, succulent pale green pointed leaves. The tiny white star-like flowers are borne in the leaf axils and open only in fine weather, the plant being the countryman's weather glass. It often stays green all year but it is in spring that it is most welcome, when "greens" are scarce. It is gathered and used fresh in salads or treated like spinach and made into purée. Countrymen use it in salads with dandelion leaves. The water in which chickweed has been boiled should be used in soups and stews or to make "stock," for it is rich in mineral salts.

A genus of a single species, native of tropical Africa, India and the East Indies, its spreading branches covered with pale grey bark, its leaves divided into 12–15 pairs of leaflets which close up at night. Gerard (1596) said that desert travellers in Africa carry with them quantities of the pulp which is sustaining and thirst quenching. The fragrant yellow flowers are followed by an oblong pod filled with an acid pulp which encloses 6–12 seeds covered with a brown shell. The rosy-red pulp contains citric and malic acid, potassium salts, also gum, pectin and grape sugar. The tree is grown in the West and East Indies as a commercial crop, the tamarinds being exported in syrup after removing the hard shell. In India and the Far East, tamarinds are used to make curries and are included in most chutneys.

A genus of bush-like trees present in warm and subtropical regions and able to survive arid conditions. They are found in deserts, on steppelands and by the seashore where their scale-like leaves reduce moisture evaporation to a minimum. The tiny pink flowers of T. mannifera appear in terminal panicles after the leaves. The plant is common in Palestine, Arabia and Sinai, growing in sand and on barren hillsides. Almost throughout the year it yields a honey-like liquid which exudes from small holes made in the bark by a scale-like insect, coccus manniparus. The gum soon hardens and falls from the tree, to be made into honey-flavored cakes which are highly nourishing. It was an important food of the Israelites during their wanderings in the desert "wilderness" but who found that the shrubs yielded little gum when they reached the cooler Promised Land.

It is native of C. Asia and the Far East, gradually working its way westwards until it is now common in S. Europe where it is found on barren ground by the roadside. It requires an open situation and a dry sandy soil. The plant's dark green entire leaves with finely toothed margins emit a sweet balsamic scent when handled. As Parkinson, botanist to Charles I of England, said, it is one of the sweetest herbs. It was used with lavender to put in muslin bags, to place among clothes and bedding while an infusion of the leaves, taken hot, is an aid to colic of stomach disorders and relieves flatulence. The plant bears large heads of deep yellow flowers and increases by its creeping rootstock. It is propagated either from seed or by removal of the offsets in spring. It requires a well drained soil and open situation.

TANACETUM VULGARE

TANSY

Compositae

224 Eur, W Asia
N Am

Perennial 2−3 ft (60−90 cm)

It is one of a genus of 50 or more species distributed across S. Europe and W. Asia and taking its name from the Greek *athanaton,* immortal, for all who drunk the tea made from its leaves, either fresh or dry, lived to old age. The leaves, finely shredded and beaten with eggs to fry as tansy cakes, were eaten in Lent in remembrance of the bitter herbs of the Passover. Today, a few leaves are included in omelettes for their pleasant bitterness. They are also used fresh or dry in stuffings and in pork sausage meat, to counteract the greasiness. Tansy is a hardy plant with branched stems and grey-green leaves divided into numerous pairs of pinnatifid leaflets. An essential oil, smelling of camphor, is stored in the leaf cells. The small yellow button-like flowers are borne in late summer in flat terminal heads. Remove them when they die back.

TARAXACUM OFFICINALE

DANDELION

Compositae

225 Temperate Zones

Perennial 4−6 in. (10−15 cm)

Widespread everywhere throughout the temperate world, it is present in grassland and by the roadside. Its long tap root makes it difficult to eradicate. It is a tiresome weed of lawns and yet its young leaves included in salads have a pleasant bitterness and contain vitamins A, B₁ (Thiamine) and C in generous amounts. From the root at soil level, the leaves appear in rosette formation. They are bluntly toothed, like a lion's teeth (the French named it dent de lion). The Arabian physician Avicenna, who knew of its valuable health-giving qualities, named it taraxacon, edible. From the roots, together with those of burdock, a tonic beer is made which is also a blood purifier. The brilliant yellow flower with radiating florets arises from the root on a 6 in. (15 cm) leafless stem. It blooms almost the whole year round and is much visited by bees. From the stem, a milky juice exudes when broken. When the white seed pappus has been blown away, the seed receptacle is bare. In Wales and in France, the roots are sliced into salads and sprinkled with lemon juice and to make the leaves more tender, cover plants with a pot to blanch them. Keeping the plants free of flowers will also increase the amount of leaf, which can also be boiled like spinach to serve with meats.

TEUCRIUM SCORODONIA

GERMANDER

Labiatae

226 W Asia, Medit
Temperate Zones

Perennial 1−2 ft (30−60 cm)

A genus of more than 300 species, native of warm temperate regions. T. scorodonia, a hairy, shrubby plant, has square stems and opposite grey-green leaves, wrinkled and toothed at the edges like those of sage. The small purple labiate flowers, borne in a terminal spike-like inflorescence, appear in midsummer when the whole plant is cut. It is often used with ground ivy, Glechoma hederacea, to which it is closely related. Both plants grow in deciduous woodlands and hedgerows, usually in chalky soils and with their bitterness make a wholesome ale or "tea." At one time ground ivy grew in every alehouse garden to put into a glass of ale to clarify it, hence its name ale-hoof. The genus takes its name from Teucer, king of ancient Troy, who according to Dioscorides made use of the plant to maintain his health.

THEA SINENSIS

TEA

Ternstroemiaceae

 227 S Asia, China, Japan
*Warm Temperate Zones
of Old World*

THEOBROMA CACAO

CACAO

Sterculiaceae

 228 S Am, Jamaica
*Tropical Zones
of New World*

THYMUS VULGARIS

THYME

Labiatae

 229 S Eur
Warm Temperate Zones

TILIA EUROPAEA

LIME TREE

Tiliaceae

 230 N Eur, Asia
North Temperate Zones

Perennial 20–30 ft (6–8 m)

T. sinensis, closely related to Camellia japonica of the East, is native of China where its use as a drink is mentioned in manuscripts dating from the 6th century AD. It provides the China tea of commerce which is milder and has a more delicate fragrance than T. assamica, Indian tea. Both species are grown commercially, T. sinensis in China and Indonesia where more than 5 million acres are under cultivation; and T. assamica in India and Ceylon. Both are much-branched evergreen shrubs, in the wild growing to 30 ft but no more than 7–8 ft (2 m) tall under cultivation. The dark green, leathery lanceolate leaves are borne on short stalks, those leaves from the middle and upper branches making the finest teas and thus commanding the top prices. The white, scented flowers are borne singly in the leaf axils and are followed by a small, round seed capsule.

Tree 12–16 ft (3–5 m)

A genus of 30 species, native of tropical America where it grows in rain forests and is a valuable commodity under cultivation. The Swedish botanist Linnaeus named it Theobroma, meaning "food of the gods." It makes a small spreading tree with a trunk about 6 ft (2 m) high, covered in smooth brown bark. The tree is continuously in leaf, flower and fruit and as it grows best under the shade of other trees, it is a valuable crop to produce commercially. The leaves are dark green and lanceolate, the small flowers crimson-red. They are followed by yellowish-red pods which are harvested when the seeds rattle in the pods. After drying, the beans are mixed with sugar and ground down to a paste, most of the fat being removed, and the result is cocoa. When the fat is left in, the product is chocolate.

**Perennial 4–8 in.
(10–20 cm)**

The common thyme is that usually grown in gardens. It is the wild thyme of mountainous places of those countries bordering the Mediterranean. It is a woody herb with branched stems and is taller growing than T. serpyllum, a plant of more northerly parts which forms a dense mat and is usually found on sunny banks. T. vulgaris is present on grassy slopes and has a more pungent smell. Since early times it has been used more than any other herb to make stuffings to counteract the richness of meats. The small elliptical leaves are set in pairs all the way up the stems and are dark green above, grey on the underside. The mauve flowers are borne in conical clusters throughout summer and are much visited by bees. T. citriodorus is the lemon-scented thyme, and there are gold (aureus) and silver leaf forms which are also strongly scented.

Tree 30–50 ft (10–16 m)

The limes are deciduous woodland trees with pale green heart-shaped leaves and bearing, in mid-summer, creamy white scented flowers in small cymes from the axils of the leaves. The upper surface of the leaves is usually covered with honey-dew caused by aphids which collect on the under-surface. The flowers contain a fragrant volatile oil soluble in alcohol. T. europaea is the common or European lime, used for street planting in town and cities because of its compact upright habit and ability to withstand clipping. It is thought to be a natural hybrid of T. cordata which has smaller leaves and flowers later. T. americana is the North American lime. It has large coarsely-toothed leaves and white flowers and from its bark, a sugary maple-like syrup is obtained.

TRAGOPOGON PORRIFOLIUS	TRAPA BICORNIS	TRIGONELLA FOENUM-GRAECUM
SALSIFY	LING	FENUGREEK
Compositae	Onagraceae	Fabaceae
231 Temperate Eur, Asia *Temperate Zones*	**232** SE Eur, Temperate Af, Asia *Warm Temperate Zones*	**233** SW Asia *Warm Temperate Zones*

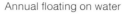

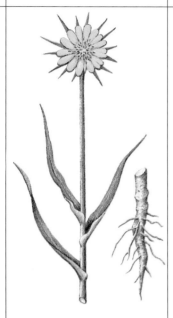

Perennial 2–3 ft (60–90 cm)

A genus of 40 species, T. porrifolius being native of the Mediterranean regions, extending into C. Europe, where it is known as the vegetable oyster for its flavor is thought to resemble that of the sea food. It is found in sandy soil on waste ground, often near the sea and its roots have the most delicate flavor of all root crops. The pale mauve flowers close at noon whatever the weather. Salsify has narrow grey-green leaves which clasp the stem and its daisy-like fowers are followed by round seed heads, like those of the dandelion. Though perennial, it is treated as an annual when grown in the garden and has become a popular food plant, seed being sown in spring in shallow drills and kept moist, for otherwise it will not germinate. Plants in the wild will, if left undisturbed until spring, produce new shoots, which are cut when 6 in. (15 cm) high and simmered to serve with meat. They have a delicate flavor all their own.

Annual floating on water

These primitive plants were more widely distributed in the Tertiary period than now. Then they covered most of N. and C. Europe; today they are found in pools and ponds from C. Europe to E. China and throughout S.E. Asia and Japan, where T. bicornis is prized for its seeds, which are ground to make flour to bake into bread and cakes; or for preserving in honey or sugar to use in confectionery. The seeds have a high protein content and are nourishing. The Singhara nut, T. bispinosa, is native mostly of tropical Asia but is also present in Kashmir. The seed is eaten raw like nuts or grated into salads. It is also boiled to make a thick pottage-like dish. The plants have two types of leaf: the finely divided submerged leaves and diamond-shaped undivided leaves which form a rosette and float on the surface. The small white flowers are followed by hard brown one-seeded fruits about 2 in. (5 cm) across, with 2 opposite pairs of horn-like projections. The fruit of T. bicornis has only 2 horns.

Annual 2 ft (60 cm)

It is native of N. Africa and the E. Mediterranean, also of India and W. Asia, trigonella denoting its 3-angled corolla and foenum-graecum meaning Greek hay, since it was used to impart its goodness to hay of poor quality. Each leaf is divided into 3 leaflets with serrated edges and the small yellow flowers are borne in the leaf axils. They are followed by sickle-shaped pods containing 12 or more seeds. The plant grows on wasteland and on rocky ground by the sea and for centuries its seeds have been used as a substitute for coffee, after drying, roasting and pounding. They are an ingredient of curry powders and have a hot bitter taste. The seeds are pale brown and oblong, with a groove which divides them into two unequal parts. They contain salts of iron and phosphorus and stimulate the appetite. The sprouted seed contains 20% protein and large amounts of choline, as well as vitamin A.

TRITICUM VULGARE	TROPAEOLUM MAJUS	TUBER MELANOSPORUM
WHEAT	NASTURTIUM	TRUFFLE
Gramineae	Tropaeolaceae	Fungi
234 Medit, S Asia *Temperate Zones*	235 Mexico, Temperate S Am *Temperate Zones*	236 C Eur

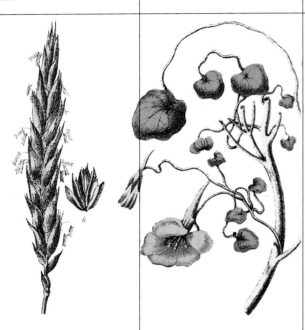

Annual 3–4 ft (1 m)

A genus of 20 species believed to be native of Asia Minor and N. Africa where it has been grown as a staple food since earliest times. In the wild, the wheats are confined to the Mediterranean region and may have originated on land now covered by the inland sea. Wheat grains have been found in Egyptian tombs of before 2000 BC and in prehistoric lake dwellings of Switzerland. Wheat has hollow stems and unbranched flower spikes which give rise to the ears of corn and change from green to golden-brown as they ripen. The wheats vary in the denseness of the spikes and in the presence or absence of awns. T. compositum is a "bearded" wheat which bears several ears to each stalk. With T. turgidum it was grown in Egypt in earliest times, when that country was the grainary of the ancient world.

Annual, trailing or climbing to 10 ft (3 m)

It is native of Chile and Peru and of most temperate regions of S. America, reaching Europe only in the late 17th century. It was named tropaeolum, a trophy, from the resemblance of the round, long stalked leaves to a Roman centurion's shield and the long spurred flowers to his helmet. The large, showy flowers which appear in shades of red, yellow, orange and pink and ease of culture soon made it a garden favorite and it flowers best in dry, poor soils. In the wild it trails over the ground and pulls itself up small trees and shrubs. In the garden, plants will cover a high trellis screen in a few weeks and be a picture of beauty as well as providing health-giving food. The leaves contain iron and sulphur and vitamin C. They were used by sailors at sea as an alternative to scurvy grass, sowing seed in boxes.

The truffles are fungi which grow underground in total darkness. They have knobby fruiting bodies filled with a maze of passages, the walls of which are covered with spore-cells which are released when the fruits decay to form further fruiting bodies. Tuber melanosporum, found only in the Périgord district of S. France, where trained dogs and pigs reveal their whereabouts by sniffing for their delicate aroma. This truffle has a black skin or peridium covered with pyramid-shaped tubers and is mostly found in deciduous forests, at the foot of oak trees. The tubers, which vary in size from 1 to 3 in. (2.5–7.5 cm) in diameter, have pinkish flesh and contain numerous white veins which are spore chambers. The Piedmont truffle of N. Italy, Tuber magnatum, is equally sought after by gastronomic establishments for its highly aromatic flesh. The tubers are brownish-yellow with a smooth skin and are usually divided into two chambers.

The flesh inside is palest pink. Fully grown tubers can weigh up to 1 lb (450 g). Choiromyces venosus is a rare tuber of the British Isles with yellowish-white skin covered in warts and shaped like a potato, often being 6 in. (15 cm) long. It is found in deciduous woods over limestone. All tubers are rare, and are mostly found in August and September.

TYPHA LATIFOLIA

REED MACE

Typhaceae

237 Temperate Zones

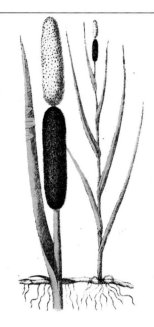

Perennial 4–6 ft (1–1.5 m)

A genus of 10–12 species, native of the temperate and sub-tropical regions of the world, and found growing by the side of ponds and in swamplands. The giant reed mace has long lance-shaped leaves which overtop the thick cylindrical pale brown flower spike which grows to 6 in. (15 cm) long and is made up of female flowers. It has a velvet-like feel when handled, hence their name of cats-tails. They appear in mid-summer and are held on a shiny leaf-less stem. The whole plant dies back in winter and begins to grow again in spring. The shoots are cut from the base as soon as they appear above the water, then about 10 in. (25 cm) long. The Lesser Reed mace, T. angustifolia is a smaller plant in every way and is usually found close to the sea, on river estuaries.

ULMUS RUBRA

RED ELM

Urticaceae

238 N Am
North Temperate Zones

Tree 8–12 ft (2–3 m)

It has long been the staple food of the Red Indian tribes of N. America, where it abounds. It is a small twiggy tree with long toothed leaves, covered on both sides with soft hairs and all parts are clothed in yellow silk. The inner bark or bast is made up of cells containing mucilage which is both nutritious and healing to the lining of the stomach. The bark is removed in spring, the entire tree and its branches being stripped naked. The tree, which should be 10 years old before it is stripped, will die but others arise in coppice-like forma-tion. The inner bark is removed in lengths of 2 ft (60 cm) and several inches wide. It is reddish-brown with a hay-like smell. The inner bark is about ⅛ in. (3 mm) thick and is extremely fibrous.

URTICA DIOICA

GREATER NETTLE

Urticaceae

239 Eur, Asia
Temperate Zones

Perennial 2–3 ft (60–90 cm)

A genus of about 50 species of hairy plants native to the temperate regions of the world. All species are covered with stiff bulbous hairs which contain and inject formic acid into the skin when handled. This causes intense irritation, and the skin forms reddish eruptions. It is one of the most useful plants known to man. The fibrous hairs were used as thread by the northern nations before the introduc-tion of flax from the East. The thread is equal to that of cotton or linen. U. dioica is the greater nettle; U. urens, the lesser nettle. The latter grows shorter and is glabrous except for the stinging hairs. U. dioica is covered in soft down in addition to the stinging hairs. The leaves are heart-shaped and toothed, while the greenish-white flowers are borne in clusters from the leaf axils. The Roman nettle, native of S. Europe, is also glabrous and grows shorter but its stings are more painful. Though perennial, the plants die back in winter and come again in spring when the young tops, steamed in a little margarine make a nourishing vegetable to serve with meats. From the tops of a tonic beer is made. Nettle "tea" made by infusing the fresh or dried leaves and a wineglassful taken daily will purify the blood and reduce blood pressure. Nettle soup is pal-atable and nourishing. Nettles are found on wasteland and in farmyards, usually growing in rich soil.

VACCINIUM CORYMBOSUM	VALERIANELLA OLITORIA	VANILLA PLANIFOLIA	VERONICA BECCABUNGA
BLUEBERRY	CORN SALAD	VANILLA	BROOKLIME
Ericaceae	Valerianaceae	Orchidaceae	Scrophulariaceae
240 Eur, W Asia	**241** Eur, C Asia *Temperate Zones*	**242** S Am *Tropical Zones*	**243** N Eur, W+N Asia *North Temperate Zones*

Perennial 1−2 ft (30−60 cm)

A large genus of low growing evergreen deciduous shrubs distributed throughout the N. temperate regions, growing on moorlands and mountain sides, usually in acid soils. The plants increase by suckers to form dense plantations. V. myrtillus, distributed across Europe and N. Asia, has bright green angular stems and small ovate leaves. The pinkish bell-shaped flowes are borne in the axils of the leaves early in summer, to be followed by black edible pea-size fruits covered in grey "bloom." V. corymbosum is the blueberry, native of E.N. America. It has larger leaves followed by large black fruits covered in grey "bloom." Also a plant of N. America is V. angustifolium which has white bell-shaped flowers followed by blue berries which are sweet and juicy, while V. parvifolium bears red berries, more acid than the others.

Annual or biennial 4−8 in. (10−20 cm)

A small genus of glabrous plants distributed throughout the N. temperate regions, especially Europe, with simple narrow unstalked leaves, pale green like those of lettuce and small pale lilac flowers in early summer. It is present on arable land and waste ground, often around the edges of corn fields (hence its name) and in hedgerows. In France and Italy especially it has been appreciated for its inclusion in winter and early summer salads. In France it is salade de prêtre and is usually at its best during Lent or at lambing time. In France it is widely grown to supply the Paris market in spring, for its succulent leaves are included in salade lorette, with beetroot and grated celery. As a garden plant it is valuable in that it stands the winter cold better than lettuce.

Perennial, climbing to 40 ft (12 m)

A genus of 90 species of epiphytic plants, native of tropical America and Indonesia, with vanilla also of Mexico where the best vanilla is produced. In their natural state the plants are found in dense woodlands where they pull themselves to the top of tall trees by aerial roots in their search for sunlight. Where grown commercially, climbing is restricted. The rootstock is as woody as the vine but the plant forms a smooth stem with thick fleshy leaves up to 8 in. (20 cm) long and terminating in a point. From the leaf nodes the aerial roots are formed and in the axils the greenish-yellow flowers are borne in a dense inflorescence. They are followed by a cylindrical pod 8 in. (20 cm) long containing small beans enclosed in black pulp. From the unripe pods, vanilla extract is obtained by a process of fermentation. The odoriferous principle is vanillin.

Perennial 4−8 in. (10−20 cm)

A prostrate plant of brooks and ponds, it is present in all parts of the N. temperate regions. In Anglo-Saxon leech books it was called broke lempe, which means "growing in the mud of brooks and ponds." It forms succulent hollow stems that creep along the mud, rooting at the leaf nodes. The whole plant has a glossy appearance and has small oval leaves which are leathery to the touch, while the bright blue flowers are borne throughout summer. With its high vitamin C content, it was eaten in salads to keep away scurvy and like watercress, it is rich in iron and calcium. At one time and until citrus fruits became plentiful, it was sold by the pound weight in the streets of London, to sailors about to embark for service abroad. Townsmen would include it in summer salads or boil it to eat as spinach.

VIBURNUM PRUNIFOLIUM	VICIA FABA	VIOLA ODORATA
WILD RAISIN	BROAD BEAN	VIOLET
Caprifoliaceae	Leguminosae	Violaceae
244 E–N Am	245 Medit, C Asia *Temperate Zones*	246 Eur *Temperate Zones*

Perennial 4–14 ft (1–4 m)

A genus of more than 200 species native of temperate and sub-tropical Asia and N. America where V. pruni-folium is found in open wood-lands from New England to Georgia. It is a tall, erect shrub or small tree with glossy bright green oval leaves which take on rich colors in autumn. In early summer it bears clusters of white flowers which are sweetly scented. It is an attractive garden shrub, for it presents a delightful picture when in bloom, while its purple-black fruits in autumn are a welcome addition to the kitchen table. They are about 1 in. (2.5 cm) long and cylin-drical and are harvested when they become soft. Viburnum opulus, the snowball tree of high cranberry, is native of N. America, the British Isles and N. Europe. An ornamental shrub, its large round flowers are followed by drooping clusters of red berries.

Annual 3–5 ft (1–1.5 m)

The broad bean is one of the oldest of man's food plants, seed having been found in Palestinean tombs of 3,000 BC. and in Bronze Age lake dwellings in Switzerland. Since then, the plant has been used as food for both humans and animals throughout Europe and Asia. It is indigenous to S. Asia and the Near East. In the wild it grows on wasteland and by the side of fields.
The broad bean, so called because the seeds (beans) are the longest of all edible beans, about 1 in. (2.5 cm) long and ¾ in. (1.8 cm) wide, is an erect single-stemmed plant. Its compound leaves consist of 2–6 leaflets, the lilac and white pea-like flowers borne in clusters in the leaf axils. They are fol-lowed by long thick shiny pods containing 4–8 greenish-white beans embedded in soft down.

Perennial 2–4 in. (5–10 cm)

A genus widely distributed throughout the cooler regions of the world, with V. odorata famed for its sweet scented flowers. The plant was so highly regarded by the ancient Greeks that it became the symbol of Athens early in her history. The flowers were cooked with game and included fresh in salads to which they give color and sweetness. Crystallized violets are used to decorate cakes which have been coated with icing sugar and are used in modern confec-tionery to decorate violet cream chocolates. The plant has a short rootstock with long runners, which root at the leaf nodes to form new plants. The heart-shaped leaves are dark green, while the purple-blue flowers are spurred and have 4 upper oblong petals and 2 side petals. It is a plant of hedge-rows and woodlands, enjoying shade and moisture, and is in bloom early in spring. It was grown in medi-aeval "knot" gardens, for the flowers were in constant demand and although their perfume exceeds that of all other flowers, it fades quickly. This is because its chemical composition contains ionine from which the word violet is derived. This substance is able to dull the senses within a short time; it is not the flower that loses its scent when inhaled but the sense of smell that is dulled. If, after a few moments the flower is again smelled, the perfume returns only to disappear again as quickly. Shake-speare wrote of the imperma-nence of its scent: "sweet, not lasting, the perfume and suppliance of a minute; no more." Violets were the favorite flower of the Empress Josephine of France and shortly before his exile, Napoleon picked flowers from her grave which on his death-bed were found in a locket around his neck.

VITIS VINIFERA

GRAPE

Vitidaceae

247 SE Eur, W+C Asia, Medit
Warm Temperate Zones

Perennial climber 6–20 ft (2–6 m)

A genus of 60 or more species distributed over the N. temperate regions. Since earliest times V. vinifera, the vine, has been one of man's most important food plants. The fresh fruit is enjoyed as dessert, especially by invalids for it is thirst quenching and sustaining, since grape sugar, unlike cane sugar, is taken immediately into the blood stream without having to be changed by the saliva. In this respect, grape sugar resembles honey. Grapes are also rich in salts of iron and potassium and are sustaining. Grapes are now grown in warm countries throughout the world for wine making, more than 30 million metric tons being made each year. The dried fruit, which has a high iron content, provides the raisins of commerce. The sultana is a seedless variety originating in Smyrna; muscatels are left on the tree to dry before being gathered. The plant takes its name from *viere,* to twist, for it climbs by tendrils which represent modified inflorescences. The leaves are 5-lobed and coarsely toothed, the greenish-white flowers being borne in large panicles and followed by the fruits in late summer. They are white, green, yellow or purple-black and vary from pea size to that of small plums.

YUCCA FILAMENTOSA

YUCCA

Agavaceae

248 SE-N Am, Mexico, West Indies
Warm Temperate Zones of New World

Perennial 4–15 ft (1–4 m)

A genus of 40 species native of S. United States and Mexico where they are known as Palm lilies. They are plants of the desert, prairies and rocky mountainous slopes and bear a rosette of pointed sword-like leaves about 2 ft (60 cm) in length with sharp teeth along the edges. From the center of the leaves the branched flower stem arises to a height of 8 ft (2–3 m) and bears in large racemes, drooping bell-shaped flowers of creamy-white which are heavily scented at night when open. They have wax-like petals. They are pollinated by the moth Pronuba yuccasella which collects pollen from one flower, rolls it into a ball and presses it into the stigma of another flower where, through a hole which she drills in the side of the ovary, she lays her eggs. Thus, development of larvae and seeds are complementary to each other. The larvae falls to the ground when the flower stem dies down, to winter in its cocoon, and emerges when the plants bloom again in spring. When the flowers begin to fall, the seedpods are gathered when green, while the large flat seeds are white and succulent. They are removed by slitting open the capsules and are boiled to serve as a vegetable to accompany meat or game. They have much of the taste of sweet corn. American Indians dry the leaves for their fiber which can be seen trailing from the edges. Y. aloifolia bears its snow-white flowers on 16 ft (5 m) stems and in large panicles often 2 ft (60 cm) long. Its glaucous leaves have an attractive white edge. The yuccas are adaptable garden plants and are found in many gardens in the British Isles and Europe and in South Africa and Australia.

ZEA MAYS

SWEET CORN

Gramineae

249 Trop S+C Am
Warm Temperate Zones

ZINZIBER OFFICINALE

GINGER

Zingiberaceae

250 S Asia
Torrid Zones

ZIZIPHUS VULGARIS

JUJUBE

Rhamnaceae

251 E Medit, C Asia
Temperate Zones

Annual 3—6 ft (1—2 m)

A genus of a single species, it is a member of the grass family, archaeological specimens found in S. America being more than 5,000 years old. Zea mays is native of S. and C. America though from early times it has been cultivated in most tropical countries, especially India. The male flowers are produced in a terminal inflorescence (the tassel) while the female flowers form in the leaf axils lower down the stem and catch the male pollen grains as they fall from above onto the pendent stigmas. Close planting ensures better pollination by wind agent. As the ears develop they are protected by large leaf sheaths which enclose the seeds (cob) completely. They take about 5 months to grow and ripen, becoming as much as 10 in. (25 cm) long and as cylindrical as a man's forearm. As many as 12 rows of seeds make up the cob, there being 30 or more seeds in a row.

Perennial 2—3 ft (60—90 cm)

A genus of almost 100 species, native to Indonesia and N. Australia, it was imported into Spain early in the 16th century and from there reached America and the West Indies soon after. The finest ginger is today grown in Jamaica and in S. China. The greyish-red roots are sold "coated" or "uncoated" with the skin still on. The roots are also known as "white" or "black". Green ginger is the young, immature roots, generally used as a sweetmeat known as preserved ginger, which is prepared by immersing the roots in hot sugar syrup after they have been boiled and scraped. In the wild, the plant grows in rain forests for it enjoys shade and a humus-rich soil. Thus it is grown commercially in the shade of trees especially planted for their crops. Ginger has lance-shaped pointed leaves, borne on a green reed-like stem. It sets no seed and reproduces itself by underground roots. At the base of each stem is produced a thick round tuber-like root. These are lifted each year when the leaf stems die back, the small roots being replanted. Dried ginger is used to flavor cakes and drinks such as ginger ale. The roots contain a volatile oil and the hot, bitter principle, gingerol.

Tree 20—25 ft (6—7 m)

A genus of 100 species, native of tropical America, Africa and Australia with Z. vulgaris (syn. Z. jujuba) native of the E. Mediterranean. The small trees or shrubs are spiny, with the stems and branches covered in rough brown bark. The oblong leaves of pale green are marked with longitudinous veins and the small greenish-yellow flowers are borne in dense cymes. They are followed by deep red fruits (drupes) of the size of olives which when ripe are sweet and juicy and become more so when dried in the sun for a short time. The fruits are used fresh to make drinks and when dry are included in cakes and other confectionery as an alternative to figs and dates. Jujube "cakes" are a pleasant sweetmeat and are a popular food in Arabia and Palestine. Z. vulgaris was introduced into Italy and France by the Romans and is grown commercially in the islands of Hyeres for export to all parts of Africa and the East.

All That Mankind Needs

Although nature provides man with every kind of nourishment, in some parts of the world there is not enough to feed everyone. Third world countries are often overcrowded and the poverty of these nations does not allow the importation of foodstuffs.

Species of plants have evolved and flourish in every part of the world, even where there is snow and ice or in the desert. Every root, leaf or fruit we collect and eat is part of Mother Nature's bounty which allows and supports life on this planet and provides us with everything we need to remain healthy.

Nature has provided man with food to ease the pangs of hunger since he first appeared on earth. As the Bible reminds us, God said: "I have given you every herb bearing seed which is upon the face of the earth and every tree in which there is fruit."

In every part of the world, in the sea and on land, there is food to feed all the people. Provided it is harvested at the right time, there are supplies available

Those who live near the coast will find a constant supply of the seaweeds, most primitive of plants, which have evolved during millions of years. Kelp, dulse and carrageen moss are present in abundance on both sides of the Atlantic and Pacific oceans, either in shallow pools of seawater or attached to rocks. Boiled in milk, they possess great nutritive value. They contain chlorophyll and also have a high iodine content.

A striking image of food distribution in India (right).

Opposite page:
In Europe wild cherry trees provided poor country people with an important part of their diet for many years. The cherries were dried and used to make "cherry soup" in the winter.

to provide man with a meal the whole year round, even in those places that are covered with snow and ice for several months of the year or where the ground is parched for want of rain – for nuts, seeds and roots can be stored, as well as a number of fruits, to feed mankind in difficult times.

Another of the primitive foods, the fungus, which contains no chlorophyll and is unable to make its own food by photosynthesis, is readily available in all parts of the globe. The field mushroom appears in generous amounts in meadows in most parts of the northern hemisphere and comes in the autumn or

113

Trees and plants need water to grow. Rain water is sucked from the ground by the roots and then evaporates from the leaves to form clouds which begin the cycle again.

Another important cycle *(right)* is that of the seasons. In winter the tree stores energy to produce buds and leaves in spring, flowers in summer and fruit in autumn, when it also loses its leaves. These, in their turn, become a natural fertilizer. Beneath the tree we can see *(left to right)* branched burre reed, true ginger and white onion.

fall, and there are others such as the chanterelle and the horse mushroom. In damp woodlands appear many other fungi, growing in decayed vegetation or attached to trees which they use as a host plant for their nourishment. Most fungi can be dried and used in winter when wild food plants may not be prevalent.

For the same reason the peoples of northerly latitudes make full use of nuts, storing them as does the squirrel, to use when other foods are scarce. In hedgerows, copses and open woodlands grow beech, hazel, sweet chestnut and oak, each of which provides man with an abundance of nut-like fruits which can be made into flour to bake as bread or cakes.

In warmer parts of the North Temperate zone the almond, walnut and pecan are found. All are deciduous trees, mostly catkin-bearing and wind-pollinated. Their nuts are eaten raw or used in confectionery. The pines are evergreen and from their cones are obtained large seeds which make nut-like eating. Among the earliest plants to inhabit the earth, they must have provided early man with much of his food. Almost as valuable were those tuberous rooted plants which could also be stored through winter and which are freely available in all parts of the world. Nowhere is this more true than in South America, where they have been the staple foods for the tribal peoples since earliest times. The potato and the ipomoea or sweet potato were to become among the most valuable of all crops when grown commercially, sustaining millions of people in winter in all parts of the western world. In the New World also grow the dahlia and arrowroot, the tuberous roots of which are highly nutritious.

In the Old World, the tuberous rooted Chinese artichoke and the garlic and Star-of-Bethlehem are bulbous plants which are nutritious and sustaining. In the far east, the yam, although a climbing plant, is the counterpart of the dahlia and potato of the New World, while in Africa, the nourishing Hotten-

All life depends on the green leaf's chlorophyll, which converts sunlight into energy and so powers the whole of organic creation.

The aim of brightly colored flowers is to attract insect or animal pollinators.

To disperse their seeds some plants wrap them in attractive and nutritious packages, designed to be eaten.

Bark is the protective covering of a circulation system so elaborate that some of its processes still defy explanation.

In their penetration of the earth to seek water and minerals roots bypass most hard obstacles but can split rock if necessary.

Left to right:
Black truffle, *Tuber melanosporum*;
Lactarius volemus;
Ramaria botrytis;
Boletus aureus;
morel, *Morchella esculenta*;
chanterelle, *Cantharellus cibarius*;
Gomphidius glutinosus and
honey fungus, *Armillaria mellea*.

Nature also provides us with feasts for the eyes such as cherry blossom *(above)*. Cherry stones have been found in neolithic dwellings. The tree is thought to have been brought to Europe from Asia by the first Aryan immigrants.

Below left to right:
Blackthorn, *Prunus spinosa*, from the same family as the plum.

An olive branch, symbol of peace.

The prickly pear, a tasty cactus fruit.

tot "bread" of the tribesmen of the same name is made from the roots of the Testudinaria which may form a tuber 10 ft (3 m) in circumference.

Peoples of northern climes obtain the same nourishment from the roots of the wild arum and from the carrot, parsnip and Jerusalem artichoke. Of the same family is the sunflower, native of South America, whose seeds were used centuries ago by the Aztec Indians to make a tasteless cooking oil, the counterpart of olive oil of the old world. Sunflower seed contains the important vitamin E, and as it is low in cholesterol (which in fatty foods forms deposits on the walls of the arteries causing blockage of the blood

flowing to the heart), it is now recognized as one of the world's most important plant foods and its use may account for the long life span of the South American tribesmen.

The grasses make a valuable contribution to the feeding of the people. Sweet corn or maize was a primary food of the South American tribesmen more than 5,000 years ago. Known as Indian meal, or Indian corn, the ripe corn is ground into flour and is also consumed as a vegetable. Other staple foods of the grass family are wild oats, which grow as far north as Scotland and Norway where they are used for making porridge and bread; also barley and wheat which have been used for flour to bake into bread since earliest times.

Another grass, rice, is a marshland plant which is native of India and South-east Asia, where for centuries it has fed the population, and which now has a world-wide distribution. Brown or unpolished rice contains the important vitamin B_{15} (Pongamic acid) which prevents premature aging and supplies the heart and blood cells with oxygen.

Of the other important seed crops, there is the broad bean which the people of the Old World have consumed since earliest times and its counterpart of the New World, the pole or runner bean. Always has nature provided man with similar products wherever he may live. The berries of allspice are available for flavoring to those living in the tropics of the New World; those of juniper serve the same purpose for those inhabiting colder parts.

Fruits, too, are there for all the people to make use of. In northerly parts, found in the wild across North America, northern Europe and Asia, there is the apple, wild cherry and sloe; the blackberry, alpine strawberry, wild rose and gooseberry – all of them plants of woodland and hedgerow. On moorlands are found bilberries and cranberries and in North America, also the huckleberry. In warmer parts, the fig, pear, melon and cucumber are plants of the Old World and with them grow the pome-

granate and persimmon, the peach and olive and the citrus fruits, rich in vitamin C. Tomatoes and eggplant are of the New World, where in the tropics grow guavas, the avocado and naranjilla, fruits which are also rich in vitamin C. The same form of nourishment is available to all the people everywhere: Not only do the plants provide food to satisfy the pangs of hunger but also the same vitamins and mineral salts needed to maintain a healthy body and active mind. In the deserts of the Old World is found the date palm: In the deserts of the New World grows the prickly pear. Both provide fruit of high nutritional value.

A plant of the northern temperate regions of both the Old and New Worlds is the arrowhead, present by the side of rivers and lakes, whose tuberous root (really a swelling at the base of the stem) is cooked as a vegetable when fresh or is dried for winter use. It has a counterpart in the tropics of the Old World in the Chinese arrowhead which also grows by rivers and lakes and is used in the same way. It grows in muddy ground which never freezes in winter, the tubers being lifted and used fresh all the year round.

Young shoots of the bamboo provide nourishing meals for the peoples of Southeast Asia, China and Japan where the climate is warm and damp and conducive to rapid growth. Bamboos

also grow in the southern United States under similar conditions. Peoples inhabiting the cooler climes of North America, Europe and Asia obtain much the same nourishment from the young shoots of pokeweed, thistle and fern when they appear in spring, a time when the fresh green shoots are eagerly sought after following the long, cold days of winter. In the warmer climes of southern Europe and North Africa, the hop and asparagus satisfy a similar demand and everywhere are found fresh green leaves in summer, full of vitamins and mineral salts to provide man with all his food requirements.

Nourishment is also obtained from the bark of certain trees. From the bark of the red elm of North America, a soothing drink is made and the chinchona tree of the tropics yields a stimulating drink.

Those living in northerly climes can make use of the syrup of the sugar maple for sweetening and those of the tropics will use the juice of sugar cane. "Behold, I have given you every herb which is upon the face of the earth ... to you it shall be for meat (food)," said the Lord God.

Arrowhead, *Sagittaria Sagittifolia (above)* is to be found near rivers and lakes in all warm climates. Its root is edible.

Below left to right:

Sunflower seeds contain the valuable vitamin E.

Pears, of which there are now more than 1,500 varieties.

Wild raspberries, to be found in the mountains.

The potato, now one of the world's major basic food substances.

Substances which are Beneficial to Health

Nature's larder has provided man with food to ease the pangs of hunger ever since he first began to feed himself and until he was endowed with sufficient intelligence to prepare it in such a way as to make his meals a pleasure as well as a necessity. The countryside everywhere is abundant with wild foods which are there for the taking, each in its season for almost the whole year round. In places covered with snow and ice for a large part of the year there are foods to store for use at that time.

everyone since time began, and it is important to have knowledge of those natural foods which are able to supply the various parts of the body with vitamins and mineral salts so that it will function well throughout a long life.

Today, in the world of advanced medical science, we tend to dismiss as irrelevant much that the old herbalists had written, and yet in recent years, much has proved to be correct. It was once thought that wormwood, which is

Frontispiece *(right)* of "Der Gart" 1485, shows a gathering of the most notable herbalists of all ages. The central three are probably *(left to right)* the Roman, Pliny; the Greek, Dioscorides, and the Arabian, Mesue or Serapion.

Early man had no knowledge of the health value of the foods he ate but consumed those foods which gave him a sense of well-being; and by trial and error he left those alone which upset his constitution. There was no one to offer advice on plants having medicinal value to restore him to health. A sick man could not travel the countryside in search of food, however plentiful it might be, just as a sick man today cannot pursue his work with vigor. To keep young and active has been the desire of

found on waste ground in most parts of the temperate world, would cure epilepsy and other nervous disorders, and the plant is believed to have brought about amazing cures until the use of herbs for food and medicine came to be neglected. As man built himself towns and cities and in them set up factories and workshops during the Industrial Revolution, he ceased to look upon wild plants as being able to supply his needs. In their place the apothecary's shop filled with man-made cures.

Seaweed *(above)* is the most primitive food substance. It contains iodine which is important for the correct functioning of the thyroid gland.

Preparations able to cure or ease body disorders there may be, but prevention of illness is of greater importance. Those who regularly included a few leaves of wormwood in salads or sandwiches were supplying the body with important potassium salts and with the B vitamins which science has found to be so necessary to fortify the nervous system. Ancient man ate wormwood leaves because he felt better for doing so, though he did not know the reason why. Wormwood is a restorative in the same way that sorrel leaves are included in soups served in most country inns of France as they have been since mediaeval times. For the same reason, the leaves are included in salads with those of dandelion and watercress, endive and lettuce. In bars and restaurants today throughout Europe where it grows wild, a leaf or two of borage is placed in a glass of beer or white wine because of its cool cucumber flavor and its powers of restoration. Indeed, modern science has shown that the juice of borage stems and leaves contains as much as 30% nitrate of potassium which acts as a powerful restorative.

The body requires these mineral salts for it to function properly. Without them the body cannot make full use of the vitamins it needs for it to remain healthy and active. Potassium is one of the minerals the body needs most, for potassium takes up excess moisture, thus making it difficult for bacteria to exist in the bloodstream. But equally important, it controls the amount of calcium in the bloodstream. Thus if a broken bone does not soon "knit" or "set," the cause may be rectified by consuming large quantities of plants rich in potassium salts. Lack of potassium allows the salts of calcium, sodium, iron and magnesium, necessary for the proper functioning of the body, to become too dominant, upsetting the balance. An excess of iron will block the lymph channels, increasing the size of the lymph glands. Lymph is the nutrient needed for healthy tissue growth; it prevents hardening of the arteries and removes waste material resulting from activity of the body's cells.

Brain activity is aided by potatoes, wheat germ, bran and nuts.

Mushrooms help prevent the effects of aging and greying hair.

The pituitary gland needs wheat germ and potatoes to function correctly.

Thyroid gland functioning can be helped by eating tomatoes, radishes, watercress, seaweeds including kelp, laver, dulse and carrageen, and tarragon.

Citrus fruit skins help tone muscles.

Plants grown in soil that lacks potash lack the ability to withstand adverse conditions. Plants grow "soft" and become liable to attacks by disease molds. There is also a restriction of the circulation of sap from stem to leaves, caused by blockage of the leaf nodes and sap channels. This is due to an excess of iron in the plant in the same way that the body reacts when deprived of potassium, allowing other minerals to become too dominant. Apple and grape juice, and also cranberry juice, are rich in potash and will correct this condition if taken regularly, a small glassful daily. Those plants richest in potassium are the tomato, eggplant and pepper. They are native of Peru whose people are among the longest living in the world.

As one grows older, the need for additional potassium becomes more im-

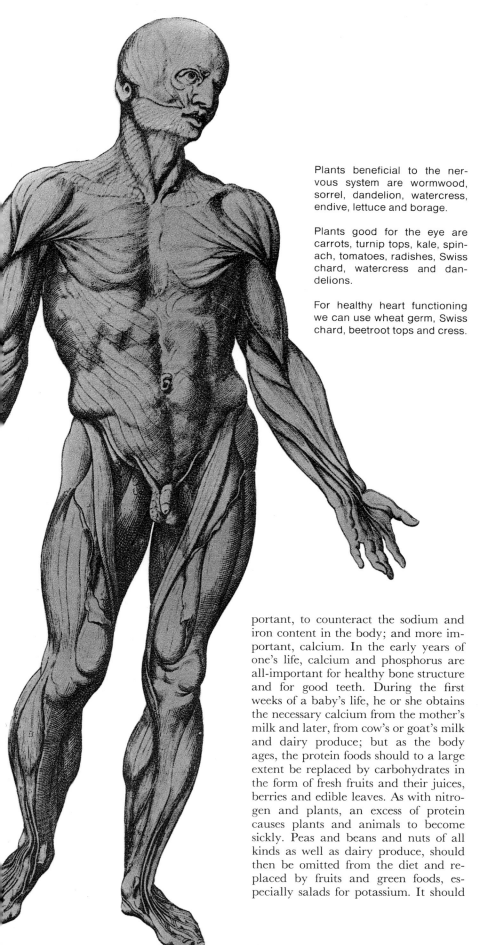

Plants beneficial to the nervous system are wormwood, sorrel, dandelion, watercress, endive, lettuce and borage.

Plants good for the eye are carrots, turnip tops, kale, spinach, tomatoes, radishes, Swiss chard, watercress and dandelions.

For healthy heart functioning we can use wheat germ, Swiss chard, beetroot tops and cress.

For the blood and the circulation: grape and apple juice, cranberries, parsley, spinach, nasturtium and watercress, while horseradish serves to clean the blood.

Kidney and urinary problems can be eased by the intake of the same plants which are good for the eyes.

The liver requires a substance present in peas, beans, black molasses and cereals.

Wheat germ and potatoes help the pancreas to function correctly.

Wheat germ is required for a healthy sex life.

For healthy bowel functioning we need bran, legumes, nuts, dates, raisins, figs and blackberries.

portant, to counteract the sodium and iron content in the body; and more important, calcium. In the early years of one's life, calcium and phosphorus are all-important for healthy bone structure and for good teeth. During the first weeks of a baby's life, he or she obtains the necessary calcium from the mother's milk and later, from cow's or goat's milk and dairy produce; but as the body ages, the protein foods should to a large extent be replaced by carbohydrates in the form of fresh fruits and their juices, berries and edible leaves. As with nitrogen and plants, an excess of protein causes plants and animals to become sickly. Peas and beans and nuts of all kinds as well as dairy produce, should then be omitted from the diet and replaced by fruits and green foods, especially salads for potassium. It should

(Right) *Lactarius deliciosus*. Mushrooms contain folic acid, an important body requirement.

Morchella conica (above) is one of many types of *Morchella*, which are all edible but should always be cooked before eating.

Bear's garlic, *Allium ursinum (below)*, is a valuable medicinal plant to be found in moist valleys and forests.

be remembered that protein foods increase the alkalinity and thickening of the blood while carbohydrates have the opposite effect. They cause a thinning of the blood, allowing it to circulate more freely (the blood makes a complete circuit of the body every 23 seconds) and preventing precipitation on the walls of the arteries. Grape juice, perhaps in the form of white wine, as well as apple and cranberry juices, are the best for giving the blood an acid condition.

Iron is an important mineral required by the body to keep it in good health. It is needed to maintain the red corpuscles in the blood, preventing anemia, but it is assimilated only where vitamin C is present, in the same way that a well limed soil is able to unlock the fertilizers it contains and make them available to plants. Iron regulates the oxygen and carbon dioxide in the blood and ensures good circulation. It keeps the hands and feet warm in cold weather and prevents fatigue and loss of vitality. Iron is present in quantity in black molasses, left over from the refining of cane sugar; in wheat germ, removed in the refining of flour; in legumes; in the leaves of parsley and spinach, nasturtium and watercress.

Pernicious anemia has been successfully treated by eating large quantities of mushrooms and other edible fungi. Dr. Williams of Texas University, in 1939, found that the important human body requirement, folic acid, was present in spinach and in mushrooms as well as in animal liver; this discovery gave the mushroom an important boost, for no longer was it looked upon as luxury food. More recently, Dr. Benjamin Frank, the American nutritionist, has suggested that greying hair and premature aging may be caused by a deficiency of folic acid which can be prevented by a generous intake of mushrooms.

A healthy body also needs a regular intake of iodine, all the more so when modern chlorinated drinking water has, in many places, replaced the crystal-clear water of springs and wells which contained most of the valuable mineral salts.

Chlorinated water may be more germ-free but it causes the body to lose its important iodine content. Iodine is necessary for the proper functioning of the thyroid gland, through which the blood passes every 17 minutes. The secretion of iodine by the thyroid gland kills weak germs that have passed into the bloodstream, and more powerful germs are made weaker and weaker as the blood circulates. If there is a low iodine intake, the thyroid gland is deprived of its needs, for in addition, it rebuilds energy in the body and also eases nervous tension.

Those plants rich in iodine include radishes, tomatoes and watercress, important additions to the summer salad bowl, and most of all the seaweeds, especially kelp, laver, dulse and carrageen which are found on rocky coasts almost everywhere. Iodine is also present in tarragon.

As the mineral salts of the soil are being continually washed away, and are carried into the seas by rivers, it is to the oceans that modern man must look in future for much of his food if his body is to obtain its mineral requirements. More than two-thirds of the earth's surface of almost 200 million square miles is covered by water. Besides the seaweeds, which have been there since the beginning of time and were a valuable source of food for early man, all shellfish have a high iodine content, including those which are almost invisible to the eye.

The continual erosion of soil, and loss of the minerals it contains, are due partly to man's own shortsightedness, for he is destroying the forest with its balanced plant life of roots, bark, leaves and fruits at a frightening rate. The roots of trees and plants have since the beginning of life on earth helped to bind together the soil, preventing it being washed into the rivers by heavy rain to be carried down to the sea. The vegetation had taken the full force of the rain before it reached the ground, thus also preventing much of the soil from being eroded. It has been calculated that each cubic mile of ocean (ca.

A thistle, *Dipsacus silvestris (left)* as depicted by Dioscorides nearly two thousand years ago. According to the text the root was mashed, mixed with wine and kept in a bronze container for use as a tincture in the treatment of boils and warts. Many plants are known as thistles although often belonging to different families. Another example is *Cirsium arvenese (above)*. The heads were once used to tease cloth, in fact thistles are also known as teasels or teazles.

Carrots *(above)* are the most valuable source of vitamin A, especially beneficial for the eyes, besides containing other vitamins and sugars which are concentrated mostly on the surface of the root, and thus should not be peeled.

The vine, *Vitis vinifera*. Grape juice helps the circulation.

4 km³) contains some 200 million tons of chemical compounds, including iodine, magnesium, bromine and other important minerals required to maintain the body in normal health. The thyroid gland needs iodine; the parathyroid requires cobalt; the adrenal needs magnesium; the pituitary gland needs mangenese. All parts of the body need different minerals in various quantities. None is more important than iodine which is available in few land plants. Sulphur is also a mineral present in certain plants, the most important being horseradish and those of the onion family. Sulphur clears the blood of impurities and helps to kill baccili of the common cold.

The pituitary gland, situated behind the nose, controls the thyroid and pancreas. It prevents the body from forming an excess of fat. Wheat germs and potatoes contain generous amounts of manganese and wheat germ is also rich in vitamin E, one of the most important vitamins needed for a healthy sex life. Wheat germ, being rich in the B vitamins, is needed by the pancreas to manufacture insulin which is required by the body to store and control its sugar content. If the pancreas is not supplied with B vitamins, it fails to produce insulin, and diabetes can result.

Primitive man had no knowledge of the presence of minerals and vitamins in the foods he ate. He consumed those foods which were readily available each in its season and mostly those foods which made him feel well. Indeed, it was not until 1912 that the name vitamin (from the Latin *vita,* life) was added to our language, to distinguish those "necessary food substances" the body required for a healthy life. Though as early as 1753, Dr. James Lind had written that the dreaded scurvy disease of sailors, caused by lack of vitamin C, could be prevented by consuming citrus fruits on their travels, it was not known why this was so and vitamin C was not isolated until 1928.

The first of the vitamins, B, considered to be a single vitamin, was discovered in 1911 by the Polish scientist Casimir Funk when he extracted a substance from the refinings of rice able to cure beri-beri disease among eaters of polished or refined rice in south-east Asia. It was in fact vitamin B1, or thiamine, the first of the important B complex vitamins which were to be discovered later. Since few vitamins are manufactured by the body, they must come from other sources. Nor is the body able to store up vitamins for long periods; hence there must be an almost daily intake. Plants supply most of the necessary vitamins and they are distributed throughout the world for man to make use of.

Vitamin A has been called the "glamour" vitamin, for those who consume it in large amounts usually have sparkling eyes and a clear skin. It is needed for healthy bone and tissue growth, especially in young children. It is essential for the proper functioning of the kidneys and to prevent urinary troubles. Above all it strengthens and clears the eyes. Without this vitamin, the eyes find difficulty in adjusting to changes of light and to seeing in the dark. Vitamin A is also needed to protect the mucous membrane of the nose and throat which acts as a filter against pollution, and as the mucous is being continually used up, it must be continually replaced.

In the vegetable world, the most valuable source of vitamin A is found in the root of carrots, wild or cultivated, from which it was first isolated. The substance is known as carotene, which is converted into vitamin A in the body. The process is helped by chopping (or chewing) the raw roots which are sprinkled over soups and stews and into salads. Carrots are available all year. They can be lightly cooked whole or diced to serve as a vegetable. Vitamin A is also present in turnip tops, kale and spinach; in tomatoes, radishes and Swiss chard which grows on the shore and by lakesides; and in watercress and dandelion leaves. It is also present in those fruits with an orange skin, especially apricots, but also in grapes. Vitamin A is stored in the liver and in fat body tissue so that some intake of fatty foods is

Broccoli *(left),* like cabbage, is a member of the cruciferous family.

All varieties of cabbage contain a wide range of vitamins and minerals. The ancient Greeks and the Romans used cabbage only as a medicinal herb. Cato said that Romans had been able to do without doctors for centuries, thanks to cabbage. In fact it has been described as "the doctor of the poor." It is good for the respiratory and nervous system and is useful in the treatment of dysentery, an infusion is an excellent depurative and the leaves, which should first be ironed to soften them, can be used as a poultice to relieve rheumatic and other pains.

necessary, but for the body to make use of it, vitamin A must be accompanied by vitamin E. This vitamin is known as Tocopherol. It strengthens the heart muscles and fortifies the sex glands. Lack of this vitamin can cause male sterility. When it became known that avocado pears possessed liberal amounts of vitamin E, they came to be eaten and used in beauty treatment in all parts of the world.

Vitamin E is also present in wheat germ; in dried peas and beans and in most green vegetables, especially Swiss chard and beetroot tops. Cress is rich in it. This vitamin reduces the need for oxygen in the body, and thus puts less strain on the heart. In the same way, asthma sufferers respond to a regular intake of this vitamin. One way of taking it is to put a large handful of mixed "greens" containing this vitamin through a juicing machine and to serve before lunch as a daily "cocktail" which will also provide the body with chlorophyll. Or use the same "greens" in a daily salad.

Usually accompanying vitamin E is vitamin F, the polyunsaturated fatty

Two varieties of lettuce: *Lactuca sativa (left)* and *Lactuca crispa (above).* Lettuce is said to have cured Emperor Augustus of a severe liver complaint. It is a refreshing and calming ingredient for salads.

The eggplant or aubergine *(above)* has a high potassium content.

Lactarius piperatus (above centre) is a bitter mushroom that should be well cooked.

Lactarius deliciosus (above) is not as tasty as its name suggests.

Watercress, *Nasturtium officinale* in flower *(right)*. It is known as "bodily health" in France.

acid that improves the skin and lowers cholesterol in the blood, preventing blockage of the arteries by fatty deposits. Vitamin F is present only in vegetable oils such as those of sunflower seeds and pumpkin nuts which the peoples of the Balkan countries consume in large amount and which they believe accounts for their living to a ripe old age.

The B vitamins, the first to be discovered, work as a team though each is of different chemical composition. There are 17 vitamins of the B complex though the merits of several of them are as yet little understood, while some are thought to be of only limited importance, though there may be a reevaluation when their values are better known.

Vitamins of the B group need to be constantly replenished as they are soluble in water and cannot be stored in the body. Thus all people need a daily intake of green foods, as animals do, if health is to be maintained.

Vitamin B_1 (Thiamine) strengthens the muscles, including the heart, and prevents fatigue. It aids the digestion, controls the adrenal glands and relaxes the nerves, preventing depression. Though wheat germ is the richest source, this vitamin is obtained from nuts, dried peas and beans, lettuce, cress and cucumbers, also cauliflower and broccoli. The same plant foods which are rich in vitamin B_1 also contain B_2 (Riboflavin) which guards the body against premature aging. It prevents the skin from wrinkling and cracking. It is mainly concerned with the conversion of protein and sugars into energy. It is present also in bran, tomatoes, apricots and in tea drinks.

Vitamin B_3 (Niacin) is needed for correct brain activity and to prevent nervous disorders. It prevents dizziness and depression; it eases migraine. It is present in potatoes, wheat germ, bran and nuts, while beer drinkers rarely suffer from a deficiency. Vitamin B_6 (Pryrodoxine) assists in the simulation of proteins and in the formation of hemoglobin in the blood. It is able to convert

amino acids to niacin and prevents the build-up of cholesterol in the blood. This vitamin is lost in freezing and canning owing to the use of preservatives. It is obtained from nuts, dried peas and beans, peanuts, wheat germ, green peppers, eggplants, lettuce and cabbage.

Lack of vitamin B_{12} may cause pernicious anemia which destroys the nerve cells. It is not present in plants (only in meat) but is closely allied to folic acid, present in mushrooms and most "green" foods, and to Pantothenic acid which with vitamin B_1 fortifies the adrenal glands. It prevents depression and loss of appetite, as well as premature greying of the hair. Sufferers from arthritis usually lack this vitamin which is present in small quantities in wheat germ, peanuts, soya beans, and dried peas and beans.

Also of the B complex is Choline which guards the liver against fatty degeneration and with Inositol lowers the cholesterol level of the blood. Inositol is a sedative and also promotes healthy hair growth. It is present in black molasses, oatmeal and in most fresh fruits.

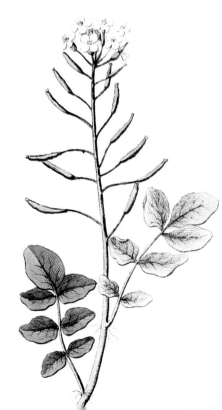

Associated with the B vitamins is Biotin, required in small amounts in the manufacture of glycogen in the liver. It is found in peas and beans, black molasses and cereals.

Vitamin C (Ascorbic acid) is necessary to prevent scurvy which causes loss of energy, premature aging and falling hair. It maintains the strength of blood vessels and prevents strokes. Its discoverer was a Hungarian, Professor Szant-Gyorgyi, who was later to realize that vitamin C was only effective when other factors were also present, that synthetic vitamin C did not produce the same results as when the juice of citrus, grapes and blackcurrants was taken. The Professsor called this hidden factor vitamin P, which is present only in plant foods.

Vitamin C is present in dandelion leaves, watercress, ladies' smock and nasturtium leaves eaten by South American Indians, who are among the longest living of all people. Fruits, especially apples and strawberries, are rich in vitamin C, also tomatoes, eggplants, rose hips and rowanberries. Vitamin D, obtained from the sun and from the skins of citrus fruits, is needed to prevent night cramps and to forestall rickets in young children. It keeps the muscles healthy and helps protect the body against the common cold. The fresh skins of all citrus fruits should be grated into salads and over stewed fruits.

The other important vitamin is K, which prevents hemorrhages and is present in most "greens," especially cabbage, kale and spinach, Swiss chard and tomatoes.

All green plants contain chlorophyll which gives leaves their green coloring and enables plants to manufacture their own food. The atomic structure of chlorophyll is made up of carbon, hydrogen, oxygen, nitrogen and a single atom of magnesium. The juice of "greens" is therefore one of nature's most important substances, for it contains all the important elements of life. A handful of "greens" put through a juicer will contain not only mineral salts and vitamins but also chlorophyll which will tone the system and sweeten the breath and prevent the stale smell of perspiration. For these reasons it is now used in toothpastes and deodorants but is better taken as a daily drink.

There is another important part played by plants in maintaining body fitness, they provide fiber or roughage for a healthy action of the bowels. This will eliminate all unwanted material from the intestines, and thus will do much to prevent cancer of the bowels. Wholemeal bread made from unrefined flour should replace white bread in the diet, for it contains the entire wheat grain after removal of the husk and has 4-times greater fiber content. Wheat bran, composed of the outer layers of wheat removed in the refining of white flour, is a rich source of fiber and should be sprinkled over stewed fruit at breakfast. Legumes are the next best sources of fiber, together with nuts of all kinds, especially almonds and fresh coconut. Of fruits, dates, raisins and figs are richest in fiber, and of fresh fruits, blackberries. Of roots, horseradish has a high fiber content, also parsnips, beetroot and potatoes. Of "green" foods, only spinach is really fibrous, many times more so than other green vegetables. It is one of nature's wonder foods.

For sweetening, the syrup of maple and birch provided man in cooler climes with his needs, and in warmer parts, sugar cane which is now refined to supply the world's sugar requirements, most of the goodness being removed as molasses. The most health-giving of all sweeteners is honey, which bees produce from the nectar of flowers and which is a sedative. Unlike white sugar, it requires no mastication but enters the bloodstream immediately. It is man's finest source of energy and is an important supplier of vitamin K.

The dog rose, *Rosa canina*, derives its name from the ancient superstition that its root cures rabies. A secretion of this rose caused by the sting of a certain insect is used in herbal medicine as a tonic, while the red part of the hip has a high vitamin content.

Habitat – Harvest time – Nutritious matter

A closer look at edible wild plants. The following pages give a breakdown of the plants showing where to find and when to harvest them, with indications as to which parts of the plant to use. The reader learns the nutritive content of each plant and in which way it is beneficial for the health.

Title page *(right)* from "The Grete Herball", 1526, shows the herbalist and his assistant harvesting fruit and flowers. In the foreground we can see two mandrakes with human forms. Mandrakes were said to emit an anguished wail when uprooted.

Opposite page:
Bees provide us with an energy-giving natural sweetener.

As more information has been acquired about nutrition, this complex subject has created a greater general interest. Unfortunately doctors are so busy diagnosing the diseases of their patients and administering the necessary treatment that they have little time to study the latest ideas that have been developed in the field of nutrition. A doctor knows how to recognize the different illnesses, but often pays very little attention to the standards and requisites of

good health. If more attention were paid to the problem of keeping well through adequate nutrition, less people would succumb to degenerative diseases.

Recent studies have shown that the average daily requirement of nutrients increases remarkably under stress. Many of us are subject to unexpected and unusual stresses from time to time, consequently we need to increase our intake of nutrients to keep healthy and to cope with these stresses. However, increasing nutrients does not necessarily mean increasing the quantity of the food we eat. Refined and processed foods,

although containing many calories, may lack all their nutrients. There are forty nutrients which cannot be made in the body. From these our bodies synthesize an estimated ten thousand different compounds essential to the maintenance of health. All forty nutrients work together, thus a lack of any one could result in the underproduction of hundreds of important compounds. Nitrates from commercial fertilizers destroy or decrease the vitamin C content of plants and can also cause serious illnesses in farm animals and babies while pesticide residues not only alter flavor and destroy various vitamins but can also inhibit the action of many enzymes.

Herbs and plants have been used as medicines since the beginning of time and still have a useful place in coping with many human ailments. We should not forget, however, that many illnesses can be prevented by following a balanced diet containing wild plants, which are the richest source of the nutrients necessary for healthy living.

Plant Lexicon Number	Where To Find	Part used	Harvesting Time	Nutritive Value	Health Benefits
AGRIMONY 4	Hedgerows	Leaves, Flowers	Summer	Vitamin C	Antiscorbutic; strengthens the blood vessels; prevents strokes; for healthy teeth and gums.
				Volatile oils	Blood purifier; Astringent.
ALEXANDERS 211	Hedgerows Wasteland	Leaves Roots	Summer Winter	Vitamin C	Antiscorbutic; strengthens the blood vessels; prevents strokes; for healthy teeth and gums.
ALFALFA 127	Grassy slopes	Seed sprouts	Summer	Vitamin B_2	Prevents premature aging; skin disorders.
				Vitamin C	Antiscorbutic; strengthens the blood vessels; prevents strokes; for healthy teeth and gums.
				Protein	For healthy gland secretion, hormones from which enter the bloodstream and regulate the chemical processes of the body.
ALLSPICE 164	Woodlands	Fruits	Autumn (Fall)	Volatile oil	Stimulant; tonic.
ALMOND 10	Woodlands	Nuts	Autumn (Fall)	Vitamin B_1	Strengthens the heart and muscles; controls the adrenal gland; fortifies the nervous system.
				Biotin	Aids respiration.
				Protein	For healthy gland secretion, hormones from which enter the bloodstream and regulate the chemical processes of the body.
AMERICAN AMARANTH 9	Wasteland	Leaves	Summer	Vitamin B_2	Prevents premature aging; skin disorders.
ANGELICA 14	Wasteland	Leaves; stems; seed; root	Summer Autumn (Fall)	Volatile oils Angelic acid	Stimulant; tonic.
ANISE 165	Wasteland	Seed	Autumn (Fall)	Choline	Lowers cholesterol level in blood; reduces risk of heart attacks.
APRICOT 178	Woodlands	Fruit	Summer	Vitamin A	Improves the sight; protects the mucous membrane of throat and nose; protects the body against infection.
				Calcium	For relaxation and sound sleep; builds healthy bones and teeth.
				Iron	Prevents anemia.
ARROWHEAD 198	Waterside	Tuber	Summer	Vitamin C	Antiscorbutic; strengthens the blood vessels; prevents strokes; for healthy teeth and gums.
ARROWROOT 126	Woodlands	Rhizome	Summer	Starch	Nutritious.
ASPARAGUS 28	Coastline	Young shoots	Spring; Summer	Vitamin A	Improves the sight; protects the mucous membrane of throat and nose; protects the body against infection.
				Vitamin B_1	Strengthens heart and muscles; controls the adrenal gland; fortifies the nervous system.

Plant Lexicon Number	Where To Find	Part used	Harvesting Time	Nutritive Value	Health Benefits
				Vitamin B_2	Prevents premature aging; skin disorders.
				Vitamin B_3	Prevents mental fatigue.
				Iron	Prevents anemia.
ASPARAGUS PEA 120	Wasteland	Seed Pods	Summer	Vitamin B_1	Strengthens the heart and muscles; controls the adrenal gland; fortifies the nervous system.
				Vitamin B_2	Prevents premature aging; skin disorders.
AVOCADO PEAR 158	Swamplands	Fruit	Summer	Vitamin E	Fortifies the sex glands; reduces the body's need for oxygen, of importance to asthma sufferers.
BALM 128	Hedgerows	Leaves	Summer	Enzymes	Tonic; carminative; reduces blood pressure.
				Vitamin C	Antiscorbutic; strengthens the blood vessels; prevents strokes; for healthy teeth and gums.
BAMBOO 25	River banks	Young shoots	Summer	Vitamin B_2	Prevents premature aging; skin disorders.
BANANA 137	Forest lands	Fruit	All Year	Carbo-hydrates	For energy; assists in assimilation of other foods.
				Phos-phorus	Prevents tooth decay and easily broken bones.
BARBERRY 35	Woodlands	Fruit	Late Summer	Vitamin A	Improves the sight; protects the mucous membrane of throat and nose; protects the body against infection.
				Vitamin C	Antiscorbutic; strengthens the blood vessels; prevents strokes; for healthy teeth and gums.
BARLEY 103	Fields	Seed	Autumn (Fall)		Nutritive Demulcent.
BASIL 143	Wasteland	Leaf	Summer	Enzymes	Tonic; carminative; reduces blood pressure.
				Potassium	Restorative; prevents an excess of iron and calcium in the blood.
BAUHINIA 33	Hillsides	Flowers; leaves	Summer	Potassium	Restorative; prevents an excess of iron and calcium in the blood.
BAY LAUREL 114	Woodlands	Leaves	All Year	Glycosides	Aids digestion.
				Bitter prin-ciples	Improves the appetite.
BEECH 84	Woodlands	Nuts	Autumn (Fall)	Bitter prin-ciples	Improves the appetite.
				Choline	Lowers cholesterol level in blood; reduces risk of heart attacks.

Plant Lexicon Number	Where To Find	Part used	Harvesting Time	Nutritive Value	Health Benefits
BEET 37	Seashore	Root; leaves; stems (seakale beet)	Autumn (Fall) Summer	Vitamin A	Improves the sight; protects the mucous membrane of throat and nose; protects the body against infection.
				Vitamin B$_2$	Prevents premature aging; skin disorders.
				Iron	Prevents anemia.
				Potassium	Restorative; prevents an excess of iron and calcium in the blood.
BERGAMOT 132	Woodlands	Leaves	Summer	Volatile oil	Stimulant; tonic.
BETELNUT PALM 19	Seashore	Leaves; nuts	Summer Autumn (Fall)	Vitamin B$_1$	Strengthens the heart and muscles; controls the adrenal glands; fortifies the nervous system.
				Vitamin C	Antiscorbutic; strengthens the blood vessels; prevents strokes; for healthy teeth and gums.
				Protein	For healthy gland secretion, hormones from which enter the bloodstream and regulate the chemical processes of the body.
BISTORT 173	Pastureland	Young shoots; leaves	Early summer	Vitamin C	Antiscorbutic; strengthens the blood vessels; prevents strokes; for healthy teeth and gums.
				Carbo- hydrates	For energy; assists in assimilation of other foods.
BITANG 110	River banks	Young shoots; leaves	Early summer	Vitamin C	Antiscorbutic; strengthens the blood vessels; prevents strokes; for healthy teeth and gums.
BLACKBERRY 194	Hedgerows	Fruits	Autumn (Fall)	Vitamin C	Antiscorbutic; strengthens the blood vessels; prevents strokes; for healthy teeth and gums.
				Calcium	For relaxation and sound sleep; builds healthy bones and teeth.
				Iron	Prevents anemia.
BLACK MULBERRY 134	Woodlands	Fruit	Late summer	Vitamin C	Antiscorbutic; strengthens the blood vessels; prevents strokes; for healthy teeth and gums.
BLACK MUSTARD 209	Arable land	Seeds	Late summer	Vitamin A	Improves the sight; protects the mucous membrane of throat and nose; protects the body against infection.
				Vitamin C	Antiscorbutic; strengthens the blood vessels; prevents strokes; for healthy teeth and gums.
BLUEBERRY 240	Moorlands	Fruits	Late summer	Vitamin C	Antiscorbutic; strengthens the blood vessels; prevents strokes; for healthy teeth and gums.
BOGBEAN 130	Wet land	Leaves	Summer	Vitamin C	Antiscorbutic; strengthens the blood vessels; prevents strokes; for healthy teeth and gums.
				Menyan- thin	Tonic properties.
BORAGE 38	Wasteland	Leaves; flowers	Summer	Potassium	Restorative; prevents an excess of iron and calcium in the blood.
				Manga- nese	For a healthy pituitary gland which controls fatty deposits.
				Mucilages	Protects mucous membranes.

Plant Lexicon Number	Where To Find	Part used	Harvesting Time	Nutritive Value	Health Benefits
BRAZIL NUT 36	Rain forests	Nuts	Late summer	Vitamin B$_1$	Strengthens the heart and muscles; controls the adrenal gland; fortifies the nervous system.
				Protein	For healthy gland secretion, hormones from which enter the bloodstream and regulate the chemical processes of the body.
				Inositol	Stimulates hair growth.
BREAD FRUIT 23	Woodlands	Fruits	Late summer	Carbohydrates	For energy; assists in assimilation of other foods.
BROAD BEAN 245	Wasteland	Seeds	Summer	Vitamin B$_1$	Strengthens the heart and muscles; controls the adrenal gland; fortifies the nervous system.
				Vitamin B$_2$	Prevents premature aging; skin disorders.
				Choline	Lowers cholesterol level in blood; reduces risk of heart attacks.
BROOKLIME 243	Ditches	Leaves and stems	Summer	Vitamin C	Antiscorbutic; strengthens the blood vessels; prevents strokes; for healthy teeth and gums.
BURDOCK 18	Wasteland	Young leaves Roots	Early summer Winter	Vitamin C	Antiscorbutic; strengthens the blood vessels; prevents strokes; for healthy teeth and gums.
BURNET 176	Pastureland	Leaves	Summer	Vitamin C	Antiscorbutic; strengthens the blood vessels; prevents strokes; for healthy teeth and gums.
CACAO 228	Rain forests	Seeds	Late summer	Theobromine	Dilates blood vessels.
				Protein	For healthy gland secretion, hormones from which enter the bloodstream and regulate the chemical processes of the body.
CAPE GOOSEBERRY 162	Coast	Fruits	Late summer	Vitamin C	Antiscorbutic; strengthens the blood vessels; prevents strokes; for healthy teeth and gums.
CAPER 42	Rocky slopes	Flower buds	Summer	Vitamin C	Antiscorbutic; strengthens the blood vessels; prevents strokes; for healthy teeth and gums.
CARAWAY 47	Wasteland	Seeds	Autumn (Fall)	Essential oil (Carvol)	Aids the digestion.
CARDAMOM 80	Rain forests	Seeds	Late summer	Potassium	Restorative; prevents an excess of iron and calcium in the blood.
				Volatile oil	Stimulant; tonic.
CAROB 50	Rocky slopes	Seeds; bulb	Late summer	Carbohydrates	For energy; assists in assimilation of other foods.
				Saccharine	Sweetening.
CARRAGEEN MOSS 52	Seashore	All parts	All year	Mucilage	Nutritive.

Plant Lexicon Number	Where To Find	Part used	Harvesting Time	Nutritive Value	Health Benefits
CARROT 75	Hedgerows	Root	Late summer	Vitamin A	Improves the sight; protects the mucous membrane of throat and nose; protects the body against infection.
CASHEW 11	Rain forests	Fruit; nut	Late summer	Vitamin B$_2$	Prevents premature aging; skin disorders.
				Vitamin C	Antiscorbutic; strengthens the blood vessels; prevents strokes; for healthy teeth and gums.
				Protein	For healthy gland secretion, hormones from which enter the bloodstream and regulate the chemical processes of the body.
CASSAVA 125	Rain forests	Roots	Late summer	Carbo-hydrates	For energy; assists in assimilation of other foods.
CASSIA 54	Rocky outcrops	Fruits; bark	Late summer	Essential oils	Promote the flow of gastric juices.
CHECKERBERRY 91	Mountain slopes	Fruits	Late summer	Vitamin C	Antiscorbutic; strengthens the blood vessels; prevents strokes; for healthy teeth and gums.
CHERVIL 16	Wastelands	Leaves; Roots	Summer Autumn (Fall)	Vitamin A	Improves the sight; protects the mucous membrane of throat and nose; protects the body against infection.
				Vitamin C	Antiscorbutic; strengthens the blood vessels; prevents strokes; for healthy teeth and gums.
				Iron	Prevents anemia.
CHICKWEED 220	Wastelands	Leaves	Spring	Vitamin C	Antiscorbutic; strengthens the blood vessels; prevents strokes; for healthy teeth and gums.
				Iron	Prevents anemia.
CHICORY 53	Meadows	Stems; roots; leaves	Winter Summer	Vitamin A	Improves the sight; protects the mucous membrane of throat and nose; protects the body against infection.
CHINESE ARTICHOKE 219	Woodlands	Tuberous roots	Winter	Vitamin A	Improves the sight; protects the mucous membrane of throat and nose; protects the body against infection.
				Iron	Prevents anemia.
CHIVE 6	Woodlands	Leaves	All summer	Vitamin A	Improves the sight; protects the mucous membrane of throat and nose; protects the body against infection.
				Vitamin B$_2$	Prevents premature aging; skin disorders.
				Vitamin C	Antiscorbutic; strengthens the blood vessels; prevents strokes; for healthy teeth and gums.
				Calcium	Makes good bones and teeth.
				Iron	Prevents anemia.
				Phospho-rus	Ensures correct glandular secretions.
CHOCHO 206	Rain forests	Fruit	Late summer	Vitamin B$_1$	Strengthens the heart and muscles; controls the adrenal gland; fortifies the nervous system.
				Vitamin C	Antiscorbutic; strengthens the blood vessels; prevents strokes; for healthy teeth and gums.

Plant Lexicon Number	Where To Find	Part used	Harvesting Time	Nutritive Value	Health Benefits
COCONUT PALM 58	Coast	Nut; milk	All year	Vitamin B$_1$	Strengthens the heart and muscles; controls the adrenal gland; fortifies the nervous system.
				Inositol	Stimulates hair growth.
				Protein	For healthy gland secretion, hormones from which enter the bloodstream and regulate the chemical processes of the body.
COFFEE 59	Rocky slopes	Bean	Late summer	Aromatic oil	Strengthens the heart.
				Caffeine	Brain stimulant.
COLA 60	Tropical forests	Nuts	Late summer	Caffeine	Brain stimulant
				Cola	Nervine.
COLEWORT 39	Wasteland	Leaves	Summer; Winter	Vitamin B$_6$	Prevents nervous tension.
				Vitamin C	Antiscorbutic; strengthens the blood vessels; prevents strokes; for healthy teeth and gums.
				Vitamin K	Prevents hemorrhages.
				Calcium	For relaxation and sound sleep; builds healthy bones and teeth.
				Iron	Prevents anemia.
COMMON ASH 88	Woodlands	Exudation	Summer	Sweet principle (Mannite)	Tonic.
COMMON ORACH 30	Rocky slopes	Leaves	Summer	Vitamin C	Antiscorbutic; strengthens the blood vessels; prevents strokes; for healthy teeth and gums.
				Potassium	Restorative; prevents an excess of iron and calcium in the blood.
COMMON SORREL 195	Field sides	Leaves	Summer	Vitamin A	Improves the sight; protects the mucous membrane of throat and nose; protects the body against infection.
				Vitamin C	Antiscorbutic; strengthens the blood vessels; prevents strokes; for healthy teeth and gums.
				Potassium	Restorative; prevents an excess of iron and calcium in the blood.
CORIANDER 62	Wasteland	Leaves; Seeds	Summer Autumn (Fall)	Volatile oil	Stimulant.
CORN SALAD 241	Arable land	Leaves	Spring	Vitamin B$_1$	Strengthens the heart and muscles; controls the adrenal gland; fortifies the nervous system.
				Vitamin B$_2$	Prevents premature aging; skin disorders.
				Vitamin C	Antiscorbutic; strengthens the blood vessels; prevents strokes; for healthy teeth and gums.
COSTMARY 223	Wasteland	Leaves	Summer	Aromatic oil	Prevents gout and rheumatism.
COWAGE 135	Tropical forests	Pods	Summer	Vitamin B$_1$	Strengthens the heart and muscles; controls the adrenal gland; fortifies the nervous system.

Plant Lexicon Number	Where To Find	Part used	Harvesting Time	Nutritive Value	Health Benefits
COWSLIP 177	Woodlands; hedgerows	Flowers; leaves	Spring	Vitamin C	Antiscorbutic; strengthens the blood vessels; prevents strokes; for healthy teeth and gums.
				Iron	Prevents anemia.
CRAB APPLE 123	Woodlands; hedgerows	Fruit	Autumn (Fall)	Vitamin C	Antiscorbutic; strengthens the blood vessels; prevents strokes; for healthy teeth and gums.
				Malic acid	Neutralizes excess of calcium in the blood.
				Phos-phorus	Fortifies the nervous system.
CRANBERRY 151	Boglands	Fruit	Late summer	Vitamin C	Antiscorbutic; strengthens the blood vessels; prevents strokes; for healthy teeth and gums.
				Citric acid	Stimulates the bile.
				Benzoic acid	Prevents decomposition.
CUBEB 167	Forest lands	Unripe fruits	Summer	Volatile oil	Stimulates the appetite
CUCUMBER 68	Hedgerows	Fruit	Summer	Vitamin A	Improves the sight; protects the mucous membrane of throat and nose; protects the body against infection.
				Vitamin C	Antiscorbutic; strengthens the blood vessels; prevents strokes; for healthy teeth and gums.
CUMIN 70	Wayside	Seeds	Late summer	Volatile oil Mucilage	Stimulates the appetite and digestive juices.
CURRY LEAF TREE 136	Woodlands	Leaves; fruits	Summer	Volatile oil	Stimulates the appetite and digestive juices.
CURRY PLANT 99	Wasteland	Leaves	Summer	Volatile oil	Stimulates the appetite and digestive juices.
DAHLIA 74	Wasteland	Tuberous root	Autumn (Fall)	Vitamin A	Improves the sight; protects the mucous membrane of throat and nose; protects the body against infection.
				Inulin	For diabetics.
DALO 61	Marshland	Tuberous root	All year	Vitamin A	Improves the sight; protects the mucous membrane of throat and nose; protects the body against infection.
DANDELION 225	Wasteland	Leaves, root	Summer	Vitamin A	Improves the sight; protects the mucous membrane of throat and nose; protects the body against infection.
				Vitamin B_1	Strengthens the heart and muscles; controls the adrenal gland; fortifies the nervous system.
				Vitamin C	Antiscorbutic; strengthens the blood vessels; prevents strokes; for healthy teeth and gums.

Plant Lexicon Number	Where To Find	Part used	Harvesting Time	Nutritive Value	Health Benefits
DATE PALM 161	Desert	Fruit	All year	Carbo-hydrates	For energy; assists in assimilation of other foods.
				Protein	For healthy gland secretion, hormones from which enter the bloodstream and regulate the chemical processes of the body.
DAY LILY 100	Wasteland	Tuberous root Flower buds	Winter Summer	Vitamin A	Improves the sight; protects the mucous membrane of throat and nose; protects the body against infection.
				Vitamin C	Antiscorbutic; strengthens the blood vessels; prevents strokes; for healthy teeth and gums.
DILL 13	Wasteland	Seed	Autumn (Fall)	Volatile oil	Stimulant; tonic.
DULSE 189	Seashore	All parts	All year	Iodine	Fortifies thyroid gland to keep the body firm and slim.
EARLY WINTER CRESS 32	Hedgerows; waste ground	Leaves	Summer	Vitamin A	Improves the sight; protects the mucous membrane of throat and nose; protects the body against infection.
				Vitamin C	Antiscorbutic; strengthens the blood vessels; prevents strokes; for healthy teeth and gums.
				Vitamin E	Reduces the body's need for oxygen and puts less strain on the heart.
				Iron	Prevents anemia.
EGGPLANT 212	Hedgerows	Fruits	Summer	Vitamin B_1	Strengthens the heart and muscles; controls the adrenal gland; fortifies the nervous system.
				Vitamin B_2	Prevents premature aging; skin disorders.
				Vitamin C	Antiscorbutic; strengthens the blood vessels; prevents strokes; for healthy teeth and gums.
				Calcium	For relaxation and sound sleep, builds healthy bones and teeth.
				Iron	Prevents anemia.
ELDERBERRY 201	Woodlands; hedgerows	Fruit; Flowers	Late summer Early summer	Vitamin C	Antiscorbutic; strengthens the blood vessels; prevents strokes; for healthy teeth and gums.
				Iron	Prevents anemia.
ENGLISH OAK 186	Woodlands; hedgerows	Nut	Autumn (Fall)	Protein	For healthy gland secretion, hormones from which enter the bloodstream and regulate the chemical processes of the body.
EVENING PRIMROSE 144	Wasteland	Leaves	Summer	Vitamin C	Antiscorbutic; strengthens the blood vessels; prevents strokes; for healthy teeth and gums.
FENNEL 86	Wasteland	Leaves	Summer	Volatile oil (Anethol)	Aids digestion; calms the nerves.
FENUGREEK 233	Rocky ground	Seeds	Late summer	Iron	Prevents anemia.
				Phos-phorus	For strong bone and teeth formation.

Plant Lexicon Number	Where To Find	Part used	Harvesting Time	Nutritive Value	Health Benefits
FERN 29	Woodlands	Young shoots Rhizomes	Early summer All year	Vitamin C	Antiscorbutic; strengthens the blood vessels; prevents strokes; for healthy teeth and gums.
FIELD CRESS 116	Pastureland	Leaves	Summer	Vitamin A	Improves the sight; protects the mucous membrane of throat and nose; protects the body against infection.
				Vitamin C	Antiscorbutic; strengthens the blood vessels; prevents strokes; for healthy teeth and gums.
				Iron	Prevents anemia.
FIELD MUSHROOM 182	Pastureland	All of it	Early autumn	Vitamin B_3	Prevents insomnia, nervous tension, depression.
				Calcium	For relaxation and sound sleep; builds healthy bones and teeth.
				Folic acid	Prevents anemia.
FIG 85	Rocky ground	Fruits	All year	Dextrose	Nutritive.
GALANGAL 7	Tropical forests	Root	Late summer	Volatile oil	Stimulant.
GARLIC 5	Rocky slopes	Bulb	Autumn (Fall)	Vitamin A	Improves the sight; protects the mucous membrane of throat and nose; protects the body against infection.
				Vitamin C	Antiscorbutic; strengthens the blood vessels; prevents strokes; for healthy teeth and gums.
				Sulphur	Clears blood of impurities.
GENTIAN 93	Mountain slopes	Roots	Autumn (Fall)	Bitter principle	Stimulates the appetite; tonic.
GERMANDER 226	Wasteland	Leaves	Summer	Bitter principle	Acts as a tonic.
GINGER 250	Rain forests	Root	Late summer	Volatile oil	Stimulant.
GINSENG 153	Hillsides	Root	Late summer	Bitter principle	Acts as a tonic.
GLOBE ARTICHOKE 73	Coast	Leafy head	Summer	Vitamin A	Improves the sight; protects the mucous membrane of throat and nose; protects the body against infection.
GOOD-KING-HENRY 51	Wasteland	Leaves	Summer	Vitamin A	Improves the sight; protects the mucous membrane of throat and nose; protects the body against infection.
				Vitamin B_2	Prevents premature aging; skin disorders.
				Iron	Prevents anemia.
				Potassium	Restorative; prevents an excess of iron and calcium in the blood.

Plant Lexicon Number	Where To Find	Part used	Harvesting Time	Nutritive Value	Health Benefits
GOOSEBERRY 191	Woodlands	Fruit	Summer	Vitamin C	Antiscorbutic; strengthens the blood vessels; prevents strokes; for healthy teeth and gums.
GRAPE 247	Rocky ground	Fruit (Fresh and dried)	Late summer Dried, all year	Vitamin C	Antiscorbutic; strengthens the blood vessels; prevents strokes; for healthy teeth and gums.
				Iron	Prevents anemia, tiredness.
				Potassium	Restorative.
GREATER NETTLE 239	Wasteland	Leaves, stems	Summer	Vitamin A	Improves the sight; protects the mucous membrane of throat and nose; protects the body against infection.
				Vitamin C	Antiscorbutic; strengthens the blood vessels; prevents strokes; for healthy teeth and gums.
GROUND NUT 17	Wasteland	Seeds	Late summer	Protein	For healthy gland secretion, hormones from which enter the bloodstream and regulate the chemical processes of the body.
GUARANA 157	Rain forests	Seeds	Late summer	Guaranine	Stimulant.
GUAVA 183	Rain forests	Fruit	Late summer	Vitamin C	Antiscorbutic; strengthens the blood vessels; prevents strokes; for healthy teeth and gums.
HAWTHORN 65	Woodlands; hedgerows	Berries	Late summer	Vitamin C	Antiscorbutic; strengthens the blood vessels; prevents strokes; for healthy teeth and gums.
HAZEL 63	Woodlands; hedgerows	Nuts	Autumn (Fall)	Vitamin B_1	Strengthens the heart and muscles; controls the adrenal gland; fortifies the nervous system.
				Choline	Lowers cholesterol level in blood; reduces risk of heart attacks.
HENBIT 113	Hedgerows	Young shoots	Spring	Vitamin C	Antiscorbutic; strengthens the blood vessels; prevents strokes; for healthy teeth and gums.
HOP 104	Hedgerows	Young shoots	Spring	Bitter principle	Tonic properties.
HORSERADISH 20	Wasteland	Roots	Winter	Vitamin C	Antiscorbutic; strengthens the blood vessels; prevents strokes; for healthy teeth and gums.
				Iron	Prevents anemia.
				Calcium	For strong bones and teeth.
				Potassium	Restorative.
HOT PEPPER 43	Rocky slopes	Fruit	Summer	Vitamin A	Improves the sight; protects the mucous membrane of throat and nose; protects the body against infection.
				Vitamin C	Antiscorbutic; strengthens the blood vessels; prevents strokes; for healthy teeth and gums.
				Vitamin P	Combines with vitamin C in fresh fruits to strengthen the blood vessels.

Plant / Lexicon Number	Where To Find	Part used	Harvesting Time	Nutritive Value	Health Benefits
HUCKLEBERRY 92	Damp woodlands	Fruit	Late summer Autumn (Fall)	Vitamin C	Antiscorbutic; strengthens the blood vessels; prevents strokes; for healthy teeth and gums.
HYSSOP 105	Rocky ground	Leaves	All year	Vitamin C	Antiscorbutic; strengthens the blood vessels; prevents strokes; for healthy teeth and gums.
				Flavonoides	Strengthens the blood capillaries.
				Volatile oil	Stimulates the appetite.
JERUSALEM ARTICHOKE 98	Wayside	Tubers	Winter	Vitamin A	Improves the sight; protects the mucous membrane of throat and nose; protects the body against infection.
JUJUBE 251	Rocky ground	Fruit	Late summer	Mucilage; sugar	Nutritious
				Vitamin C	Antiscorbutic; strengthens the blood vessels; prevents strokes; for healthy teeth and gums.
JUNIPER 109	Woodlands	Berries	When ripe	Volatile oil	Stimulant.
KALINGA 76	Rain forests	Fruits	Late summer	Vitamin C	Antiscorbutic; strengthens the blood vessels; prevents strokes; for healthy teeth and gums.
				Vitamin P	Strengthens the blood vessels; gives resistance to disease.
KAVA 168	Rain forests	Stems, roots	Summer; Winter	Carbohydrates	For energy; assists in assimilation of other foods.
KIE-KIE 89	Rain forests	Fruit	Summer	Vitamin C	Antiscorbutic; strengthens the blood vessels; prevents strokes; for healthy teeth and gums.
LADY'S SMOCK 44	Meadows	Leaves	Summer	Vitamin C	Antiscorbutic; strengthens the blood vessels; prevents strokes; for healthy teeth and gums.
				Iron	Prevents anemia.
				Calcium	For strong bones and teeth.
LAVER 174	Seashore	All parts	All year	Vitamin C	Antiscorbutic; strengthens the blood vessels; prevents strokes; for healthy teeth and gums.
				Iron	Prevents anemia.
				Calcium	For strong bones and teeth.
LEMON 56	Rocky ground	Fruit	All year	Vitamin C	Antiscorbutic; strengthens the blood vessels; prevents strokes; for healthy teeth and gums.
				Vitamin D	Present in oil ducts in fruit skin, fortified by sunlight. This vitamin must be present before calcium is absorbed into the blood and into bones.
				Vitamin P	Always present with vitamin C, protecting it from oxidization in the body. Protects the body against infection.

Plant Lexicon Number	Where To Find	Part used	Harvesting Time	Nutritive Value	Health Benefits
LENTIL 115	Fields	Seeds	Late summer	Vitamin B_1	Strengthens the heart and muscles; controls the adrenal gland; fortifies the nervous system.
				Protein	For healthy gland secretion, hormones from which enter the bloodstream and regulate the chemical processes of the body.
LIME TREE 230	Woodlands; hedgerows	Flowers; leaves	Early summer	Chlorophyll	For internal healing; sweetens the breath; increases hemoglobin in blood.
				Volatile oil	Prevents insomnia.
LING 232	Pools; ponds	Seed (nuts)	Late summer	Protein	For healthy gland secretion; hormones from which enter the bloodstream and regulate the chemical processes of the body.
LIQUORICE 96	Hedgerows; waste ground	Root	Autumn (Fall)	Calcium	For relaxation and deep sleep; builds healthy bones and teeth.
LITCHEE 119	Woodlands	Fruit	Late summer	Vitamin C	Antiscorbutic; strengthens the blood vessels; prevents strokes; for healthy teeth and gums.
LOTUS LILY 142	Rivers; lakes	Roots; seeds	All year	Protein	For healthy gland secretion, hormones from which enter the bloodstream and regulate the chemical processes of the body.
LOVAGE 118	Hedgerows; Wasteland	Leaves; stems; roots	All year	Vitamin C	Antiscorbutic; strengthens the blood vessels; prevents strokes; for healthy teeth and gums.
MAIDENHAIR TREE 94	Woodlands	Fruit (nuts)	Late summer	Protein	For healthy gland secretion, hormones from which enter the bloodstream and regulate the chemical processes of the body.
MANGO 124	Woodlands; hillsides	Fruit	All summer	Vitamin C	Antiscorbutic; strengthens the blood vessels; prevents strokes; for healthy teeth and gums.
MANGOSTEEN 90	Rain forests	Fruit	Late summer	Vitamin C	Antiscorbutic; strengthens the blood vessels; prevents strokes; for healthy teeth and gums.
MARIGOLD 40	Fields	Flowers; leaves	Summer	Vitamin C	Antiscorbutic; strengthens the blood vessels; prevents strokes; for healthy teeth and gums.
MARJORAM 148	Hilly pastures	Leaves	All year	Volatile oil and bitter principles	Stimulates the appetite, improves the digestion.
MARSH MALLOW 8	Woodlands; river banks	Leaves; roots	Summer; Autumn (Fall)	Vitamin C	Antiscorbutic; strengthens the blood vessels; prevents strokes; for healthy teeth and gums.
MAY APPLE 171	Woodlands	Fruit	Late summer	Vitamin C	Antiscorbutic; strengthens the blood vessels; prevents strokes; for healthy teeth and gums.
MEDLAR 131	Woodlands	Fruit	Late summer	Vitamin C	Antiscorbutic; strengthens the blood vessels; prevents strokes; for healthy teeth and gums.

Plant Lexicon Number	Where To Find	Part used	Harvesting Time	Nutritive Value	Health Benefits
MELON TREE 46	Rain forests	Fruit	Late summer	Vitamin A	Improves the sight; protects the mucous membrane of throat and nose; protects the body against infection.
				Vitamin C	Antiscorbutic; strengthens the blood vessels; prevents strokes; for healthy teeth and gums.
MILK CAP 111	Woodlands	All parts	Late summer	Protein	For healthy gland secretion, hormones from which enter the bloodstream and regulate the chemical processes of the body.
				Calcium	For relaxation and deep sleep; builds healthy bones and teeth.
MILKWEED 27	Fields; wasteland	Young shoots	Early summer	Vitamin C	Antiscorbutic; strengthens the blood vessels; prevents strokes; for healthy teeth and gums.
MILLET 216	River valleys; hedgerows	Seed (corn)	Late summer	Calcium	For relaxation and deep sleep; builds healthy bones and teeth.
				Potassium	Restorative; controls the function of calcium and iron, preventing deposits of calcium on blood vessels.
MOREL 133	Grassy woodlands	All parts	Mid-summer	Protein	For healthy gland secretion, hormones from which enter the bloodstream and regulate the chemical processes of the body.
NARANJILLA 213	Shrubland (high ground)	Fruit	Mid-summer	Vitamin C	Antiscorbutic; strengthens the blood vessels; prevents strokes; for healthy teeth and gums.
NASTURTIUM 235	Wasteground	Seed; leaves	Summer	Vitamin C	Antiscorbutic; strengthens the blood vessels; prevents strokes; for healthy teeth and gums.
				Iron	Prevents anemia.
NUTMEG, MACE 138	Rain forests	Fruit	All year	Volatile oil	Aids digestion; stimulates the appetite.
NUTMEG PLANT 141	Waste ground	Seeds	Late summer	Volatile oil	Aids digestion; stimulates the appetite.
OAT 31	Field sides	Seeds	Late summer	Vitamin B_1	Strengthens the heart and muscles; controls the adrenal gland; fortifies the nervous system.
				Iron	Prevents anemia.
OKRA 101	Waste ground; hedgerows	Fruit; seeds	All summer	Vitamin C	Antiscorbutic; strengthens the blood vessels; prevents strokes; for healthy teeth and gums.
OLIVE 145	Hilly ground	Fruit	All summer	Vitamin E	Strengthens the heart muscles; fortifies the sex glands.
				Vitamin F	Improves the skin; lowers cholesterol in the blood.
OREGON GRAPE 122	Woodlands	Fruit	Late summer	Vitamin C	Antiscorbutic; strengthens the blood vessels; prevents strokes; for healthy teeth and gums.
ORPINE 207	Mountain slopes	Leaves	Early summer	Vitamin C	Antiscorbutic; strengthens the blood vessels; prevents strokes; for healthy teeth and gums.

Plant Lexicon Number	Where To Find	Part used	Harvesting Time	Nutritive Value	Health Benefits
PAPAW 15	Tropical forests; ravines	Fruit; seeds	Late summer	Vitamin C	Antiscorbutic; strengthens the blood vessels; prevents strokes; for healthy teeth and gums.
				Volatile oil	Aids the digestion; stimulates the appetite.
PARAGUAY TEA 106	River banks	Leaves	All summer	Caffein	Prevents too rapid wasting of tissues of the body.
PARSLEY 159	Rocky wasteland	Leaves; seed	All summer	Vitamin A	Improves the sight; protects the mucous membrane of throat and nose; protects the body against infection.
				Iron	Maintains red blood corpuscles; prevents anemia.
PASSION FRUIT 155	Tropical forests	Fruit	All summer	Vitamin A	Improves the sight; protects the mucous membrane of throat and nose; protects the body against infection.
				Vitamin C	Antiscorbutic; strengthens the blood vessels; prevents strokes; for healthy teeth and gums.
PEA 170	Wasteland; sand-dunes	Seed	All summer	Vitamin A	Improves the sight; protects the mucous membrane of throat and nose; protects the body against infection.
				Vitamin B_1	Strengthens the heart and muscles; prevents fatigue.
				Vitamin B_2	Prevents premature aging; skin disorders.
				Vitamin B_3	Keeps the mind clear; eases tension.
				Vitamin B_6	Helps the body assimilate protein.
				Vitamin E	Reduces the body's need for oxygen and puts less strain on the heart.
				Choline	Lowers cholesterol in blood.
PEACH 181	Mountain woodlands	Fruit	All summer	Vitamin A	Improves the sight; protects the mucous membrane of throat and nose; protects the body against infection.
				Iron	Maintains blood corpuscles; prevents anemia.
PEAR 185	Woodlands	Fruit	Late summer	Calcium	For healthy bones and teeth.
				Iron	Prevents anemia.
				Phosphorus	Transfers the sugar in the blood to the liver where it is stored as the energy producing glycogen.
PECAN 48	River banks; woodlands	Nut	Autumn (Fall)	Vitamin B_1	Strengthens the heart and muscles; controls the adrenal gland; fortifies the nervous system.
				Inositol	For healthy skin; prevents baldness; prevents insomnia.
PERSIMMON 78	Tropical forests	Fruit	Late autumn	Vitamin C	Antiscorbutic; strengthens the blood vessels; prevents strokes; for healthy teeth and gums.
PINEAPPLE 12	Tropical forests	Fruit	Late summer	Vitamin C	Antiscorbutic; strengthens the blood vessels; prevents strokes; for healthy teeth and gums.

Plant Lexicon Number	Where To Find	Part used	Harvesting Time	Nutritive Value	Health Benefits
PINE-NUT 166	Mountain slopes	Cones	All year	Vitamin B_1	Strengthens the heart and muscles; controls the adrenal gland; fortifies the nervous system.
				Choline	Lowers cholesterol level in blood; reduces risk of heart attacks.
PISTACHIO 169	Mountain slopes	Nut	Late summer	Vitamin B_1	Strengthens the heart and muscles; controls the adrenal gland; fortifies the nervous system.
				Choline	Lowers cholesterol level in blood; reduces risk of heart attacks.
POKEWEED 163	Field sides	Young shoots	Early summer	Vitamin B_1	Strengthens the heart and muscles; controls the adrenal gland; fortifies the nervous system.
				Vitamin B_2	Prevents premature aging; skin disorders.
				Choline	Lowers cholesterol level in blood; reduces risks of heart attacks.
POLE BEAN 160	Woodlands; hedgerows	Beans	All summer	Vitamin B_1	Strengthens the heart and muscles; controls the adrenal gland; fortifies the nervous system.
				Vitamin B_2	Prevents premature aging; skin disorders.
				Vitamin B_6	Enables the body to assimilate proteins.
				Iron	Prevents anemia.
POMEGRANATE 184	Mountain slopes	Fruit	All year	Vitamin C	Antiscorbutic; strengthens the blood vessels; prevents strokes; for healthy teeth and gums.
POTATO 214	Coastal areas	Tuber	Late summer; Autumn (Fall)	Vitamin B_3	Eases tension; keeps the skin healthy and quick healing.
				Vitamin C	Antiscorbutic; strengthens the blood vessels; prevents strokes; for healthy teeth and gums.
				Iron	Prevents anemia.
				Carbo-hydrates	Increases energy.
				Protein	For healthy gland secretion, hormones from which enter the bloodstream and regulate the chemical processes of the body.
PRICKLY PEAR 146	Desert lands	Fruit	All year	Vitamin C	Antiscorbutic; strengthens the blood vessels; prevents strokes; for healthy teeth and gums.
PURSLANE 175	Wasteland	Leaves	Summer	Vitamin A	Improves the sight; protects the mucous membrane of throat and nose; protects the body against infection.
				Iron	Prevents anemia.
				Calcium	For healthy bones and teeth.
QUINCE 72	Woodlands	Fruit	Late summer	Vitamin C	Antiscorbutic; strengthens the blood vessels; prevents strokes; for healthy teeth and gums.
RADISH 187	Sandy soils	Root	All year	Calcium	For healthy bones and teeth.
				Iodine	For a healthy thyroid gland.

Plant Lexicon Number	Where To Find	Part used	Harvesting Time	Nutritive Value	Health Benefits
RAMPION 41	Roadsides	Shoots; roots	Early summer, Winter	Vitamin C	Antiscorbutic; strengthens the blood vessels; prevents strokes; for healthy teeth and gums.
RED ELM 238	Woodlands	Bark	Spring	Mucilage	Soothes the linings of stomach and intestines; nourishing.
RED POPPY 154	Fields	Seeds	Summer	Protein	For healthy gland secretion, hormones from which enter the bloodstream and regulate the chemical processes of the body.
				Volatile oil	Stimulates the appetite.
REED MACE 237	Ponds and lake side	Young shoots	Early summer	Vitamin C	Antiscorbutic; strengthens the blood vessels; prevents strokes; for healthy teeth and gums.
RHUBARB 188	River banks	Leaf stems	All summer	Potassium	Restorative; regulates other mineral salts in the body.
RICE 150	Flooded land	Seed	Late summer	Vitamin B_6	Helps the body assimilate protein.
				Vitamin B_{15}	Supplies the heart and blood cells with additional oxygen.
				Carbo-hydrates	For energy.
ROCKET 82	Wasteland	Young shoots	Spring	Vitamin C	Antiscorbutic; strengthens the blood vessels; prevents strokes; for healthy teeth and gums.
ROSEMARY 193	Rocky ground	Leaves	All year	Volatile oil	Strengthens the nervous system.
				Bitter principles	Stimulates the appetite; regulates flow of bile.
				Phyton-cides	Destroy germs in the body.
ROWAN 215	Woodlands; Rocky ground	Berries	Autumn (Fall)	Vitamin A	Improves the sight; protects the mucous membrane of throat and nose; protects the body against infection.
				Vitamin C	Antiscorbutic; strengthens the blood vessels; prevents strokes; for healthy teeth and gums.
RUE 196	Rocky ground	Leaves	All year	Rutin	A glycoside, it strengthens the blood capillaries.
				Bitter principle	Stimulates the appetite.
SAFFRON 67	Hillsides	Stigma	Late summer	Bitter principle	Stimulates the appetite; calms the nerves.
SAGE 200	Rocky ground	Leaves	All summer	Volatile oil; Bitter principle	Stimulates the appetite; increases the flow of bile.
SALOP 147	Woodlands	Tubers	Autumn (Fall)	Bassorin	Soothing to lining of stomach; nourishing.
SALSIFY 231	Sandy coastal areas	Root	Winter	Vitamin A (small amounts)	Necessary for proper functioning of the kidneys; strengthens the eyes.

Plant Lexicon Number	Where To Find	Part used	Harvesting Time	Nutritive Value	Health Benefits
SAMPHIRE 66	Sea cliffs	Leaves; fruits	Summer	Vitamin C	Antiscorbutic; strengthens the blood vessels; prevents strokes; for healthy teeth and gums.
SASSAFRAS 202	Woodlands	Roots; berries	Winter; Autumn (Fall)	Volatile oil; Bitter principle	Stimulates the appetite.
SAVORY 203	Rocky ground	Leaves	Summer; Winter	Volatile oil; Bitter principle	Stimulates the appetite.
				Mucilage	Soothes the linings of stomach and intestines.
SCOLYMUS 204	Sandy ground	Root	Winter	Vitamin A (small amounts)	Strengthens the eyes; protects mucous membrane of throat and nose.
SCORZONERA 205	Sandy ground	Root	Winter	Vitamin A (small amounts)	Strengthens the eyes; protects mucous membrane of throat and nose.
SCURVY GRASS 57	Waste ground	Leaves	Summer	Vitamin C	Antiscorbutic; strengthens the blood vessels; prevents strokes; for healthy teeth and gums.
				Iron	Prevents anemia.
				Potassium	Restorative; regulates other mineral salts in the body.
SEA BUCKTHORN 102	Sandy ground	Fruit	Summer	Vitamin A	Improves the sight; protects the mucous membrane of throat and nose; protects the body against infection.
				Vitamin C	Antiscorbutic; strengthens the blood vessels; prevents strokes; for healthy teeth and gums.
SEA HOLLY 83	Sandy ground	Young shoots; roots	All year	Vitamin C	Antiscorbutic; strengthens the blood vessels; prevents strokes; for healthy teeth and gums.
SEAKALE 64	Seashore	Young shoots	Winter	Vitamin C	Antiscorbutic; strengthens the blood vessels; prevents strokes; for healthy teeth and gums.
SEA SPINACH 199	Seashore	Leaves	Summer	Vitamin C	Antiscorbutic; strengthens the blood vessels; prevents strokes; for healthy teeth and gums.
				Iron	Prevents anemia.
				Potassium	Restorative; prevents an excess of iron and calcium in the blood.
SESAME 208	Tropical forests	Seeds	Late summer	Vitamin E	Fortifies the sex glands; reduces the body's need for oxygen.
SKIRRET 210	Sandy ground	Roots	Winter	Vitamin A	Improves the sight; protects the mucous membrane of throat and nose; protects the body against infection.
SNAKEROOT 26	Woodlands	Root	Autumn (Fall)	Aromatic oil Bitter principle	Stimulates the appetite; tonic benefits.

Plant Lexicon Number	Where To Find	Part used	Harvesting Time	Nutritive Value	Health Benefits
SOLOMON'S SEAL 172	Woodlands	Young shoots	Spring	Vitamin B₁	Strengthens the heart and muscles; controls the adrenal gland; fortifies the nervous system.
				Vitamin B₂	Prevents premature aging; skin disorders.
SORREL TREE 152	Woodlands	Leaves	Summer	Vitamin C	Antiscorbutic; strengthens the blood vessels; prevents strokes; for healthy teeth and gums.
SOYA BEAN 95	Sandy ground	Seeds	Summer	Vitamin B₁	Strengthens the heart and muscles; controls the adrenal gland.
				Vitamin B₂	Prevents premature aging; skin disorders.
				Vitamin E	Fortifies the sex glands; reduces the body's need for oxygen.
				Inositol	Promotes healthy skin tissue; prevents baldness.
				Protein	For healthy gland secretion, hormones from which enter the bloodstream and regulate the chemical processes of the body.
SPEARMINT 129	Hedgerows	Leaves	Summer	Volatile oil	Stimulates the appetite; aids the digestion.
SPINACH 217	Waste ground	Leaves	Summer	Vitamin K	Regulates coagulation of the blood; prevents hemorrhages.
				Iron	Prevents anemia.
				Potassium	Controls other minerals in the body.
				Chloro-phyll	Increases hemoglobin in the blood.
SQUASH 69	Field sides	Fruit	Late summer	Vitamin A	Improves the sight; protects the mucous membrane of throat and nose; protects the body against infection.
				Vitamin B₂	Prevents premature aging; skin disorders.
				Vitamin B₃	Keeps the mind clear; eases tension.
STAGHORN 190	Woodlands; thickets	Berries	Summer	Vitamin C	Antiscorbutic; strengthens the blood vessels; prevents strokes; for healthy teeth and gums.
STAR-OF-BETHLEHEM 149	Rocky hillsides	Bulb	Autumn (Fall)	Protein	For healthy gland secretion, hormones from which enter the bloodstream and regulate the chemical processes of the body.
STRAWBERRY 87	Woodlands; hedgerows	Fruit	Summer	Vitamin C	Antiscorbutic; strengthens the blood vessels; prevents strokes; for healthy teeth and gums.
				Iron	Prevents anemia.
SUGAR CANE 197	Open ground	Juice	Late summer	Carbo-hydrates	For energy; assists in assimilation of other foods.
SUGAR MAPLE 1	Woodlands	Juice	Spring	Carbo-hydrates	For energy; assists in assimilation of other foods.
SUNFLOWER 97	Waste ground	Seeds	Late summer	Vitamin E	Fortifies the sex glands; reduces the body's need for oxygen and puts less strain on the heart.
				Iron	Prevents anemia.

Plant Lexicon Number	Where To Find	Part used	Harvesting Time	Nutritive Value	Health Benefits
SWEET CHESTNUT 49	Woodlands	Nuts	Autumn (Fall)	Vitamin B$_1$	Strengthens the heart and muscles; controls the adrenal gland; fortifies the nervous system.
				Protein	For healthy gland secretion, hormones from which enter the bloodstream and regulate the chemical processes of the body.
SWEET CICELY 139	Hedgerows	Leaves; roots	Summer	Vitamin C	Antiscorbutic; strengthens the blood vessels; prevents strokes; for healthy teeth and gums.
				Volatile oil	Stimulates the appetite and gastric juices.
SWEET CORN 249	Wasteland	Seeds (cob)	Late summer	Vitamin B$_1$	Strengthens the heart and muscles; controls the adrenal gland; fortifies the nervous system.
				Vitamin B$_2$	Prevents premature aging; skin disorders.
				Iron	Prevents anemia.
SWEET POTATO 107	Hedgerows; sandy ground	Tubers	Late summer	Vitamin A	Improves the sight; protects the mucous membrane of throat and nose; protects the body against infection.
SWEET RUSH 3	Ponds and rivers	Root	Late summer	Volatile oil	Stimulates the appetite; increases flow of gastric juices.
TAMARIND 221	Tropical forests	Bulb	Summer	Potassium	Restorative; controls other minerals in the body.
				Malic acid	Neutralizes an excess of calcium in the blood, preventing gout.
TAMARISK 222	Steppelands; sea coast	Gum	Summer	Potassium	Restorative; controls other minerals in the body.
TANSY 224	Wastelands	Leaves	Summer	Volatile oils Bitter principle	Stimulates the appetite; aids the digestion.
TARRAGON 22	Hedgerows	Leaves	All year	Iodine	Fortifies the thyroid gland.
				Potassium	Restorative; controls other minerals in the body.
TAWA 34	Woodlands	Fruits	Late summer	Vitamin C	Antiscorbutic; strengthens the blood vessels; prevents strokes; for healthy teeth and gums.
TEA 227	Hillsides	Leaves	Late summer	Caffeine Tannin	Stimulant; aids the digestion.
TEA TREE 117	Rocky slopes	Leaves	All year	Caffeine Tannin	Stimulant; aids the digestion.
THISTLE 45	Wastelands	Young shoots	Summer	Vitamin C	Antiscorbutic; strengthens the blood vessels; prevents strokes; for healthy teeth and gums.
				Potassium	Restorative; controls other minerals in the body.
				Flavonoides	Strengthens the capillaries.

Plant Lexicon Number	Where To Find	Part used	Harvesting Time	Nutritive Value	Health Benefits
THYME 229	Dry banks; mountain slopes	Leaves	All year	Phyton-cides	Destroy germs.
				Volatile oil	Stimulates the appetite.
TOMATO 121	Wastelands	Fruit	Summer	Vitamin A	Improves the sight; protects the mucous membrane of throat and nose; protects the body against infection.
				Vitamin C	Antiscorbutic; strengthens the blood vessels; prevents strokes; for healthy teeth and gums.
				Vitamin E	Reduces the body's need for oxygen and puts less strain on the heart.
				Iodine	Fortifies the thyroid gland.
				Potassium	Restorative; controls other minerals in the body.
TRUFFLE 236	Woodlands	Fungus	Late summer	Protein	For healthy gland secretion, hormones from which enter the bloodstream and regulate the chemical processes of the body.
TURMERIC 71	Rocky hillsides	Roots	Winter	Volatile oil	Stimulates the appetite; clears the kidneys of impurities.
VANILLA 242	Tropical forests	Pods	Autumn (Fall)	Vanillin	Strengthens the heart.
VIOLET 246	Woodlands; hedgerows	Flowers	Spring	Glucosides	Energy producing.
WALNUT 108	Woodlands	Nut	Autumn (Fall)	Vitamin B_1	Strengthens the heart and muscles; controls the adrenal gland; fortifies the nervous system.
				Choline	Reduces cholesterol level in blood, preventing deposits on wall of arteries.
				Inositol	For healthy skin; prevents baldness.
WATER CHESTNUT 79	Ponds, lakes, marshland	Tuber	All year	Vitamin A	Improves the sight; protects the mucous membrane of throat and nose; protects the body against infection.
WATERCRESS 140	Rivers, ponds	Leaves, stems	All year	Vitamin A	Improves the sight; protects the mucous membrane of throat and nose; protects the body against infection.
				Vitamin E	Fortifies the sex glands.
				Iron	Prevents anemia.
				Iodine	Fortifies the thyroid gland.
				Chloro-phyll	Heals the linings of the stomach; prevents ulcers.

Plant Lexicon Number	Where To Find	Part used	Harvesting Time	Nutritive Value	Health Benefits
WATER MELON 55	Hedgerows; waste ground	Fruit	Summer	Vitamin A	Improves the sight; protects the mucous membrane of throat and nose; protects the body against infection.
				Vitamin B_1	Strengthens the heart and muscles; controls the adrenal gland; fortifies the nervous system.
				Vitamin B_2	Prevents premature aging; skin disorders.
				Vitamin C	Antiscorbutic; strengthens the blood vessels; prevents strokes; for healthy teeth and gums.
WHEAT 234	Fields; hedgerows	Seed	Late summer	Vitamin E (wheat germ)	Fortifies the sex glands; strengthens the heart.
				Iron	Maintains red blood corpuscles; prevents anemia.
WILD ARUM 24	Hedgerows	Tuber	Late summer	Carbohydrates	For the body to be active, energetic.
				Calcium	For strong bones and teeth; stabilizes the nerves
				Potassium	Regulates other minerals in the body.
WILD CHERRY 179	Woodlands; hedgerows	Fruit	Mid-summe	Vitamin A	Improves the sight; protects the mucous membrane of throat and nose; protects the body against infection.
				Vitamin C	Antiscorbutic; strengthens the blood vessels; prevents strokes; for healthy teeth and gums.
				Iron	Maintains red blood corpuscles; prevents anemia.
WILD LETTUCE 112	Field sides; waste ground	Leaves	Summer	Vitamin A	Improves the sight; protects the mucous membrane of throat and nose; protects the body against infection.
				Vitamin B_1	Strengthens the heart and muscles; controls the adrenal gland; fortifies the nervous system.
				Vitamin B_6	Calms the nerves; encourages sound sleep.
				Vitamin C	Antiscorbutic; strengthens the blood vessels; prevents strokes; for healthy teeth and gums.
WILD PARSNIP 156	Hedgerows	Root	Winter	Calcium	For strong bones and teeth, stabilizes the nerves.
				Iron	Maintains red blood corpuscles, prevents anemia.
WILD PLUM 180	Woodlands; hedgerows	Fruit	Mid summer	Vitamin A	Improves the sight; protects the mucous membrane of throat and nose; protects the body against infection.
				Vitamin B_1	Strengthens the heart and muscles; controls the adrenal gland; fortifies the nervous system.
WILD RAISIN 244	Woodlands; hedgerows	Fruit	Late summer	Vitamin C	Antiscorbutic; strengthens the blood vessels; prevents strokes; for healthy teeth and gums.

Plant Lexicon Number	Where To Find	Part used	Harvesting Time	Nutritive Value	Health Benefits
WILD ROSE 192	Woodlands; hedgerows	Hips	Late summer	Vitamin C	Antiscorbutic; strengthens the blood vessels; prevents strokes; for healthy teeth and gums.
				Malic acid	Neutralizes excess calcium in the blood; prevents gout.
WILLOW HERB 81	Waste ground	Young shoots; leaves	Summer	Vitamin C	Antiscorbutic; strengthens the blood vessels; prevents strokes; for healthy teeth and gums.
				Mucilage	Protects stomach linings; prevents ulcers.
WORMWOOD 21	Waste ground	Young shoots; leaves	Summer	Potassium	Restorative, regulates other minerals in the body.
				Bitter principle	Stimulates the appetite.
WOUNDWORT 218	Ponds and ditches	Young shoots; tuberous roots	Summer	Vitamin A	Improves the sight; protects the mucous membrane of throat and nose; protects the body against infection.
				Iron	Maintains red blood corpuscles; prevents anemia.
YAM 77	Hedgerows	Tubers	Winter	Carbohydrates	For energy.
				Iron	Maintains red blood corpuscles; prevents anemia.
YUCCA 248	Prairie lands	Seeds	Late summer	Calcium	For strong bones and teeth, stabilizes the nerves.
ZAPODILLA 2	Tropical forests	Fruit	Late summer	Vitamin C	Antiscorbutic; strengthens the blood vessels; prevents strokes; for healthy teeth and gums.

Nutrition and Primitive Peoples

This chapter describes various studies that have been carried out on primitive tribes. They show that these people not only have a well-balanced diet but are more resistant to disease than people of the civilized world.

San mother and children crack and eat mongono nuts around a fire *(right)*. Kalahari Desert, Botswana.

Nature's supply of food is of such importance that some tribes have made deities of their crops. The Mochican maize goddess *(above)* dates back to two thousand years ago.

Opposite page:
The walnut tree, owing to the value of its wood, is sadly disappearing. The Romans dedicated this tree to Jupiter. Walnuts are highly nutritious.

The only real difference between primitive and so-called civilized peoples is that the primitive tribes have to hunt and search for their food while those who are civilized have their food grown for them. The tribesman eats food as he finds it, growing either above or below ground, mostly without any preparation

before it is cooked, though some poisonous plants such as the manioc of the Montana Indians of Peru are edible only if steeped in water and then roasted. The urban populations, wherever they may live and work, are fed by others: they work while others feed them with food grown by specialists in all parts of the world and so prepared that most of the valuable vitamins and mineral salts have been systematically removed. This is done so as to present the food as attractively as possible. For Westerners' enjoyment, wholemeal bread and brown sugar must be made white, while rice is polished to give it a glistening whiteness and the health-giving husk is removed as it is when corn is

processed to make into bread. Chemicals are added to food so that whether it is to be canned or frozen, it will remain edible for as long a period as possible. Modern man has only a few hours a day to prepare and consume his food. Thus chemicals (which destroy most of the goodness) are added to preserve the col-

or and eating qualities of pre-frozen or canned food; it will remain edible for two years or more, during which time it will have lost much of its goodness, though time will be saved in obtaining more. Primitive man on the other hand, inhabiting those inhospitable parts which man has found difficult to tame by modern engineering methods, obtains his food only when he needs it, eating it fresh whenever he can while those who live in cold climates store roots and nuts to use only in winter.

Civilized man has always believed that those who hunt and search for their food in remote parts must devote almost the whole of the daylight hours to obtain sufficient amounts. This is not so.

An important food item of the Montana tribes of the Amazon basin is manioc *(above)*, a kind of tapioca which is poisonous unless soaked in water and then roasted.

(Right) Kung bushmen raiding a wild bees' nest in a baobab tree. This tribe finds sufficient food even when people in nearby towns are dying of starvation.

Dr. James Woodward, reporting on a year spent with the Hadza tribe of East Africa, said that the menfolk spent only about two hours each day finding the daily intake of food for themselves and their families. Although the area was teeming with animals and game birds of all types which would have provided meat for a large part of their diet, at least 80 percent of their food requirements was obtained from just ten species of plants, while the rest of their diet was made up of wild honey and meat in about equal amounts. The medical team headed by Dr. Woodward said that the health of the tribe was in every way outstanding, rickets, scurvy and vitamin B deficiency among the children being almost unknown. A similar excellent bill of health was given to various groups of Aboriginals visited by medical teams in Australia in recent years. As long ago as 1841, Professor George Grey, who spent several years in the Australian desert studying the food habits of the Aboriginals, found their diet consisted of the roots of 29 different plants; 4 different fruits; the leaves of 2 mesembryanthemums; 4 kinds of gum; 2 species of cyad nuts; 7 edible fungi and manna provided by the flowers of 2 species of Banksia.

Dahlia tubers *(left)* as stored throughout the winter for food, or to grow flowers in summer.

The dieticians Irven de Vore and Richard Lee who spent more than a year with the Kung bushmen of the North Kalahari desert in 1964–1965 (a time of severe drought in the region which in an average year receives less than 10 inches of rain) reported that the bushmen were able to feed themselves well even though people living in nearby townships were dying of starvation and needed outside help with their food supplies to survive. The doctors confirmed the observations of Dr. Woodward and the Hadza tribe when they estimated that the Kung bushmen collected all the food they required in less than two hours a day. They knew more than 200 species of plants, half of which they used as food, the Mongongo nut being the most important item in their diet because of its high calorie and protien value and its year-round availability. Their daily intake of food provided the bushmen with about 2500 calories and 100 grams of protein, equal to 5 lbs (2 kilos) of rice and 28 lbs (12 kilos) of lean meat, an intake of calories and protein not exceeded by those of any country of the Western world.

Not only are the primitive tribes able to feed themselves well during times of famine, since they do not rely upon one or two staple foods such as corn and potatoes which may be decimated by adverse weather or by pest and disease; but in times of drought they have a wider variety of plants available to them that are able to survive these conditions, being able to store up moisture in their roots and fleshy leaves. The dahlia and prickly pear of the Mexican desert are examples.

Working among the Xavante tribesmen of South America, medical men have reported finding the gamma-globulin levels in the blood, which give an indication of an ability to resist infectious diseases, are twice as high as those of civilized people. Dr. Prior of Wellington Hospital, New Zealand, who spent some years comparing the health of those who inhabited the Westernized island of Rarotonga and those of the more primitive Pukapuka, has

reported that on the latter island, he found only 2 percent with high blood pressure and associated deseases, compared with 21 percent of the men and twice as many of the women living on Rarotonga. This was due entirely to the foods they ate, people of Pukapuka living on a natural diet of fish and fresh plant foods while those of Rarotonga enjoyed a westernized diet.

In their book *Farewell to Eden*, Matthew Huxley and Cornell Capa, who spent several years with the Montana tribes of the Amazon Basin, have told that when their diet consisted of manioc (tapioca), sweet potatoes, maize, green bananas, peanuts and watermelons which the Amahuaca tribesmen grew in clearings and found in the rain forests, their health was outstanding in every way; they were eating a completely balanced diet of calories, protein and carbohydrates and all the vitamins they contained, augmented by a small amount of lean meat, mostly birds. The only adverse condition they could discover was the high proportions of dental decay brought about by the manioc remaining too long in the mouth as starch so as to cause fermentation. The diet of the tribesmen consisted of those foods grown in virgin soil in which humus and nutrients had accumulated since the beginning of time. The canopy of the silk cotton trees prevented the heavy rains leaching the nutrients from the soil.

In their book *Western Diseases: Their Emergence and Prevention* published in 1981, Drs. Hugh Trowell and Denis Burkitt tell of their experiences among the Kikuyu tribe of East Africa during the 1930's and later. It was, reports Dr. Trowell, 20 years before they saw their first case of heart disease and blood pressure. Indeed, when the doctors first arrived in Kenya, they began documenting the health of the Kikuyu as they first came under the influence of European settlers. At the beginning, high blood pressure was unknown among the tribesmen and a detailed survey of four tribes actually showed a decline in blood pressure as they aged.

Nyatunyatijara woman *(above)* winnowing wangunu seed. Australia.

Overleaf:
Lotus plants are harvested in the Shantung province of China. Quite distinct from the lotus of the ancient Greeks, this species of water lily is a sacred plant of India and China. The entire plant is utilized. The root stem is stuffed with rice, seeds, stalk and fruit are also eaten. The leaves are used in salads, as packing material and, as can be seen, as improvised clothing.

The two photographs *(above)* show the wide variety of wild food gathered by a San woman in one day. In most tribes it takes only about two hours to find sufficient food to feed a family.

Their diet consisted of maize, millet, sweet potatoes, peanuts and green bananas (known as plantains). It was a diet similar to that of the tribesmen of the Amazon Basin and they too showed no symptoms of heart disease or high blood pressure, the two diseases of the western world which are giving most concern. The vegetarian diet of the tribesmen was augmented by a small amount of lean meat, and honey was used for sweetening. It was not until they were introduced to the use of salt and refined sugar in their diet by the Europeans that western diseases began to make their appearance.

Denis Burkitt, an eminent surgeon and now the world's leading authority on fiber intake, has reported that appendicitis, unknown among the natives of East Africa before 1939, is now as common among the tribesmen as it is among white people. This is due, Dr. Burkitt believes, to the removal of fiber from many foods during the refining processes and the elimination of nuts and roots from the diet, each of which provided valuable roughage.

When the American nutritionist Nathan Pritikin of the Longevity Centre, California, devised a diet for the heart patients there based on that of East African tribesmen, consisting of whole grain products, potatoes, pulses, nuts and roots, with refined sugar and salt completely eliminated, he found that after only four weeks, people confined to their beds for many months were able to walk six miles a day and of 32 certified diabetics, 16 were able to survive entirely without insulin, provided they continued with their diet. It was found that these natural foods do not flood the system with sugar as do products made from processed flour. This was confirmed by Dr. Daphne Humphries, working with diabetics and patients with heart disease at the Royal Berkshire Hospital, Reading, England, who found that when patients were put on a similar diet of natural foods, 25 out of 32 patients reduced their high blood pressure immediately and 7 out of 11 of those

suffering from heart disease were soon able to walk 3 or 4 miles a day.

Mr. Fairfield Osborn in his book *Our Plundered Planet* confirmed the belief of many nutritionists that man's health is entirely related to the health of the food he eats, and the health of that food to the earth from which it comes. If soils in which plants are grown have become leached and impoverished (through the removal of natural vegetation), the food from them will be deficient in its energy and health-giving value. To feed the teeming population of the world's industrial cities, large tracts of land have been used year after year to grow crops so that virtually every scrap of goodness has been removed from the soil and it is kept productive only by the application of expensive artificially made fertilizers. All organic manures, the products of nature accumulated over the years, have long since vanished. There is no "body" in the land and the food it produces is lacking in goodness.

Soil erosion is an even greater problem. This process, known as laterization, takes place when forests and hedgerows deprive the land of natural cover and wind protection.

From his clinic in the Harz Mountains, Adolph Just expressed the thought that the only hope for man in leading a healthy life, free from cancer and heart disease and all the illnesses of modern life, was to return to nature, to harvest and consume those fruits, nuts, roots and leaves of woodland, field and hedgerow and to eat them raw or lightly cooked, for they would provide man with all his needs.

(Left) San women collecting food with their children. Kalahari Desert, Botswana.

(Above top) Topnaar Hottentot woman collecting Nara melons. Namib Desert, Namibia.

(Above) A pygmy woman preparing the evening meal with members of the family.

159

Harvesting and Storing Wild Foods

For centuries man has used the processes of fermentation and distilling to produce alcoholic drinks. This ancient woodcut *(below right)* shows the process of distilling and conserving liquor (probably rum for sailors) in wooden barrels.

Just as the squirrel *(above)* stores nuts for the winter, so man has developed many ways of storing, conserving and processing food to meet his requirements during the lean months of the year. This chapter explains how best to collect and conserve wild food.

Opposite page:
Besides containing a refreshing drink, the white meat of the coconut can be dried for storage. From this coconut oil is extracted and used mainly for making soap, of which it is one of the world's principal sources.

In the history of man, roots, bulbs, nuts and seeds have always been considered the most important part of his diet simply because they retained their food value after plant growth had died down and could be lifted from the ground whenever required; or they could be stored throughout winter and spring and used until such time as the fresh green shoots of plants were ready to eat in early summer. Roots such as parsnips are frost-hardy and may be left in the

ground all winter, as indeed can celery and leeks which are not roots botanically but require the exclusion of light to become blanched and thus tender. Those roots such as beets or carrots which are not winter hardy should be lifted in autumn, cleaned of surplus soil, stored in boxes of dry soil, peat or sand and placed in a frost-free room.

As with all food crops, lift roots when at their best, before they have become hard and woody, for by then they will also have lost flavor and eating qualities. Do not allow them to remain too long in the ground or they grow too large. Parsnips should be about 12 in. (30 cm) in length and about 4 in.

(10 cm) in diameter at the top. Lift the roots with care, using a garden fork and inserting it deeply into the soil close to the roots, which are gently pressed upwards and out of the ground. This will be more easily done if the tops are held with the free hand and pulled upwards, and should be done when the soil is dry. Leave the roots on the surface exposed to the sun and wind for several hours to dry; then all surplus soil is shaken away and the top foliage screwed off, rather than cut off. This will prevent the roots "bleeding" at the point where the tops are removed. Should they do so, they will lose nutritional value and flavor and their keeping qualities will be reduced. Roots will store better when dry (wet roots will decay), though they must be kept away from strong sunlight or artificial heating which will cause them to shrivel. They will retain their condition all winter if stored in a cold, dark, frost-free room.

Some plants with thick roots, like dandelion, chicory and seakale, are lifted in autumn and forced into new top growth during winter to provide salad "green" at this time.

There are many ways of storing mushrooms, which should be picked with care not to confuse them with poisonous varieties. After cleaning they can be sliced, threaded, and hung up to dry *(right)*.

Another way of conserving mushrooms is to boil them in water with a little vinegar, drain, cover in oil and store in jars with bay leaves *(above)*.

Capers, which grow on rocks and walls in warm climates, can be pickled with peppercorns *(below)*.

Bulbs such as onions and shallots, native of the Near East, grow on top of the soil and are lifted as soon as the foliage has turned brown and died down. They are best lifted when the soil is dry, and dried on sacking. They are strung up by their foliage or hung up in string bags to complete their drying in an airy room; or they may be placed on shelves away from strong sunlight. When quite dry, the foliage may be removed, but not the outer brown skin of the bulbs which will protect them from decay during winter. For the same reason, do not damage the skins when lifting the bulbs.

Potato tubers require different treatment. Early varieties are lifted as required late in summer. They can be stored for special occasions in winter by shaking away surplus soil and placing them in a sack enclosed in a tin box or in peat and burying the container 12 in. (30 cm) beneath the ground, marking the position with a stone.

Sweet as well as ordinary potatoes are lifted late in autumn while the soil is still dry and before the winter frosts begin. The haulm (top), having died back, is removed and the tubers are spread out on sacking to dry. They are then placed in sacks or in tea chests, covered with peat and moved to a cool, frost-free place. Keep them in the dark or the tubers will turn green. Or they may be moved to a corner of a cellar, shed or garage and kept in place by fixing strong boards across and to a depth of about 2 ft (60 cm). They are then covered with 6 in. (15 cm) of straw and over the top is placed a 6 in. (15 cm) layer of dry soil. This will exclude frost and light.

From earliest times, cereals and legumes (lentils, peas and beans) which do not need artificial drying in warm climes were grown in large quantities to feed the people. In Egypt, broad beans are sown in October and harvested in March, the seed being ground when dry. The large kidney-shaped seeds are removed from the pods and dried on trays in the sun. They are then placed in wooden boxes in a dry room, and after soaking in water for several hours, are cooked (boiled) to serve with meats in winter. Peas are treated in the same way. Both peas and beans can be blanched and placed in the freezer as an alternative method of keeping them fresh.

Every autumn, the woodlands and hedgerows will yield their quota of nuts which, if gathered when fully mature, will keep in condition through winter. Walnuts, sweet chestnuts, hickory and hazel nuts are among the most nutritious. After gathering, spread out the nuts on trays in an airy room to dry. This will take about four weeks. Then remove the outer covering, the husk, and store the nuts on shelves.

Those plants whose seeds are used for flavoring, the herbs such as sweet cicely, dill and coriander, cumin and wild celery, must be harvested with care. They should be fully ripe, otherwise the seeds will not retain their flavor, nor will the flavor be fully developed.

As the growing season comes to an end, make regular inspection of the plants. The seed heads will first turn yellow, then brown, at which point the seed capsules will begin to split open. It is now time for the heads to be removed, before the seeds are shed and lost. Cut away the heads and place in a clean cardboard box with the name of the plant written on the side. The heads should be dry, otherwise the seeds will deteriorate if not dried quickly and this is not always possible. Place the boxes in a dry airy room, on a table or shelf, turning the seed heads daily so that they will dry as quickly as possible, then the seeds will leave the capsules and fall into the box. Remove the heads and gather up the seeds, which are placed in small boxes depending upon the amount. If there is chaff among the seeds, put them through a fine mesh sieve to remove this. Do not use a tin box to store the seeds or they will sweat and turn moldy. Use wooden or cardboard boxes or glass jars, correctly labelled.

Some seeds, such as those of nasturtium and capers, are best preserved in

Dried chili peppers can be used for seasoning a wide variety of dishes. They can also be kept in oil, thus producing "hot" oil. The plant can be grown on balconies or window-sills.

vinegar as they are harvested. They should be removed as soon as they reach a reasonable size and pickled while succulent and juicy, while green. Place the seeds in a screw-top glass jar, then fill almost to the top with tarragon vinegar that has been boiled with 15 g (½ oz) salt and a few peppercorns and allowed to cool. Pickled nasturtium seeds can be used as a substitute for capers to accompany fish.

Other crops which are preserved by pickling when harvested include gherkins (small cucumbers), red peppers, beetroot and shallots, though beetroot will store for several months and shallots (after drying), all winter.

Many health-giving plants have leaves which are used for flavoring and to make stuffings for meat and for sauces. They are used fresh in summer and those that are evergreen are available all year. Those herbs such as lemon balm, tarragon, sage and mint which die down in winter can be preserved for winter use by drying. Thyme, hyssop and winter savory, although evergreen, can also be dried and their full flavor preserved. The stems are cut late in summer when at their best and before they begin to die back. Use a sharp knife or pair of scissors and cut them on a dry day. Place the stems on sacking on a table or shelf in a dry airy room, turning them daily for several weeks until the leaves are dry and crisp. They are then placed on sheets of clean paper and rubbed down. Rub the stems between the hands to remove the leaves. Place the leaves in wooden or cardboard boxes and store in a dry place from

which strong light is excluded. Or the stems, after cutting, may be gathered together and made into small bunches. They are strung up in an airy room to dry. Correctly dried herbs should crackle when pressed; they should have retained their full scent and be free of "mustiness", an unpleasant quality they will take on if too wet when harvested or if dried too slowly. When fully dry, the bunches can be enclosed in muslin bags which will retain any falling leaves and will keep the herbs free from dust.

Parsley, which grows on rocky outcrops along the Mediterranean coastline, is with its thick crinkled leaves the most difficult of herbs to dry and needs hours of warm sunlight or a warm oven heated to a temperature of 34°C (100°F) which is held for 10 hours. Leave the oven door slightly open for any dampness to escape.

The stems of certain plants, angelica for example, can be cut and used during the entire growing season. The young stems are rich in mineral salts and impart their unique muscat flavor to fruits such as rhubarb and apples when stewed with them. The freshly cut stems, when candied, make a delicious sweetmeat.

Many herbs will keep fresh in the freezer for some time. Tarragon, parsley, hyssop and thyme come readily to mind; or the leaves can be frozen in ice cubes and placed in a refrigerator to flavor summer drinks.

Flowers too may be harvested and dried for culinary use in winter. Petals of the old red rose *(Rosa gallica)* or Apothecary's Road, one of the oldest plants known to man, are used to flavor trifles and flans. The flowers are harvested when at their best and dried in the sun. The petals will retain their scent and flavor for several years and should be included in every well made pot-pourri to perfume the home. Violets and clove-scented pinks *(Dianthus plumarius)* may be used in the same way. Like rose petals, they can be crystallized and used to decorate cakes and ice creams.

The hips (seed vessels) of wild roses with their high vitamin C content, and

Freezing is a good way of keeping green foods and fruit. *(Above)* Frozen leeks with parsley and oil. Vegetables should be blanched before freezing.

Curative tisanes and delicious refreshing teas can be made from carefully dried herbs and stored in jars *(Top of page)*.

the fruits of mountain ash *(rowan)* and crab apple are harvested late in summer and have several uses. The hips should be gathered when fully ripe and are used immediately.

Along the coastline of northern Europe, the edible seaweeds have been used as food by the maritime populations since earliest times, especially dulse *(Rhodymenia palmata)* and carrageen moss *(Chondrus crispus)* which grow at the bottom of deep pools. They are present about the rocky coastlines of Iceland and Ireland, Norway and the Isles of Orkney and Shetland. The forked fronds are of reddish-brown coloring and when dry can be stored for some weeks. From them, a nourishing drink is made and when stewed with cloves and lemon peel, a pleasantly edible jelly.

The seaweeds are valuable sources of iodine, which is necessary to fortify the thyroid gland. After gathering, one washes the seaweeds in fresh water and then lays them out to dry in the sun, turning the fronds frequently. When dry, they become covered with white powder called "manite" which gives them a sweet taste. When quite dry, the fronds are placed in wooden or cardboard boxes and kept in a dry, airy room to use as required, though in many parts the fronds are available all the year. A seaweed called laver *(Porphyra laciniata)* becomes of a slimy gelatinous consistency when boiled. Until quite recent times it was served each day at the London Reform Club, always in a silver saucepan, to accompany roast leg of mutton. It was also pickled and served with salad oil and lemon juice for fish dishes. Because it is so wholesome and prevents scurvy, it was taken on long sea voyages of exploration, for it will keep in condition a long time in tightly closed glass jars. Citrus fruits have now taken its place.

Whereas early man relied upon the storing of roots and nuts in his cave dwelling to provide him and his family with food in winter, modern man has the benefit of the deep freeze unit in which to store fresh green foods to maintain a healthy diet in winter. Most green foods will have died back by the late autumn or will have become unpalatable. They should always be harvested when at their peak of perfection, while still soft and succulent. If blanched correctly before being placed in the freezer, they will retain these desirable qualities for at least a year. In addition to their eating qualities, they will retain their full complement of vitamins and mineral salts which will not have been destroyed through the process of canning or by the addition of preservatives. Even if kept for a year or more without using, the greens will remain in exactly the same condition as when harvested from the wild or from the garden. The chart of harvesting times of the food crops described in the book will be a guide as to when they will be at their best. Fruits should be fully ripe, but not overripe or they will be too soft to freeze well. Neither should they be underripe, for then they will be hard and lacking flavor. Only for a few days will they have reached and remain

Blackcurrants *(left)* and red currants *(below)* are an excellent source of vitamins and are best conserved by freezing.

in perfect condition and this is the time to harvest them. The leaves of those plants which provide health-giving vitamins should be gathered while still young, before they have become hard and tough.

Where electric power is available, the use of a freezer will ensure that, even if severe weather should cause a shortage of fresh food crops, there will be green foods and fruits available in the home at all times. Usually root crops are lifted and stored in a cellar or shed or left in the ground to use as required, though in those parts where severe winter weather is experienced, it is better to lift the roots in autumn. It is not necessary to put them in the freezer, which should be used to store those foods which cannot be kept by other means.

Vegetables and herbs need "blanching" (usually for 5 minutes), before placing in the freezer. Most fruits do not require this treatment. Blanching is the operation of scalding the vegetables in boiling water for seconds or minutes before placing them in thin plastic bags or in polythene boxes or waxed cardboard containers before consigning to the freezer. The scalding is to render the enzymes in the cells inactive so that color, quality (and this includes the preservation of the vitamin content) and flavor are retained during the time they are in the freezer. They will not deteriorate but will come out in exactly the

same condition as they went in. This is why it is so important to pick them in perfect condition and to put them in the freezer as quickly as possible, for they will begin to deteriorate as soon as picked.

After preparing them – shelling peas; cleaning and slicing carrots; dividing other vegetables to small bunches or pieces each with about 2 in. (5 cm) of stem attached – put in a wire basket for blanching. Place in a large saucepan containing 6 pints of water for each pound of vegetables and add a little salt. Bring the water to the boil and immerse them for about 5 minutes depending upon the vegetable. Time the blanching carefully from the moment the vegetables enter the water, for if they are blanched a minute too long, the eating and keeping qualities will be impaired. At exactly the right time, lift out and immerse in cold water for the same length of time. Drain and place in polythene bags which are tightly closed with plastic-covered ties. Or place in plastic containers with a tightly closing lid, for it is important that the fruits and vegetables do not become dehydrated through moisture evaporation while in the freezer. When they have been placed in the freezer, switch to "rapid" for an hour to freeze as quickly as possible, then return to normal running. Mushrooms and sweet corn should be thawed out before cooking, otherwise all veg-

Chestnuts *(above)* can be roasted while fresh *(above right),* or stored for winter. Chestnut jam is delicious and highly prized while dried chestnuts can be ground into flour and used in the preparation of various dishes.

etables can be emptied from the bags and cooked as required.

These are the required blanching times:

Vegetable	Method of Preparing	Time
Bean, broad	Remove from pods	5–6 min
Beetroot	Remove tops	Until tender
Carrot	Slice into rings	5 min
Kale, curly	Use young shoots	3–4 min
Mushroom, small	Trim stem and simmer in butter	2 min
Mushroom, large	Peel and trim stem	Place straight in freezer
Parsley	Make into bunches	3–4 min
Peas	Remove from pods	2 min
Potatoes	Wash away soil (If no other storage facilities are available)	5–6 min
Spinach	Use young leaves	3–4 min
Sweet corn	Remove husk and stem	5–6 min

With the exception of apples, fruits do not require blanching but each should be given individual treatment to preserve them at their best.

APPLE. If there is room to store apples, they can be kept in this way through winter and used when required. An attic, dry cellar or garden shed will be suitable. Spread out the apples on a bench, or they can be kept in a freezer for 2 years or more. Peel and core, then cut into segments or rings. Blanch for 2 minutes and put into plastic bags. Or for purée, stew for ½ hr before placing into plastic containers.

APRICOT. They freeze well if not peeled. Cut into halves, remove the stone, place in a plastic box and cover with syrup. After putting in the freezer, switch on the current to "rapid" for an hour.

BILBERRY. The berries are smaller than blackcurrants and about half the size of American blueberries, which are hybrids of *Vaccinium corymbosum* and *V. australe.* Allow the fruits to become fully ripe before picking them. They will have turned from green to red and then black, covered in a blue grape-like "bloom". Cover the fruit with sugar (1 oz or 28 g to each ½ lb or 225 g of fruit) mixed with a teaspoonful of cornflour and the juice of a lemon. Place into small tinfoil dishes and cover with pastry. Place in the freezer and bake when required.

BLACKBERRY. Pick on the point of ripening. If overripe they will like raspberries become "mushy". Spread on trays and cover with sugar (3½ oz or 100 g to 1 lb or 450 g of fruit). Then place in polythene boxes and close up tightly. The sugar coating encourages rapid freezing and there will be a minimum of enzymic change.

BLACKCURRANT. They will keep in condition for a year or more. Gather when black but before bursting their skins. To prevent the skins becoming tough, blanch in boiling water for 20 seconds. Place in polythene boxes with a lid and turn on "rapid" switch for 1 hour, then maintain a steady temperature. With soft fruits, temperature fluctuations will damage the cell structure. Thaw for 6 hours before using.

CHERRY. Sweet black cherries freeze better than white (yellow). Cut into halves, remove the stone, place in plastic containers and cover with syrup. The Myrobalan cherries (used for cooking and not dessert) freeze better than sweet cherries.

CRANBERRY. Pick when fully ripe, when bright red, place in polythene

A convenient way of freezing herbs and spices is to chop them, divide into portions and wrap in tin foil *(left)*.

Nuts, including hazel nuts *(above left)* are stored easily while rose-hips *(above top)* with their high vitamin C content, should be used immediately. Apples *(above)* can be dried and mixed with breakfast cereals, or used in cake making.

bags or plastic containers and cover with syrup.

DAMSON. No need to give them a sugar coating. Leave on the skins but remove the stones before placing in polythene bags. The fruits must be fully ripe before harvesting or they will be hard and flavorless.

GOOSEBERRY. Pick when ripe but before the skins burst. Top and tail them. Blanch for 30 seconds, cool and place in plastic bags with the freezer at "rapid" for 2 hours.

GRAPE. Grapes freeze well if not over-ripe and white grapes better than black for they keep firmer. Cut the fruits into halves, remove the pips (seeds), place in plastic containers and cover with syrup. They may be included in a mixed fruit salad to put in the freezer.

MELON. The small melons, of grapefruit size, freeze best. Remove when ripe (when the base "gives" slightly when pressed with the thumbs) and place each fruit in a plastic bag and close with a wire "twister."

MULBERRY. Harvest when the berries have turned dark red and as they retain the core, they freeze well. Place in plastic containers and cover with syrup. Before serving as dessert (or in tarts and flans) remove the core.

PEACH. They need special treatment if they are to freeze well. Pick when ripe and place in a pan of boiling water for 1 minute (no longer); then into cold water immediately, keeping the fruits submerged to prevent discoloration. The skin is then easily removed. Cut into halves to remove the stone. If a little ascorbic acid is added to the syrup to be placed over the fruits in the plastic containers, this will prevent them becoming dark colored. Ascorbic acid is obtained from drugstores. For each 1 lb or 450 g of fruit, add 500 mg ascorbic acid to each ½ pint of syrup.

PLUM. Crimson and purple varieties freeze best and need no sugar covering. Pick when quite ripe but firm. Do not remove the skins but cut in two and remove the stone, then place in plastic bags.

RASPBERRY. Pick when just on point of ripening and when dry or they will be "mushy," but unripe fruit (pink) will have no flavor and it will not mature in the freezer. Treat as for blackberries. The fruit will retain its quality for a year or more.

RED CURRANT. When the berries have turned red, cut away the bunch with scissors, cover with sugar and place (with the stems on) in plastic cartons with a lid. Have the freezer at "rapid" for 2 hours.

RHUBARB. Pull the sticks when young and early in the season. With a gentle tug, they will come away readily at the base. They will be red and firm. Old sticks are soft and stringy. Remove the leaves, cut into pieces 1 in. (2.5 cm) long, sprinkle with sugar and put into polythene bags.

STRAWBERRY. Those that ripen orange-red and are wedge-shaped freeze better than those that ripen crimson-red and are conical. Pick when dry and remove the green calyx. Place the fruits on a tray, not touching each other, and put in the freezer (on "rapid") for an hour until they are frozen hard. Then sprinkle them with sugar; place in polythene boxes with a lid and put back into the freezer. In this way, they keep their shape and will keep in condition for up 2 years.

To defrost fruits, place in refrigerator for 5–6 hours to thaw slowly before serving or cooking. Those that have not been sugared before freezing can have this added when being served. The freezer will need defrosting every 12 months.

To guard against loss through a power cut, ensure for this hazard. There are several fruits which do not freeze well but improve with keeping. Among these are the medlar, quince and pear. Medlars should not be gathered from the tree until they have been frosted. This improves the quality, making them juicy and softer. Pears are harvested with care so as not to cause bruising, or they will turn brown and will quickly decay in storage. The fruits are placed on trays of cotton wool or on dry bracken in a dark airy room. The fruits must not touch each other and should be inspected often, using or removing those which show signs of deterioration. If harvested in October or November they will keep until the end of January but will be at their best over Christmas.

Pears do not freeze well, becoming discolored, and after thawing are too soft to use. The fruits are ripe when, upon lifting with the palm of the hand, the stalk parts from the tree without undue pressure. Then place the fruits, broad end down, on trays lined with cotton wool. They require more warmth stored than do apples, a temperature of 50° F (10° C) being ideal, and they keep better in diffused light. Inspect them frequently for signs of decay.

Apples present no difficulties in storage. If harvested late in autumn when fully mature and placed on shelves in a cool, airy room, they will usually keep sound through winter. In this way, they will not take up necessary space in the freezer though some can be stored in this way.

During recent years, by government decree in many countries, certain wild plants are protected. This means they cannot be dug up or the flowers removed, under the severe penalty of large fines. Only a limited number of food plants are "protected" but the wanton destruction of plants in the wild by the careless handling of the flowers and leaves is much to be deplored. When harvesting fruit and leaves from the wild, do so with care.

Use and Preparation

Over the years many recipes have been developed to bring out the flavor of the plants we eat and make eating more enjoyable. The following pages describe the uses of the various plants in the kitchen and provide the reader with some of these useful recipes.

The beneficial effects of eating fruit and vegetables are often cancelled by the harmful presence of nitrates and pesticide residues. Care should therefore be taken to choose plants grown without chemical fertilizers and poison sprays. Overcooking fresh vegetables should be avoided as it can destroy or drastically reduce nutritional value. Fruit can be eaten fresh, bottled, dried or used for making jam or wine. This chapter gives some of the basic rules for the preparation and use of wild foods.

(Right) Woodcut showing cherry picking from the "Kreuterbuch," 1577.

The uses of wild plants for food are many. Fresh leaves and the young shoots of many plants are removed as they appear in spring and early summer and are simmered in a little water or in their own juice, to serve with meat or fish. The leaves of many plants can be included in summer salads and provide the body with valuable vitamins. The leaves of some plants can be dried to use for stuffing fish or meat and to make sauces.

spinach which have a high mineral salt content should also be cooked in two waters to remove any bitterness.

Fruits are harvested when ripe, though medlars and wild figs will need storing for several months in order to become soft and suitable to use. Fruits are used for making cooling drinks and in fresh fruit salads, though apples, sloes and wild cherries, found in northerly climes, as well as bilberries and cranber-

Opposite page:
Corn is tied in bundles and hung in the sun to dry. It can be boiled, baked or ground into flour and used to make polenta. In Mexico it is used to make an alcoholic drink called "chicha."

Tuberous roots are dug as required or, in a hard winter climate, they are lifted in autumn and stored for winter use. After cleaning of soil and washing, they are cooked in a little water until tender to use as a vegetable. Roots which have poisonous tendencies should be cooked in two waters and then baked. Thus they will be free of all poisonous matter, while baking brings out their full flavor. Those greens such as orach, sorrel, orpine and

ries are more palatable after cooking and can be made into pies and flans. Fruits are also used for preserves and jellies and to make pickles and chutneys.

Nuts such as hazel and almond are used fresh in confectionery after removing the shell, while sweet chestnuts and acorns are first boiled in water before the shell is removed so that the nuts will be soft and mealy.

Plant Lexicon Number	Uses	Part Used	Recipes
AGRIMONY 4	Tonic drinks Salads	Leaves Flowers	*Agrimony Beer* Put a handful of the herb (leaves, flowers) in a jug with a sliced lemon and tablespoon of honey and pour over ½ liter of boiling water. Stir well and leave for an hour, then strain and drink cold from the refrigerator or hot in winter.
ALEXANDERS 211	Salads Soups Sauces	Leaves	*Alexanders Sauce* To make a sauce to accompany fish, chop finely a handful of leaves and stir into 1 oz (25 g) of melted butter and the same of flour. Season with salt and pepper and stir in half a cupful of cream until it is of a smooth consistency. Simmer for several minutes and serve hot, pouring it over fish or meat.
ALFALFA 127	Salads Omelettes	Sprouting seeds	*Alfalfa Omelette* To serve 4 people, mix the yolks of 4 eggs with ½ cupful of grated cheese and a tablespoonful of cream. Beat the egg whites until stiff and with the alfalfa sprouts, fold into the yolk and cheese mixture. Melt a small piece of butter in a frying pan and pour in separately sufficient of the mixture for each person. Cook over a low flame and when ready, fold over the omelette and serve hot, sprinkled with chopped parsley or chives.
ALLSPICE 164	To flavor cakes, bread, stewed fruit	Fruit	*Gingerbread* It has the flavor of cinnamon, cloves and nutmeg combined and can be used in place of these spices. Put 2 lb (1 kilo) of flour in a basin with 4 oz (100 g) brown sugar, 1 oz (25 g) ground ginger and ½ oz (13 g) allspice and mix well. To the mix work in 4 oz (100 g) of butter, warmed and beaten to a cream and 1 lb (400 g) golden syrup. Dissolve a teaspoonful of bicarbonate soda in a cup of warm water and add to the mix, with an egg whisked in a little milk. Stir the contents well, put into a well greased tin and bake for 1 hour in a medium oven.
ALMOND 10	Confectionery Cakes Sweets Puddings	Nuts	*Cobourg Trifle* Slice across the center several small sponge cakes, cover with a layer of apricot jam and replace the other portions. Place in a glass bowl and cover with macaroons then pour over a small glass of pale sherry and ½ liter of custard. Whip a cupful of thick cream and after the custard has set, pile the cream on top. Garnish with candied angelica and blanched almonds.
AMERICAN AMARANTH 9	Vegetable Omelettes	Leaves	*Amaranth Purée* The leaves of the green amaranth, an obnoxious weed of the United States, make a spinach substitute served either boiled or as a purée, perhaps folded into an omelette. Remove the stalks and wash the leaves. Fill a saucepan with them, sprinkle with salt, add a cupful of water and simmer for 30 minutes, constantly pressing them down. Then strain and rub through a sieve. Replace the purée in the pan, add 1 oz (25 g) of butter, 2 tablespoons of cream and a sprinkling of flour. Cook slowly for 10 minutes until of the right consistency. Serve on fried bread or buttered toast or fold into an omelette.
ANGELICA 14	Confectionery Salads Trifles Cakes	Stems Leaves	*Candied Angelica* Harvest the stems before they become old and hard and cut into 2 inch (5 cm) lengths. Boil for a few minutes until soft enough to peel, then boil again in a little water. After the water has evaporated, cover the stems with fine sugar, allow to stand for 3 days and boil clear. When cool, place the stems in a large jar and use as required to decorate and flavor cakes and trifles. The fresh stems impart a muscat flavor when stewed with apple or rhubarb.
ANISE 165	Flavoring Sweetmeats Teas	Seeds Leaves	*Aniseed Tea* Seed is used to flavor bread and to make a "tea", to take hot or cold. Place 1 oz (25 g) of seed and the chopped peel of an orange in a jug and pour over it ½ liter of boiling water. Leave for 2 hours, strain and place in the refrigerator. Take a wineglass ice cold with a meal. The leaves make a pleasant addition to a salad.
APRICOT 178	Tarts and flans Puddings Preserves Dessert	Fruit	*Apricot and Rice Salad* Boil a large cupful of rice (preferably unpolished) in ½ liter of salted water for 20 minutes until soft. Drain and let cool. Stew ½ lb (200 g) of fresh apricots in half a cup of water and cut them up. Peel and dice a large cucumber and add to the apricots and in another bowl, mix a small cupful of wine vinegar and one of salad cream, then stir it into the rice. Add the contents to the apricots and cucumber, mixing well, put in a sprinkling of finely chopped parsley and season. Place in a refrigerator for an hour before serving.
ARROWHEAD 198	Vegetable Soups Salads	Tubers	*Arrowhead Soup* The bulbous roots are of walnut size and can be sliced raw into salads and served with oil and vinegar, or baked like chestnuts and served hot. They make a nourishing soup. Clean and scrape 1 lb (½ kilo) of tubers and place in a saucepan with a chopped onion. Cover with ½ liter of meat or vegetable stock. Cook slowly for 40 minutes. Remove the ingredients and mash them. Return to the pan and bring to the boil. In a cup, mix a tablespoonful of cornflour with a little milk and a beaten egg. Add to the stock and simmer for 5 minutes. Season and serve with snippets of fried bread.
ARROWROOT 126	Drinks Blancmange Soufflé	Root	*Arrowroot Soufflé* Mix 1 oz (25 g) of powdered arrowroot with a little milk to make a smooth paste. Boil ½ liter of milk and pour it into the arrowroot, mixing it briskly. Return to the saucepan, add ½ oz (13 g) of sugar, a few drops of vanilla essence and a pinch of salt. Stir over a low flame until creamy then allow to cool and beat in the yolks of 2 eggs separately then the whites which have been whisked. Pour into a pie dish and bake in a warm oven for 20 minutes. Serve hot.

Plant Lexicon Number	Uses	Part Used	Recipes
ASPARAGUS 28	Vegetable Salads Sauces	Shoots	**Asparagus Pudding** Asparagus is usually enjoyed as a vegetable or on toast, served with melted butter. It is also delicious in a pudding. Cut away the green tops (about 2 inch or 5 cm pieces) of the shoots and chop up quite small. Put in a basin with 2 beaten eggs, 2 tablespoons of flour and 2 of minced ham or bacon, 1 oz (25 g) of butter and seasoning. Mix the ingredients and add a little milk to bring to a smooth consistency. Place in a large basin, cover with a cloth or tin foil and put in a large pan of water. Boil for 2 hours, then turn onto a dish and serve with asparagus sauce.
ASPARAGUS PEA 120	Vegetable Salads	Pods	**Buttered Asparagus Peas** Though neither asparagus nor a pea, it has the flavor of both. The pods are cooked whole when about 1 inch long and their full flavor is retained if steamed for 10–15 minutes. When tender, drain off surplus moisture and cover with melted butter and grated cheese, place in a hot oven for a few minutes to brown and serve at once with fish dishes.
AVOCADO PEAR 158	Salads Preserves Dessert	Fruit	**Avocado and Anchovy Salad** Peel and stone an avocado and cut into slices. Place 3 small tomatoes into boiling water and after 30 seconds, lift out and remove skins. Put the tomatoes and the avocados into a bowl with 6–8 stoned olives and 2 oz (50 g) of anchovy fillets, season and add a tablespoonful of olive oil and a sprinkling of lemon juice. Thoroughly mix the ingredients before serving.
BALM 128	Tonic drinks Salads	Leaves	**Balm "Tea"** Gather a handful of leaves in summer and place in a jug. Add a sliced lemon and tablespoon of honey to sweeten then pour on ½ liter of boiling water. Stir and leave for an hour, then strain and drink cold from the refrigerator.
BAMBOO 25	Vegetable Salads	Young shoots	**Bamboo in Lemon Sauce** Like many plants, the young shoots can be used in several ways to serve with chicken or fish. Tie the shoots into bundles and place in a saucepan of boiling water, add a teaspoonful of salt and simmer for 30 minutes until tender. Drain, remove the ties and serve on toast with lemon sauce. To make, simmer the rind of a lemon in a cupful of chicken stock and a little milk. Melt 1 oz (25 g) butter and mix in the same of flour and heat for 5 minutes in another pan. Add the stock and simmer 20 minutes, then the juice of the lemon and 2 tablespoons of cream. Serve hot.
BANANA 137	Drinks Jellies Fritters Flans	Fruit	**Banana Fritters** Cut the bananas lengthwise into strips and dip them in batter. This is made by placing 4 oz (100 g) of flour into a basin. Add ½ oz (13 g) of melted butter, a pinch of salt, a tablespoonful of cream and an egg yolk. Stir until smooth and add 2 tablespoons of warm water. Beat well, leave for 30 minutes, then add the stiffly whisked egg whites and it is ready to use. Dip in the batter and place the bananas in hot vegetable oil. Fry until nicely brown and serve hot, topped with whipped cream.
BARBERRY 35	Tarts Pickles Sauces	Fruit	**Barberry Tart** Gather the berries when red, remove the stalks and place the fruit in a preserving pan. To every 1 lb (½ kilo) of fruit add a cupful of sugar and simmer slowly over a low flame until the fruit is soft. Then boil for 15 minutes, removing any scum as it forms. Use the fruit to cover a plate lined with pastry (see blackberry) and bake in a hot oven until brown. Cover with whipped cream and serve hot or cold.
BARLEY 103	Drinks Soups Stews	Seed	**Barley Cream Chicken** Mince ½ kilo of uncooked chicken and place in a pan. Boil 1 oz (25 g) of pearl barley in a large cupful of water for 3 minutes, strain and add the barley to the pan containing the chicken. Add a cupful of water and seasoning and cook gently for 2 hours. Strain and rub the contents through a sieve, then stir in ½ liter of partly whipped cream or milk, re-heat and serve hot on toast.
BASIL 143	Flavoring	Leaves	**Basil Seasoning** To season sausage meat and for turkey or game, or to sprinkle over tomato salads and into soups, take 1 oz (25 g) of dried bay leaves and 1 oz (25 g) each of cloves and peppercorns, 2 oz (50 g) of dried basil, marjoram and savory mixed together; ½ oz (13 g) of cayenne pepper and a small clove of garlic. Pound in a mortar until they are all well broken down and store in a jar with a tightly fitting top to use as required.
BAUHINIA 33	Salads	Flowers	**Chinese Salad** The purple flowers are sweet and juicy in a salad. Make a base of Chinese lettuce, diced cooked sweet potatoes and sliced green beans. Then add flakes of tuna or similar fish, a cupful of bauhinia flowers, and one of black olives, sliced tomato and a hard boiled egg. Season and sprinkle with tarragon vinegar.
BAY LAUREL 114	Flavoring sauces, stews	Leaf	**Bechamel Sauce** This is one of the most useful of all sauces and has the unmistakable flavor of a bouquet garni. It is made by placing in a muslin bag a fresh bay leaf or two, with a few stems of thyme, savory and oregano and immersing into ½ liter of milk or chicken stock in a saucepan. Add a small onion and a few peppercorns, season and bring to the boil. Melt 2 oz (50 g) of butter and the same of flour in another pan, stir into the spiced milk or stock, bring to the boil and let simmer for 20 min. Remove the bouquet garni and strain through a cloth. The sauce is then ready to use.

Plant Lexicon Number	Uses	Part Used	Recipes
BEECH 84	Dessert Nut meat Bread	Nuts (mast)	*Beech-nut Mince* Melt 1 oz (25 g) of butter in a frying pan and to it add 8 oz (200 g) of ground beech nuts after removing from the shells. (This is best done by placing them in boiling water for several minutes.) Put the nuts through a mill and with them mix 6 oz (150 g) of bread crumbs and a finely chopped onion. Fry over a low flame until nicely brown, then pour over ½ liter of vegetable stock and season. Cook for several minutes more when the mince will take on a crumbly appearance. Around a dish, make a border of mashed potato and diced vegetables and place the mince inside. Garnish with finely chopped parsley or chives and serve hot with strips of bacon and fried bread.
BEET 37	Salads Pickles Vegetable	Roots	*Savory Beet* To cook beetroot, screw off the leaves (do not cut them off or the roots will bleed) and boil until tender. While warm, peel off the skins with the fingers and slice the roots into a pan. Put in a tablespoonful of stock and a teaspoonful of flour. Add a small sliced onion, a small handful of well chopped parsley or of chervil, bring to the boil and simmer for 15 minutes. Remove from the flame and pour in a tablespoonful of thick cream. Serve at once.
BERGAMOT 132	Salads Drinks	Leaves	*Oswego Tea* To make a health-giving "tea" to take hot or cold, gather a large handful of leaves, place them in a saucepan with 2 pints (1 liter) of water. Bring to the boil and simmer for 15 minutes. Strain and sweeten with a little honey and add lemon juice instead of milk. It is a tranquilizer taken before bed time.
BETELNUT PALM 19	Vegetable Salads Dessert	Tree tops Nuts	*Braised Cabbage Palm* The center growth at the top of a cabbage palm makes a succulent vegetable but its removal is liable to harm the tree. The cabbage-like growth is cut into halves. Place in a large saucepan, give a sprinkling of salt and almost cover with water. Boil 15 minutes to part-cook and drain. In the pan, place bacon slices, then replace the cabbage after trying the halves together. Around them put a chopped onion or two and a few carrots. Add seasoning and a bay leaf and pour in ½ liter vegetable stock. Cover and simmer for an hour. When cooked, take out the cabbage, remove the ties and serve with meat or poultry.
BISTORT 173	Vegetable Puddings	Leaves	*Bistort Pudding* Take 1 lb (½ kilo) each of bistort and nettle leaves gathered early in summer when young and tender. Finely chop them, place in a large saucepan and add a cupful of barley which has been soaked overnight. Add half a cupful of oatmeal and a few chopped chives, season and boil slowly in a linen bag tied at the top for about 2 hours. Turn out into a bowl and while still hot, add a small piece of butter and a beaten up egg, mixing in well. Serve hot.
BITANG 110	Vegetable Salads	Young shoots	*Pork Casserole* Skin and slice a large onion and fry until soft in a little olive oil. Place in a casserole dish with several chopped bitang shoots. Slice and fry 2 red or green peppers for a few minutes and add to the casserole. Cut up 1 lb (½ kilo) lean pork, browned in the reheated oil and place in the casserole. Mix in 2 tablespoons of flour, season with salt and paprika, add ½ liter of meat stock and cook for 1½ hours in 350°F (180°C). Just before serving stir in a cupful of yogurt.
BLACKBERRY 194	Pies Tarts Jellies Preserves	Fruit	*Blackberry and Apple Pie* First make the pastry. Put 6 oz (150 g) of flour and a pinch of salt in a bowl, rub in 1½ oz (40 g) of lard and margarine and sufficient cold water to make into a dough. Then peel and slice ½ kilo of cooking apples into a pie dish and over them place 8 oz (200 g) ripe but firm blackberries. Sprinkle in 2 oz (50 g) of sugar. Roll out the pastry and fit over the edge of the pie dish. Cut out a 1 in. (2.5 cm) square at the top for the steam to escape and dampen the pastry with milk. Dust with caster sugar and place in an oven heated to 450°F (220°C) for 10 minutes, then reduce to 380°F (200°C) and bake for another 30 minutes. Serve hot with whipped cream.
BLACK MULBERRY 134	Tarts and flans Souffles Preserves	Fruit	*Mulberry Soufflé* Whisk the yolks of 2 eggs with 6 oz (150 g) sugar and the juice and grated peel of 2 lemons. Add ½ oz (13 g) gelatine dissolved in a little water and ½ lb (200 g) mulberries beaten to a pulp. Then add the whisked egg whites and a cupful of whippel cream. Pour into a soufflé dish and place in the refrigerator until it firms and serve cold.
BLACK MUSTARD 209	Salads Sauces Mustards	Seeds Leaves	*Mustard Sauce* As a spread to accompany fried herrings or sausages, melt 1 oz (25 g) of butter and stir in the same amount of flour. Add a cupful of water and bring to the boil. In a basin place 2 teaspoonfuls of black mustard powder obtained from the dry seeds and the same of lemon juice, mix together and add to the butter while on the boil. Then add half a cup of cream and use while still hot, pouring it over fish or meat.
BLUEBERRY 240	Pies Tarts Preserves Jellies	Fruit	*Blueberry Pie* Cook 1 lb (½ kilo) of blueberries with 2 tablespoons of sugar and a small cupful of water for about an hour in a slow oven. Place in a pie dish and cover with pastry, cutting out a small hole in the center for the steam to escape. Brush the pastry with milk, sprinkle with caster sugar and bake for 15 minutes in a hot oven, reducing to 350°F (180°C) then bake for 30 minutes more. Serve hot with whipped cream.

Plant Lexicon Number	Uses	Part Used	Recipes
BOGBEAN 130	Vegetable Salads Beer	Leaves Roots	*Egg and Bogbean Salad* Place a handful of young bogbean leaves in a salad bowl. Cover with mayonnaise into which a cupful of cream has been whipped to stiffen it. Then add a layer of thinly sliced hard boiled egg and another layer of bogbean leaves until the bowl is filled. Garnish with a tablespoon of capers and sprinkle with, finely chopped parsley. Serve with cold meats.
BORAGE 38	Tarts Salads Drinks	Leaves Flowers	*Borage Tart* Collect a large cupful of fresh flowers and part-boil in a little water for a few minutes. Strain and whip into the yolks of 3 eggs and a basin full of boiled apple purée. Cover a large plate with pastry (see Blackberry) and spread the mixture over it. Bake until nicely browned. Serve hot or cold. The leaves fried in batter make delicious fritters. Serve covered with hot or grated cheese.
BRAZIL NUT 36	Confectionery Dessert	Nut	*Torrijas* A sweet of Spanish origin which is popular in S. America. Cut strips of bread ½ in. (1.25 cm) thick and 1 in. (5 cm) wide. Place in a dish of melted butter, then put onto a flat tin for baking. On the top of each strip, put a layer of custard and over it, naranjilla jam. Top up with flaked brazil nuts (in Spain almonds are used) and place in an oven heated to 350°F (180°C) for 15 minutes until lightly browned. Eat hot or cold with coffee drinks.
BREAD FRUIT 23	To use as bread	Fruits	*Baked Bread Fruit* When golden-brown, the melon-like fruits which are a feature of Pacific islands are baked in their hard skins in tins over a low fire. After an hour, the soft inside becomes firm and mealy with the consistency of well baked bread. The fruits are cut into halves and the contents used in place of bread to accompany chicken dishes.
BROAD BEAN 245	Vegetable Soufflé Soup	Beans (seeds)	*Broad Bean Soufflé* Both the beans and their skins are rich in mineral salts and should be gathered as soon as the beans are seen through the outside of the pod, before becoming hard. After removing form the pod, boil beans for 30 minutes, throw away the water and remove the skins with the fingers when they begin to lose heat. Rub the beans through a sieve and to every cupful of purée add ½ cupful of water and 1 oz (25 g) each of butter and flour, mix together and season. Bring almost to the boil and remove from the flame before stirring in the yolks of 2 eggs separately. Then fold in the whipped whites. Half fill a soufflé dish and bake 10 minutes in a hot oven. Serve at once.
BROOKLIME 243	Vegetable	Leaves	*Brooklime Purée* A valuable blood purifyer, it is included in salads as a substitute for cress or used as a purée, with spinach, chickweed or lamb's lettuce, to serve with meat. Gather 8 oz (200 g) of brooklime and lamb's lettuce and place in a saucepan with ½ liter of vegetable or chicken stock. Simmer for 30 minutes until tender, then rub through a sieve. In a separate pan, melt 1 oz (25 g) butter and mix with it 1 oz (25 g) flour. Add ½ liter of milk, then the purée. Season and simmer for 10 minutes and serve hot.
BURDOCK 18	Vegetable Drinks	Young shoots; Roots	*Burdock Beer* Its roots, boiled with those of the dandelion, make a tonic drink or the young shoots, peeled and boiled, can be eaten like asparagus or chopped raw into a salad. Serve with salad oil and vinegar. The roots have a sweet taste. To make a tonic drink, lift them in late summer with those of the dandelion, wash and cut into small pieces and boil for 10 minutes, then simmer for a further 30 minutes. Use 2 oz (50 g) of root to ½ liter of water, sweeten with a little honey, strain and take a cupful daily hot or cold.
BURNET 176	Salads	Leaves	*Shrimp and Burnet Salad (Salade d'Ecrevisses)* To a large cupful of picked shrimps, stir in 2 tablespoons of mayonnaise. Place in a salad bowl and add half a cucumber sliced and peeled and a cupful of salad burnet leaves which also have a cucumber flavor. Mix well and serve in individual glasses as hors d'œuvre or with cold meats with cold cooked potatoes in mayonnaise sauce.
CACAO 228	Confectionery Puddings Sauces	Seed	*Chocolate Soufflé* Put a large cupful of milk and 2 oz (50 g) grated chocolate in a saucepan and simmer until the chocolate is dissolved. In a second pan, melt 1 oz (25 g) of butter and stir in 3 oz (75 g) flour, add the chocolate mixture and bring to the boil. Take off the boil and add ½ teaspoon of vanilla essence, 2 oz (50 g) sugar and 2 egg yolks. Beat and add the whisked whites. Turn into a mold and steam for about 50 minutes. Serve hot.
CAPE GOOSEBERRY 162	Dessert Preserves Tarts and flans	Fruit	*Tipparee Conserve* Tipparee is the South African name for this fruit where it has become naturalized. Place the fruits in a pan, just cover with water and simmer for 20 minutes until tender. For each kilo of fruit add one of sugar and a tablespoonful of lemon juice, then simmer for 30 minutes, removing the scum. Before it is quite cool, pour the jelly into screw-top jars and use with cold meats or as a sweet.
CAPER 42	Pickles Salads	Flower buds	*Cod and Capers* Place several cod cutlets in a frying pan with 2 tablespoons of olive oil and fry briskly until the fish is brown on both sides. Add several stoned and well chopped olives and a tablespoon of caper buds. Sprinkle with lemon juice and simmer for 20 minutes. Serve with sweet potatoes and a salad.

Plant Lexicon Number	Uses	Part Used	Recipes
CARDAMOM 80	Seasoning	Seeds	**Kedgeree** Cut into rings 2 large onions and fry in butter until brown. Remove them and add a cupful of rice to the fat and simmer until absorbed. Just cover with stock, add a few slices of green ginger, 2 or 3 peppercorns and a few cardamom seeds and cook slowly until the rice is tender. Serve hot and garnish with the fried onions.
CARAWAY 47	Flavoring cakes; bread; pickles	Seeds	**Caraway Cake** Beat 1 lb (½ kilo) of butter to a cream. Add 1 lb (½ kilo) of caster sugar, ¼ oz (6 g) of caraway seeds and a pinch of nutmeg, mixing in well. Whisk 4 eggs separately into the mixture, then stir in 1 lb (½ kilo) of flour, adding a little milk to make it a nice smooth consistency. Turn into a greased cake tin and cook for 2 hours in a moderate oven.
CAROB 50	Tarts and flans Puddings Sorbets	Pods	**Carob Sorbet** Dissolve 6 oz (150 g) sugar in ½ liter of water, then boil 10 minutes. In a bowl put the pulp and mashed seeds from several carob pods and add the sugar syrup when off the boil. Stir in and when cold, place in the refrigerator to freeze to a creamy consistency. Whisk 2 egg whites to a thick foam, fold into the carob purée and return to the refrigerator for 2 hours to set. Serve cold.
CARRAGEEN MOSS 52	Milk drinks Sauces Soups Jellies Blancmange	All parts	**Carrageen Blancmange** Place a large cupful of carrageen moss in a cloth bag and put in a saucepan of cold water for 30 minutes. Drain off the water and pour in a liter of milk, a tablespoon of sugar and a pinch of salt. Cook over a low flame until the milk will solidify when a little is placed on a saucer. Add a few drops of vanilla essence and pour into a mold to set. Serve cold with fresh or stewed fruit.
CARROT 75	Vegetable Soups Salads	Root	**Carrot Pie** Wash and cook 2 lb (1 kilo) of carrots until soft but still firm. Peel and cut into halves lengthwise. Remove the cores and rub the rest through a sieve together with a small raw onion. Beat 8 oz (200 g) of butter or margarine to a cream and mix in the vegetables. Put them in a pie dish and bake for 30 minutes in a hot oven. Serve hot with sauce made by beating together 1 oz (25 g) margarine, the yolk of an egg, a teaspoonful of cream, a few drops of lemon juice and a pinch of salt. Heat but do not boil. Garnish the pie with chopped parsley and hard boiled egg.
CASHEW 11	Salads Salted for dessert Fricassée	Nuts	**Cashew Fricassée** Melt 1 oz (25 g) of butter in a saucepan and finely chop 2 sticks of celery and a small onion and part-fry for a few minutes. Stir in 2 oz (50 g) of flour and ½ liter of milk as it simmers; add 2 oz (50 g) or whole or chopped cashew nuts and a pinch of salt, cook gently for 15 minutes and allow to cool before stirring in a small cupful of cream. Make a circle of cooked peas or mashed potato and diced carrots around a dish and pour inside the cashew fricassée which will be of a thick creamy consistency.
CASSAVA 125	Thickening soups Stews Puddings	Root	**Tapioca Pudding** Tapioca, obtained from cassava root, is used as a thickening agent for soups and stews. It also makes a nourishing milk pudding. Put 2 oz (50 g) of tapioca and 1 oz (25 g) sugar into a pie dish and cover with ½ liter of milk. Add a small pinch of nutmeg and cook gently for 2 hours in an oven at 250°F (120°C).
CASSIA 54	To flavour cakes; puddings; stewed fruit	Bark	**Apricot Loaf** The brown bark is the cinnamon of commerce and has more uses than any spice of the Far East. Sweet and aromatic, it is used in cakes puddings and to flavor stewed fruit. Cut up 8 oz (200 g) dried apricots and place in a saucepan with a cupful of water. Add 6 oz (150 g) caster sugar, a teaspoonful of ground cinnamon, 3 oz (75 g) lard or cooking fat and a generous pinch of salt. Simmer 5 minutes and let cool. Mix 8 oz (200 g) flour and a teaspoon of bicarbonate of soda and stir in the apricot mix and 2 beaten eggs. Pour into a greased loaf tin and bake for 1 hour in 350°F (180°C).
CHECKERBERRY 91	Sauces Preserves Drinks	Fruit	**Checkerberry Sauce** From the leaves a "tea" is made and from the red fruits, a preserve and sauce to accompany game. Gather the berries when ripe and to every 8 oz (200 g) add 6 oz (150 g) sugar and a cupful of water. Boil for about 3–4 minutes until the fruit is soft, mix in a teaspoonful of cornflour, then simmer for 10 minutes and serve hot.
CHERVIL 16	Salads Herb "butters" Flavoring	Leaves	**Maitre d'Hotel Beurre** To make a "butter" to serve with steak, place a small piece of butter in a basin, add a few drops of lemon juice, half a teaspoonful of chopped parsley and one of chervil, season and beat to a cream. Serve a teaspoonful or more on the top of each portion of grilled fish or steak.
CHICKWEED 220	Vegetable Stews	Leaves	**Chickweed Purée** Chickweed and bladder campion boiled together make a tasty vegetable to serve with meats or to include in soups. Use as an early summer substitute for spinach or sorrel and serve with meat or scrambled eggs. Place two handsful of chickweed in a saucepan with a cupful of water, sprinkle with salt and simmer for 20 minutes. Strain and put through a sieve. Put the purée back in the pan with 1 oz (25 g) butter and 2 tablespoons of cream, season and stir over a low flame for 10 minutes, adding a little flour if necessary to thicken. Serve hot on toast.

Plant Lexicon Number	Uses	Part Used	Recipes
CHICORY 53	Salads Vegetable	Leaf hearts (heads)	*Chicory Salad* Take 4 heads of forced (blanched) chicory and chop into small pieces using a stainless steel knife to prevent discoloration. Add 4 oranges which after peeling are sliced into circles as thin as possible, removing any seeds. Mix with the chicory. Place in a salad bowl and sprinkle with a little tarragon vinegar. Serve chilled from the refrigerator to accompany cold meats.
CHINESE ARTICHOKE 219	Vegetable Fritters	Tubers	*Chinese Fritters* Wash the small knobby tubers and steam with a cupful of chopped bean sprouts for about 40 minutes. Serve on thin fried or buttered toast with melted butter poured over; or after cooking fry the tubers and sprouts in butter until nicely brown.
CHIVE 6	Salads Stews Soups Omelettes	Leaves	*Chive and Rice Salad* Place in a salad bowl ½ cupful of chopped chives and the same of parsley, a bunch of watercress or field cress and ½ cupful of fenugreek or mung bean sprouts. Season and stir in ½ small cupful of tarragon vinegar and 3 large cupfulls of cold boiled rice. Mix well and serve chilled with sauté potatoes to accompany cold meats.
CHOCHO 206	Chutneys Preserves	Fruit	*Chocho Jam* Slice the melon-like fruit, remove the seeds and put the pulp in a bowl. Then make a syrup by boiling 1 lb (½ kilo) brown sugar with ½ liter of water and pour onto the pulp. After 24 hours strain off surplus liquid and to the pulp add the peel and juice of a lemon and ½ oz (13 g) ground ginger or its substitute. Place in a preserving pan and to every pound (½ kilo), add the same of sugar. Boil slowly until clear and when cool, pour into screw-top jars.
COCONUT PALM 58	Vegetable Puddings Confectionery	Flesh of nut	*Coconut Corn* A popular dish of S.E. Asia is made by using grated fresh coconut and its milk (or use desiccated coconut and goat's milk) and the corn stripped from a large cob of maize after it has been cooked. Place the ingredients in a saucepan, add a tablespoonful of olive oil and a pinch of salt. Simmer for 5 minutes and serve hot with game or chicken.
COFFEE 59	Flavoring Drinks Ice-cream	Seeds (beans)	*Iced Coffee* Make a liter of strong coffee from freshly ground beans. Place a large cupful of milk, 6 oz (150 g) of sugar and a teaspoonful of vanilla essence in a pan, bring almost to the boil and add the coffee. Allow to cool, then stir in a cupful of cream. Place in the refrigerator for an hour to give it the consistency of thick cream and serve with fresh fruit.
COLA 60	For bread and cakes; to flavor drinks	Nuts	*Cola Pudding* The nuts are dried and ground to make bread and puddings. Mix 2 tablespoonsful and 2 of ground Indian maize with a little milk for a smooth consistency. Add a tablespoon of sugar and the finely grated peel of an orange. Stir in ½ liter of milk and cook gently for 5 minutes. When cool, add 2 beaten eggs and bake in a warm oven for 30 minutes. Serve hot almost like a soufflé.
COLEWORT 39	Vegetable	Leaves	*Colewort Slaw* To accompany cold meats, take a colewort or cabbage which may be growing wild as a garden escape and shred it. Mix with it a cupful of sprouting seeds, one of chopped onion or chives and a pinch of celery seed. Then mix in a cupful of yogurt or sour cream and serve cold from the refrigerator.
COMMON ASH 88	Pickles	Seed pods	*Pickled Ash Keys* Gather the green "keys" (seed pods) as they fall in late summer, put in a large saucepan of boiling water, add 1 oz (25 g) of salt and simmer until tender. Drain off the water and put the "keys" in large stone jars with several peppercorns and horseradish shavings. Boil equal parts vinegar and cider, pour over the "keys" and place the jars in a warm oven for an hour. Then close the jars and stand in a cool place. After about a month, begin to use the "keys" with cold meat.
COMMON ORACH 30	Vegetable Salads	Leaves	*Orach Purée* The red-tinted leaves are attractive and tasty used in salads or as purée to serve on fried bread with poached eggs, or with cold meats. Pick a saucepan of leaves, wash them well and add a little water. Season and cook for 20 minutes. Drain, put through a sieve, add 1 oz (25 g) butter, 2 tablespoons of cream and a little flour to bring it to a creamy consistency and cook for 10 minutes, continually stirring. Fry slices of bread, cover with the purée and top with a firm poached egg. Sprinkle with finely chopped parsley or chives.
COMMON SORREL 195	Vegetable Sauces Soups	Leaves	*Sorrel Soup* Collect 4 large handfuls of sorrel leaves, place in a saucepan containing roux, made by cooking for a few minutes a tablespoon of flour with a knife-end of butter. While hot, pour in a liter of milk and simmer for 5 minutes. Strain and serve hot, with small squares of fried bread or in summer, cold from the refrigerator.
CORIANDER 62	Flavoring jellies; curries; pickles; chutneys	Seeds	*Fish Curry* To make a curry powder to use with chicken, fish or mutton, pound and mix 8 oz (200 g) turmeric; 6 oz (150 g) coriander seed; 2 oz (50 g) cardamons and the same of cumin and fenugreek; 1 oz (25 g) cloves and 1 oz (25 g) peppercorns. Put through a fine sieve and then into jars. To curry fish, take 2 lbs (1 kilo) of boiled fish, cut into small pieces and fry lightly with a chopped onion. Add a cupful of milk, ½ oz ((13 g) green ginger and the same of curry powder. Simmer for 15 minutes and serve with boiled rice.

Plant Lexicon Number	Uses	Part Used	Recipes
CORN SALAD 241	Salads	Leaves	*Spring Salad* It produces leaf early and is the base for spring salads. Gather a bowlful of leaves, wash and mix with a boiled chicken cut into small pieces, the bones being discarded. Add 10–12 stoned and chopped olives, a tablespoon of capers and 2 sliced tomatoes (if available). Mix carefully and sprinkle in a tablespoon of finely chopped chives. Season and sprinkle over it tarragon vinegar. Serve cold as hors d'œuvre or with cold meats.
COSTMARY 223	Soups Stews	Leaves	*Cream of Sago Soup* With their balsamic fragrance, the leaves are included in soups and stews. They were also used to impart their taste to ale. They are an ingredient of cream of sago soup. Place a liter of vegetable stock in a saucepan with a few costmary leaves and bring to the boil. Then stir in 2 oz (50 g) sago and simmer for 20 minutes. Add ½ liter of milk and seasoning. In a bowl, beat 3 egg yolks and a cupful of cream and add to the soup, stirring in until it thickens but not letting the soup boil, or the egg will curdle. Take out the costmary and serve hot or chilled.
COWAGE 135	Soups Stews Chutneys	Seeds	*Indian Soup (Mulligatawny)* The seeds have a spicy flavor and are used in Indian cookery. Stew some mutton bones in ½ liter of water and in a saucepan fry 2 sliced onions, 2 carrots and 2 apples for 15 minutes in a little fat. Mix in 2 tablespoons of flour, add a bay leaf and a tablespoon of cowage seed. Then pour in the stock and simmer for 2–3 hours. Strain and add the juice of a lemon and seasoning. Put back to boil for a few minutes and serve with small squares of fried bread.
COWSLIP 177	Tarts and flans Salads Wine	Flowers Leaves	*Cowslip Tart* Gather 8 oz (200 g) of the flowers, snipping them off at the top of the stems, pound them in a mortar and add them to ½ liter of cream. Bring to the boil, simmer for a few minutes, cool and beat in 4 eggs. Sweeten with a little honey and the mix should now be of a thick consistency. Cover an enamelled tin plate with pastry and pour on the mixture. Bake for an hour in a hot oven and serve hot or cold. (In some countries cowslips are now a protected flower.)
CRAB APPLE 123	Pies and tarts Preserves Jellies	Fruit	*Crab Apple Jelly* To make a preserve to accompany meat, peel and core the ripe fruit and place in a preserving pan. Just cover with water and simmer until tender. Strain off any surplus liquid and to each kilo of fruit, add 1 kilo of sugar, a taste of ginger and a few cloves. Boil until such time as the liquid solidifies when a little is placed on a saucer. Then, before it cools, pour into screw-top jars and store in a cool place.
CRANBERRY 151	Jellies Preserves Tarts Flans	Fruit	*Cranberry Sauce* Cranberry sauce is the traditional accompaniment to turkey in the USA and elsewhere. Place half a kilo of the ripe fruit into a preserving pan with the same amount of sugar and 1 pint (600 ml) of water. Bring to the boil and simmer for an hour, stirring often. When a little placed on a saucer quickly sets it will be done. As it cools, pour into small jars and store in a cool place.
CUBEB 167	To flavor sauces; soups; stews	Fruits Seeds	*Curry Sauce* For a hot sauce to accompany beef, chicken or prawns, chop up 2 onions and 2 apples and add to a frying pan in which a tablespoon of cooking oil and 4 oz (100 g) of butter are being heated. Cook gently for 7–8 minutes. Stir in 2 oz (50 g) curry powder made up of equal parts cubebs, cardamons, cinnamon and cumin and to which a pinch of nutmeg and clove is added. Cook for 5 minutes then add 2 oz (50 g) cornflour, stirring all the time, and mix in ½ liter meat stock. Bring to the boil, add 2 tablespoons tomato purée, 2 of sweet chutney and the juice of ½ lemon and cook slowly for 40 minutes.
CUCUMBER 68	Salads Hors d'œuvre Soups Sauces	Fruit	*Tabasco Cucumber* Peel a large cucumber and cut it into ½ in. (about 1 cm) thick slices cut diagonally. Mash the pulp of a small avocado and whip with a little cream into purée. Mix into it a cupful of alfalfa or lentil sprouts, season and add a dash of tabasco. Spread the cucumber slices with the mixture and top with slices of tomato. Serve with cold chicken or meats.
CUMIN 70	Flavoring cakes, bread, pickles	Seeds	*Seed Biscuits* Beat 4 oz (100 g) of butter to a cream and mix in 12 oz (150 g) flour, a teaspoonful of crushed cumin seed and 4 oz (100 g) of sugar. Then beat in 2 eggs that have been well whisked. The mixture should be a stiff paste. Roll out to about ½ in. (1.25 cm) thickness and cut out the "biscuits" with a metal cutter. Place on a greased tray and bake in a moderate oven for 15 minutes. Then brush the biscuits with a little milk and sprinkle with caster sugar. Keep in an air-tight tin or jar.
CURRY LEAF TREE 136	To flavor rice; soups; stews	Leaves	*Curry Leaf Rice* The fresh or dried leaves of the curry leaf tree give a special pungency to rice to be served with chicken, eastern style. Dissolve 4 oz (100 g) creamed coconut in a small basin of hot water. Place 2 tablespoons of olive oil in a frying pan and add a small well chopped onion, a cupful of rice, a few curry tree leaves, ⅔ cloves and ⅔ cardamons, a mustard spoon of saffron, a teaspoonful of salt and a few peppercorns. Fry over a low flame until the rice yellows. Place the coconut in a saucepan, bring to the boil and stir in the contents of the frying pan. Simmer for 20 minutes and serve hot.

Plant Lexicon Number	Uses	Part Used	Recipes
CURRY PLANT 99	For curries	Leaves	**Kari de Volaille** Cut up a chicken into portions and fry in 1 oz (25 g) butter until brown. Remove and put in the pan a well chopped onion. Fry for 3 minutes. Add a tablespoon of flour and one of finely chopped dried curry plant leaves. Then stir in a large cupful of stock and bring to the boil. Put back the chicken pieces, add a tablespoonful of fresh chopped coconut, 1 of Indian chutney, a chopped apple and juice of a lemon. Season and cook gently for 1 hour. Remove the chicken pieces and into the liquid stir a small cupful of cream and serve hot with cooked rice.
DAHLIA 74	Vegetable	Roots	**Dahlias with Asparagus Sauce** Lift and wash free of soil a large root, separating the tubers. Then place each in a saucepan with a cupful of water, season and boil for about 30 minutes until tender. Serve with asparagus sauce. To make, cut off 2 in. (5 cm) of the green ends of about 12 sticks, boil them in salt water and drain. Melt ½ oz (13 g) of butter in a saucepan, cook the asparagus in it for 6–7 minutes, add white sauce made by mixing flour with vegetable stock and milk, season and simmer for 15 minutes. Strain and add a few drops of lemon juice. Serve hot with dahlia or day lily roots to accompany chicken or game.
DALO 61	Vegetable	Tubers	**Baked Polynesian Pork** The large tuberous roots are cleaned and washed before boiling in two waters, draining away the first after 10 minutes to remove any toxic matter. Then boil for 30 minutes more in fresh water. Drain and cut the roots into small pieces. Place in a baking tin around a leg or loin of pork, together with several small onions or shallots. Sprinkle mixed herbs over the pork and cook in a moderate oven, allowing 20 minutes for each 1 lb (½ kilo) weight and basting often. Serve with the baked dalos and other vegetables.
DANDELION 225	Vegetable Salads Wine Coffee substitute	Roots Leaves Flowers	**Dandelion Wine** Blanched dandelion leaves are a valuable addition to summer salads or as a vegetable. The roasted roots also make an alternative to coffee and are free of caffeine while from the flowers, a wine is made. Collect a large saucepan of flowers and pour over them 2 liters of boiling water and cover. Leave for 48 hours stirring often. Strain into a preserving pan then add the rind of an orange and a lemon cut into strips, 3 lb (1½ kilos) of sugar and a piece of ginger. Boil for 30 minutes and let cool. Add 2 tablespoons of brewers yeast and let it stand 48 hours, then turn the contents into a cask. Keep the stopper firmly in for 8 weeks, strain and bottle.
DATE PALM 161	Cakes Confectionery Puddings Dessert Salads	Fruit	**Date Salad** For a delicious salad to serve with cold meats, spread lettuce leaves at the bottom of a bowl and over them place a cupful of soya bean sprouts, 2 sliced bananas, half a cup of stoned and chopped dates and a tablespoon of chopped walnuts. Squeeze in the juice of half a lemon and mix in half a cupful of yoghurt. Serve chilled with a pinch of cinnamon to each helping.
DAY LILY 100	Salads Omelettes Vegetable	Flower Buds Roots	**Beauty Bud Omelette** It takes its name from Greek words *hemera*, day and *kallos*, beauty, for the flowers retain their beauty for only a day. The unopened buds are pickled or used in omelettes while the roots can be stewed and served with meats. For an omelette, beat 2 eggs (per person) with a tablespoon of milk and add a pinch of salt. Heat 1 oz (25 g) of butter in a frying pan, pour in the mixture and stir until it sets. Sprinkle on the day lily buds, fold over and serve hot.
DILL 13	Salads Soups Sauces Pickles	Leaves Seeds	**Pickled Gherkins** In most European countries, gherkins pickled in dill vinegar are popular served with cold meats. Place the gherkins in a large bowl and cover with salt. Let them stand for 2–3 days, shake off the brine and place in layers in wide-topped earthenware jars. Sprinkle each layer with dill seed. In a pan, boil sufficient vinegar to cover the gherkins. Include a few peppercorns with the vinegar and strain before covering the gherkins when the vinegar cools. Let the gherkins remain a week or so before using.
DULSE 189	Jellies Milk drinks	All parts	**Dulse Jelly** Collect a large handful from rocks or the sea shore, wash away the sand and soak overnight in fresh water. Put into a stewpan and cover with ½ liter of fresh water. Simmer for 5 hours and strain. Add a large cupful of milk and sweeten with a little honey. To make more palatable, add a wineglass of pale sherry and turn into a mold. Use from the refrigerator. It is a nourishing food for invalids.
EARLY WINTER CRESS 32	Salads	Leaves	**Winter Cress Salad** Pick a large bunch of the cress (or watercress), wash and chop into a bowl. Add a cupful of soya or mung bean sprouts and a tablespoon of finely chopped chives. In a separate bowl mix together 2 tablespoons of olive oil, one of malt vinegar and 1 of soy sauce; add a teaspoonful of sugar and mix together. Then pour over the greens and serve with chicken or game.
EGGPLANT 212	Vegetable Salads	Fruit	**Stuffed Eggplant** Do not peel but steam for 30 minutes, slice off the top and remove some of the pulp. Mix with finely chopped chives and parsley and a hard boiled egg. Place in a casserole dish, sprinkle with grated cheese and breadcrumbs and add a few pats of butter on top. Place in a hot oven until brown on top, then fill the eggplants with the mixture and serve at once.

Plant Lexicon Number	Uses	Part Used	Recipes
ELDERBERRY 201	Sauces Pickles Pies Preserves	Fruit	*Elderberry Sauce* Gather 3 large cupfuls of ripe fruit, remove the stalks and place in a fire-proof dish. Cover with 1 pint (½ liter) of malt vinegar and place in the oven set at lowest heat, for about 5 hours. Strain into a saucepan, add a teaspoonful of salt, a few cloves and some peppercorns and a small finely chopped onion. Bring to the boil and simmer for 15 minutes. When cool, pour into screw-top jars.
ENGLISH OAK 186	Bread and cakes	Nut	*Acorn Bread* The large amount of tannic acid in acorn nuts must first be removed. Break the hard outer shell and put the nuts in a saucepan. Cover them with water and boil for 2–3 hours changing the water often. Drain and roast the nuts in a hot oven until crisp. Put through a grinder and mix with an equal weight of wholemeal flour. To 2 lb (1 kilo) of each, mix ½ oz (13 g) of yeast dissolved in ½ liter of warm water into which ½ oz (13 g) of salt has been dissolved. In a bowl make a smooth dough and stand in a warm place for 3 hours. Turn out and cut the dough into pieces for the baking tins. Stand for an hour and bake in a moderate oven.
EVENING PRIMROSE 144	Vegetable Salads	Roots	*Evening Primrose Fritters* The roots taste like parsnips and are cooked like sweet potatoes. Clean and scrub 1 lb (½ kilo) and boil in a little water for 30 minutes until tender. Drain and mash. Then mix in 1 oz (25 g) warm butter, a tablespoon of flour, 2 eggs and a pinch of salt. The mixture should be stiff. Then make into flat cakes, coat with egg yolk and breadcrumbs and fry until brown. Serve with fish or meat. The boiled roots when cold are sliced into salads and stews.
FENNEL 86	Salads Sauces Vegetable	Leaves Roots	*Finnochio au Gratin* Stew the roots of Florence fennel (really the swollen base of the stems) in a little water or vegetable stock for an hour or until soft, drain and slice into a pie dish. Cover with fennel-leaf sauce, sprinkle with grated cheese and bread crumbs and add a few pats of butter or margarine. Cook in a hot oven for 20 minutes and serve with fish or game.
FENUGREEK 233	Vegetable Salads	Seed sprouts	*Curried Fenugreek* Into a frying pan place 2 cupfuls of finely chopped fenugreek sprouts, obtained by sprouting the seeds, and a small chopped onion. Add 2 tablespoons of cornstarch in ½ a small cup of hot water and add to the pan. Cook over a low flame until the mixture has nicely thickened and serve hot to accompany game or chicken.
FERN 29	Vegetable Salads Brewing	Rhizomes Young shoots	*Fern Cakes* The rhizomes are first roasted, then peeled before grinding to flour. Mix 8 oz (200 g) with the same of oat or barley meal and add 2 teaspoons of baking powder and 1 of salt. Mix in a beaten egg and a cupful of maple or sugar syrup, using a little milk to make a dough. Bake for 30 minutes in a bread tin(s) or cut out into small cakes.
FIELD CRESS 116	Salads Soups Stews	Leaves Seed pods	*Cress Salad (Salade du Cresson)* For a cress salad, gather watercress and any of the field cresses, wash and trim and place in a salad bowl. Scatter in a tablespoon of chopped chives, a sliced hard boiled egg and a sliced tomato. Mix well and dress with mayonnaise. Serve with chicken or cold meats.
FIELD MUSHROOM 182	Sautes Stewed Fried Pickles	All parts	*Mushrooms a l'Arlesienne* Put 1 lb (½ kilo) of large mushrooms and 1 lb (½ kilo) red tomatoes, peeled and sliced, in a fire-proof dish or bowl, add a teaspoonful of chopped onion or chives and one of parsley; the juice of a lemon and season with salt and pepper. Add a teaspoonful of olive oil and bake in a hot oven for 30 minutes. Serve hot with fried or buttered toast.
FIG 85	Puddings Cakes Dessert	Fruit	*Fig Pudding* Wild figs, like medlars, need keeping in a dry room for several weeks before using, until they become soft. Fig pudding served with fig sauce made from the juice is delicious. Chop up 8 oz (200 g) of the fruit and mix with it, using a large pudding basin, the same amount of chopped suet, 4 oz (100 g) of bread crumbs and the same of flour and sugar. Beat 2 eggs into a large cupful of milk, then stir into the mixture. Cover the basin with a cloth and steam for about 2 hours. Serve hot.
GALANGAL 7	To flavor soups; stews; puddings	Roots	*Thai Chops* The roots are known as Thailand ginger and are of the same family as ordinary ginger. They are grated into stews and salads. Take 4 pork chops and cut away the meat. Mix a teaspoonful of soy sauce and one of ground galangal; 2 tablespoons of tomato sauce and 2 of white wine. Put in the meat and soak (marinate) for 30 minutes. Fry 2 well chopped onions, add the meat and a pinch of salt and fry until tender. Serve with sliced tomatoes and sauté potatoes.
GARLIC 5	Flavoring	Bulb (clove)	*Soup a l'Italienne* Melt 1 oz (25 g) of butter in a good sized pan, add a teaspoonful of flour and mix to a paste (roux). Add a small well chopped onion, a few chopped olives and a small clove of garlic. Put in 6 skinned tomatoes and season, then a small handful of macaroni. Just cover with chicken or vegetable stock and simmer for 15 minutes. Put through a sieve, return to the saucepan, add a teaspoonful of sugar and a cupful of grated cheese. Simmer for a few minutes and serve hot with small squares of fried toast.
GENTIAN 93	Tonic drinks	Roots	*Gentian Bitters* From the roots, which will have been washed and sliced, a tonic drink is prepared, alcoholic or otherwise. The root is simmered for 1 hour in a liter of water with that of sweet flag, using 1 lb (½ kilo) of each, the peel and juice of an orange and a teaspoon of cardamon seed. Drain and take a wineglassful of the drink as an aperitif before a meal. It should be used from the refrigerator.

Plant Lexicon Number	Uses	Part Used	Recipes
GERMANDER 226	Stuffings Salads Drinks	Leaves	*Pork Stuffing* Cut and slice 1 lb (½ kilo) of onions, cover with a little water, bring to the boil and simmer for 5 minutes. Melt 2 oz (50 g) butter and in it fry the onions for 15 minutes without browning. Add 2 oz (50 g) breadcrumbs and a teaspoonful of finely chopped germander (wood sage). Mix well and season and cook for a few more minutes and serve with leg or loin of pork.
GINGER 250	Flavoring Puddings Dessert Preserves	Root	*Ginger Pudding* (Pouding au Gingembre) Mix together in a pudding basin 12 oz (300 g) of flour and 6 oz (150 g) of finely chopped suet; 1 oz (25 g) of well chopped green ginger and a teaspoonful of baking powder. Add a pinch of salt and stir in 8 oz (200 g) of golden syrup and a small cupful of milk. Cover the basin with a cloth and steam for 2 hours. Serve with custard or sauce.
GINSENG 153	Bread Cakes Scones	Root	*Ginseng Scones* Place 8 oz (200 g) self-raising flour in a bowl, mix in a teaspoonful of baking powder, ½ of salt and to it, 2 oz (50 g) margarine. Into the mix, work in a tablespoon of grated ginseng root and stir in enough milk to make a smooth dough. Roll it out to ¾ in. (2 cm) thick and cut out circles as for biscuits. Place on an oven tin, brush the dough with beaten egg and bake for 10 minutes or until lightly brown in 450°F (230°C).
GLOBE ARTICHOKE 73	Vegetable	Fleshy heads	*Stuffed Artichoke* Steam the heads for an hour until tender, then remove the center leaves to make room for the stuffing. This can be of minced chicken or chicken liver bound together with hard boiled egg and spinach purée. Place in a saucepan and make hot over a low flame. Fill the hollowed artichokes with the stuffing, stand them close together in a dish and place in a hot oven for 10 minutes to become well warmed before serving with sauté potatoes and game.
GOOD-KING-HENRY 51	Vegetable Salads	Leaves	*Stewed Good-King-Henry* Earthing up the young shoots increases their tenderness. Cut when about 6 in. (15 cm) tall and stew for 30 minutes in chicken or vegetable stock. Drain and serve with gherkin sauce to accompany chicken or game. To ½ liter of brown sauce, add half a cupful of finely chopped gherkins and season. Simmer for 10 minutes and pour over the vegetable shoots when ready to serve hot.
GOOSEBERRY 191	Pies and tarts Chutneys Preserves	Fruit	*Gooseberry Fool* Gooseberries are delicious eaten hot in a pie or cold as in a ''fool.'' Top and tail 1 lb (½ kilo) of ripe fruits, early in summer and simmer in a saucepan containing a cupful of water and a generous sprinkling of sugar. When cooked, rub through a fine sieve and let cool. Whip a large cupful of cream and stir into the purée, to which a few drops of lemon juice have been added. Serve cold in individual glasses and grate chocolate over.
GRAPE 247	Jellies Preserves Chutneys Drinks	Fruit	*Crème of Black Grapes* Cut into halves 2 oz (50 g) black grapes and remove the stones. Place them in a jelly mold and pour lemon jelly dissolved in hot water, over them to a depth of 2 in. (5 cm) and let set. Put ½ liter of milk into a saucepan and boil. Add 2 oz (50 g) quick-cook macaroni and simmer for 10 minutes let cool. Beat in an egg yolk, cook gently for 2 minutes and let cool. Mix the egg white and fold into the macaroni. Whip a cupful of cream and fold into the macaroni with the rest of the jelly. Place in the refrigerator to set and turn out just before required.
GREATER NETTLE 239	Vegetable Tonic drink Soups	Leaves	*Nettle Soup* Make hot some fat in a frying pan and add 1 lb (½ kilo) of nettle tops after washing and cutting them up. Chop 2 or 3 small onions and add these. Fry for 5 minutes. Put ½ liter of water in a saucepan, bring to the boil, add the nettles and onions and seasoning. Boil for 30 minutes with the lid on. Mix in a basin a tablespoon of flour to a thin paste, using liquid from the saucepan. Add to the saucepan a knife end of margarine and simmer until the soup thickens, stirring all the time.
GROUND NUT 17	Preserves Fritters Salted	Seeds	*Ground Nut Fritters* Chop up a cupful of sprouted soya seed and a small onion. Grind half a small cup of peanuts, add a cupful of wholemeal breadcrumbs and seasoning. Place in a bowl, mix well and pour in half a cupful of vegetable stock to bind the ingredients. Make into small balls and drop them into a pan of hot olive oil. Leave for 2 minutes until brown and crisp and serve hot with chicken or ham, or as a vegetarian luncheon dish.
GUARANA 157	To flavor cakes; puddings	Nuts	*Lexington Apples* The finely ground nuts are made into a paste which is rolled and used like cinnamon in the New World to flavor cakes and bread. Peel and core 4 large apples (for 4 people) and steam for 20 minutes until half cooked. Mix 1 oz (25 g) flour and 1 oz (25 g) sugar and coat the apples with the mixture. Sprinkle with guarana (or cinnamon) and brush with egg yolk. Cover with breadcrumbs and fry in hot fat for 30 minutes. Fill the centers with chopped pineapple and serve with pineapple syrup.
GUAVA 183	Preserves Jellies Drinks	Fruit	*Guava Preserve* Place 2 kilos of guavas in a preserving pan with 2 kilos of sugar, the juice of 4 limes and 2 liters of water. Bring to the boil and simmer for an hour or so, stirring often and removing any scum as it forms. The jam is done when a little is placed on a saucer and it sets. When the contents begin to cool, pour into screw-top jars and store in a cool place.

Plant Lexicon Number	Uses	Part Used	Recipes
HAWTHORN 65	Preserves	Fruit	**Hawthorn Conserve** Gather the bright red berries when fully ripe. Wash and place in a preserving pan and to each cupful of fruit, add ½ cupful of water. Simmer for 30 minutes until the berries are soft. Mash them and place in a muslin bag for the juice to drip all night into a saucepan. Replace the juice in the preserving pan and to each cupful of juice add one of sugar. Bring quickly to the boil, add the juice of a lemon and stir frequently until such time as the jam "firms" when a little is put on a saucer. When it begins to cool, pour into screw-top jars.
HAZEL 63	Confectionery Sweets	Nuts	**Hazel and Apricot Meringue Cake** Soak 4 oz of dried apricots overnight. Whisk the whites of 3 eggs until stiff and whisk in 4 oz of caster sugar. Then fold in 4 oz of ground hazel nuts. Place half in each of two sandwich tins lined with greaseproof paper and bake in 350°F (180°C) for 20 minutes. While cooking, put the apricots in a saucepan, add the juice and peel of a small orange, 1 in. (2.5 cm) of cinnamon stick; a tablespoonful of sugar and a very little water. Simmer 10 minutes, remove the peel and mix in 2 teaspoons of arrowroot, stirring over a low heat so that the mixture thickens. When cold, spread over one of the meringues and cover with the other. Top with whipped cream and whole hazel nuts.
HENBIT 113	Vegetable Salads	Leaves Flowers	**Dead Nettle Omelette** It is the dead nettle and is of the mint family with the same minty flavor. Gather the tops including the flowers and with other greens, fill a saucepan and add a cupful of water, seasoning, then simmer for 30 minutes. Strain and place the greens in a frying pan with a knife end of butter and fry for 2–3 minutes. Take out and roll into a plain omelette. Serve with grated Parmesan cheese.
HOP 104	Vegetable Salads Drinks	Young shoots Flowers	**Hop Bitters** Gather a handful of flowers when at their best, place in a large jug with a handful of angelica (leaves and stem) or agrimony. Pour over ½ liter of boiling water and let it stand for an hour. Strain and drink cold from the refrigerator with a slice of lemon.
HORSERADISH 20	Sauces Pickles	Root	**Horseradish Sauce** Dig up the roots of well established plants, wash clean of soil, scrape them and grate. Take 2 heaped tablespoonfuls, place in a bowl, add a sprinkling of salt and stir in a large cupful of thick cream. Mix together, then stir in a small cupful of malt vinegar. The sauce should be of a nice consistency, neither too stiff nor too runny to accompany meats.
HOT PEPPER 43	Chutneys Sauces	Fruit	**Indian Chutney** Place 1 liter of malt vinegar in a stew-pan, bring to the boil and dissolve in it 8 oz (200 g) salt and 2 lbs (1 kilo) of brown sugar. Take off the boil and add 4 lbs (2 kilos) cooking apples (peeled and cored), 2 lbs (1 kilo) sultana raisins, ½ lb (200 g) ginger root, 4 sliced onions, 2 oz (50 g) mustard seed, and 4 oz (100 g) hot peppercorns or chilies. Simmer for about 2 hours, until the ingredients are tender, then when it begins to cool, pour into screw-top jars.
HUCKLEBERRY 92	Puddings Pies Preserves Chutneys	Fruit	**Huckleberry Pudding** Mash 1 lb (½ kilo) of huckleberries (or blueberries) and add them to a batter made of 6 oz (150 g) flour, ½ teaspoonful of cream of tartar and a pinch of salt, made moist with a little milk. Then stir in 2 eggs, add 2 large cups of milk and beat well. Give a pinch of bicarbonate of soda, then add the fruit, mixing it in well. Turn into a large basin and steam for 1½ hours. Serve hot with sauce made from the juice of the fruit.
HYSSOP 105	Flavoring soups, stews, savory dishes	Leaves	**Hyssop and Tomato Soup** Peel and slice 2 lbs (1 kilo) of fresh tomatoes and an onion. Place in a frying pan with 2 oz (50 g) of butter and fry for a few minutes. Sprinkle in a teaspoonful of finely chopped hyssop and cook for a further 5 minutes. Put through a sieve and place the purée in a stew-pot. Add a liter of water and seasoning, then bring to the boil and stir in 1 oz (25 g) of tapioca. Cook for another 15 minutes until it thickens. Serve with croutons of fried bread. For 6 people.
JERUSALEM ARTICHOKE 98	Vegetable Salads Stews	Tubers	**Artichoke Salad** Wash and steam the tubers until cooked right through. Then peel and slice thinly into a lettuce and tomato salad and serve with tarragon mayonnaise to accompany cold meats.
JUJUBE 251	Puddings Chutneys Preserves	Fruit	**Jujube Loaf** The fruits are the size of olives and are a substitute for figs and dates in chutneys, cakes and puddings. Remove the pointed stones and cut the fruits into pieces. Mix in a large bowl 12 oz (300 g) wholemeal flour, 2 teaspoons of baking powder and ½ one of salt. Add 2 oz (50 g) of raisins or sultanas and 2 oz (50 g) margarine and 2 tablespoons malt extract and in another bowl, mix a little milk with 2 beaten eggs and mix with the malt. Then add to the flour mix, stirring well. Turn into 2 greased loaf tins and bake in 325°F (160°C) for 1 hour. When cool, use as a cake or loaf. It also freezes well wrapped in tin foil.
JUNIPER 109	To flavor soups; meats; drinks	Berries	**Ham in Spiced Cider** To cook a leg or joint of gammon, first soak for 12 hours in a large pan, pour off the water and add a liter more, together with ½ liter dry cider, an onion, 2 or 3 bay leaves and 2 or 3 cloves, also 6–8 juniper (only the blue ripe berries are used) or allspice berries. Bring to the boil and simmer, allowing 15 minutes for each 1 lb (½ kilo) weight of the joint. When cooked, lift out and remove the skin and put in a baking tin. Moisten with cider, sprinkle with brown sugar and a teaspoonful of dried juniper or allspice and bake in a hot oven, basting with the liquid. Allow 10 minutes baking for every 1 lb (½ kilo) weight. After baking, allow 24 hours before the ham is cut into.

Plant Lexicon Number	Uses	Part Used	Recipes
KALINGA 76	Sauces Purées	Fruit	*Prawn Kalinga* The pulp of the kalinga fruit has a pleasant sourness, like unsweetened apple, and is used in place of curry sauce. Heat the ripe fruits in a little water for 10 minutes and put through a sieve. Put the purée back in the pan and with it 1 oz (25 g) of peeled prawns (or scampi) per person. Heat gently in a saucepan for 30 minutes. Serve with long-grain boiled rice and slices of peeled cucumber.
KAVA 168	Drinks	Tubers	*Yaqona* The black underground stems are washed and boiled in milk or water to make a nourishing drink like arrowroot and known as yaqona. It is demulcent. Boil for 30 minutes, strain and sweeten with sugar or honey and drink hot, but taken regularly it has a stupefying effect.
KIE-KIE 89	Tarts and flans Puddings Dessert	Fruit	*Tropical Fruit Salad* Scoop out the flesh from 2 ripe mangoes and chop up. Peel the kie-kie fruits and slice them around the mangoes, pieces of which are placed in individual fruit bowls. Cut 8 dates into halves, remove the stones and place between the kie-kie slices. Put a tablespoon of yogurt or whipped cream over the mangoes, then grate on top a little nutmeg or cinnamon and sprinkle with, a few finely chopped walnuts. Serve ice cold.
LADY'S SMOCK 44	Salads	Leaves	*Lady's Smock Salad* Remove a large cupful of leaves from the stems and place in a salad bowl. Add ½ cupful of finely chopped chives and thinly slice 2 large tomatoes and 2 hard boiled eggs. Sprinkle with tarragon vinegar or a little olive oil and serve chilled.
LAVER 174	Jellies Milk drinks Sauces	All parts	*Laver and Mushrooms* Boil the seaweed in slightly salted water for 3–4 hours. Heat 1 oz (25 g) of butter in a saucepan, add the cooked laver, the juice of a lemon and seasoning, and cook over a low flame for several minutes. Serve hot over grilled mushrooms on hot buttered toast.
LEMON 56	Flavoring Cakes Puddings Ice Cream	Fruit	*Lemon Sorbet* Allow 1 lemon and 1 oz (25 g) of sugar per person. To serve 4, place 4 oz (100 g) of sugar and ½ liter of water in a pan. Let it dissolve and bring to the boil. Add the juice of 4 lemons and the grated rind of 2, simmer for a few minutes. Strain and let cool. Beat in the whisked white of an egg and 1 oz (25 g) caster sugar, freezing to the necessary consistency. Serve in individual glasses.
LENTIL 115	Soups Stews Salads (sprouts)	Seeds Sprouts	*Sautéed Lentils* In a skillet or frying pan, fry strips of bacon until nicely browned, then remove and keep hot and in the fat, add a thinly slice onion and brown over a brisk flame. Add a large sliced tomato, half a cupful of chopped parsley and 2 large cups of sprouted lentils. Mix well and season and cook for 10 minutes over a low flame. Serve hot with the bacon slices and sauté potatoes.
LIME TREE 230	Salads Teas	Flowers	*Lime Flower Tea* Place a cupful of freshly gathered flowers into a jug, add a teaspoonful of honey and the sliced rind of a lime fruit. Pour over ½ liter of boiling water and let stand for 2 hours, or strain and use after a few minutes if required hot or take a wineglassful chilled with a meal.
LING 232	Confectionery Vegetable	Seeds	*Ling and Orange Sauce* The seeds are preserved in honey to use in confectionery and are boiled to serve as a vegetable with a suitable sauce. The seeds swell when boiled and a handful placed in a saucepan with a large cupful of water and boiled for 30 minutes will provide sufficient for 4. Serve with orange sauce with chicken or meats. For the sauce, boil ½ liter milk, add 1 oz (25 g) sugar and the juice and grated peel of an orange. Simmer for 5 minutes and let cool. Beat the yolks of 2 eggs in a little milk and pour into the pan, stirring until it thickens.
LIQUORICE 96	Sweetmeats Drinks	Roots	*Liquorice Fizz* It is used as a sweetener for cakes and puddings and to make a nourishing drink. The roots are lifted in autumn, washed and either crushed or cut into pieces about 1 in. (2.5 cm) long. They are boiled for 2 hours using ½ liter of water for every 2 lb (1 kilo) of root. Cover the pan with a lid and when the extract is a thick brown syrup, strain and let cool. Put into bottles and use a tablespoonful in a tall glass with ice. Pour into it milk to fill half the glass and top up with soda water.
LITCHEE 119	Tarts and flans Cakes Puddings Dessert	Fruit	*Litchee Sponge Pudding* Peel off the thin brittle shell to reveal the translucent white flesh with the flavor of muscat grapes. Place 1 lb (½ kilo) into a saucepan with a small cupful of water and simmer 30 minutes. Cut open the fruits to remove the stone then cover a sponge pudding or sponge cake with the fruits and serve hot or cold. To make the pudding, put 5 eggs in a bowl and 4 oz (100 g) sugar. Add the grated peel of a lemon and whisk until stiff. Stir in (slowly) 2 oz (50 g) flour then pour the mixture into a circular tin and bake for 1 hour in a hot oven. Have the litchees ready cooked and top with whipped cream.
LOTUS LILY 142	Vegetable Bread and cakes	Rhizomes Seeds	*Lotus Seed Bread* The rhizomes are baked as a vegetable; the seeds are roasted and ground to use in bread, cakes and puddings. The seeds are ground to make a crisp sweet bread. Put 4 lbs (2 kilo) wheat and lotus seed flour (in the proportion of 3 to 1) in a bowl and make a well in the center. Separately wet 1 lb (½ kilo) cornflour, then pour onto it ½ liter boiling water and stir. When it cools, add 1 oz (25 g) yeast and let stand 2 hours. Dissolve ½ oz (13 g) salt and add to the cornflour, then to the flour. Knead it to a dough. Leave an hour, then cut into pieces for the tins and bake in a moderate oven for 50 minutes until brown.

Plant Lexicon Number	Uses	Part Used	Recipes
LOVAGE 118	Vegetable Salads Soups Sauces	Leaves	*Lovage Sauce* Melt 2 oz (50 g) of butter in a saucepan and mix in 1 oz (25 g) of flour. In another pan, place a handful of lovage leaves in a little water and boil for 15 minutes. Put through a sieve and add the purée to the flour and butter, at the same time stirring in a cupful of milk. Season and simmer for 15 minutes. Serve with boiled carrots or parsnips.
MAIDENHAIR TREE 94	Bread and cakes Vegetable	Seeds	*Peperoni ripieni* Melt a knife point of butter and chop 2 onions. Fry until almost brown. Add 1 lb (½ kilo) lean and minced pork and fry for 10 minutes. Stir in cupful of mushroom sauce, add a tablespoon of ginko seeds, 4 chopped tomatoes, season and simmer. Then slice the stem end off 4 sweet peppers or eggplants, remove the seeds and stuff with the mixture. Place in a casserole dish and bake for 40 minutes in 350°F (180°C). Serve hot for 4.
MANGO 124	Pies and flans Preserves Dessert Chutney	Fruit	*Mango Chutney* Place 1 kilo of green mangoes, peeled and sliced, in a preserving pan and cover with salt. Leave for 24 hours, then cover with ½ liter of malt vinegar. Bring to the boil and simmer for 15 minutes, then add ½ kilo of stoned tamarinds and the same of raisins, half a cupful of ginger, a small teaspoonful of powdered cinnamon and half a small cupful of salt. Simmer for a further 15 minutes then stir in a syrup made by boiling ½ liter of vinegar with a kilo of sugar. Stir and boil until of a firm consistency, then scoop into screw-top jars.
MANGOSTEEN 90	Pies Tarts Puddings Dessert	Fruit	*St. Domingo Pie* Cut 1 lb (½ kilo) of fruits into halves, remove the stones, sprinkle with sugar and simmer 20 minutes in a cupful of water. Place 8 oz (200 g) flour in a bowl and rub in 2 oz (50 g) each of lard and margarine. Mix with a little water to bring it to a smooth consistency. Roll out and line a pie dish to a depth of 1½ in. (4 cm). Mix the mangosteen syrup with a teaspoonful of cornflour, then add the fruit and pour into the pie dish. Roll out the rest of the pastry for a lid, brush with milk and bake 1 hour in 400°F (200°C).
MARIGOLD 40	Soups and stews Salads	Flowers	*Marigold Stew* To serve 4, take 2 lbs (1 kilo) neck of mutton, cut up and remove excess fat. Wash, peel and slice 4 lbs (2 kilo) potatoes and a large onion. Place a layer of potatoes and some sliced onion in saucepan and cover with a layer of meat and a generous sprinkling of marigold petals, repeating until the materials are used up but finishing with a top layer of potatoes. Season and add ½ liter of meat stock. Put a lid on the pan and cook gently for between 1–2 hours and serve with stewed mushrooms.
MARJORAM 148	Flavoring soups; stews; salads	Leaves	*Greek Salad* Stone and cut up 12 black olives and quarter 6 medium size tomatoes. Place in a salad bowl, season and sprinkle over them a teaspoonful of finely chopped oregano (marjoram). Mix well but carefully, add a peeled and sliced cucumber, lettuce leaves, chives and at intervals, place a spoonful of cottage (cream) cheese about the salad. The black, red, white and green colors give it an attractive appearance.
MARSH MALLOW 8	Vegetable Sweetmeat	Roots Shoots	*Marsh Mallow Sweets* (Pâte de Guimauve) The roots are washed and boiled in a little water. Into the juice, 4 oz (100 g) of gum arabic is soaked until soft. Heat gently until dissolved and strain. Return the warm liquid to the pan, add 8 oz (200 g) icing sugar, stir in the whites of 3 eggs and whisk until stiff. Add a few drops of vanilla and allow the mix 12 hours to set. Cut into small squares and dust with icing sugar.
MAY APPLE 171	Jellies Preserves Tarts and flans	Fruit	*May Apple Jelly* Gather the lemon-shaped ripe fruits when golden-yellow. Peel 4 lbs (2 kilos) of fruit, put in a preserving pan and just cover with water. Boil for an hour, strain and replace the juice in the pan. To each cupful of juice add 6 oz (150 g) of sugar. Add the juice of a lemon and boil for another hour or until a little of the jelly sets when placed on a saucer. Turn into screw-top jars or pots and use with cold meats or in cakes.
MEDLAR 131	Preserves Chutneys	Fruit	*Medlar Jelly* Wash and cut up 4 lbs (2 kilos) of medlars ripened by the frost or after storing for several weeks. Put in a preserving pan, just cover with water and simmer until the fruit becomes pulp. Strain through muslin or a jelly bag. Return the juice to the pan and to every liter (2 pints) allow 12 oz (300 g) sugar. Add the juice of a lemon and boil for 30 minutes until the jelly sets when a little is put on a saucer. Stir continuously and remove any scum. As it cools, fill the jars before the jelly sets.
MELON TREE 46	Pies and tarts Preserves Chutney	Fruit	*Melon Pie* The fruits are as large as watermelons and when ripe have a hard orange skin. The flesh is also orange. Cut into halves, scoop out the seeds and remove the flesh. Slice it into a pie dish in layers. Over each layer, sprinkle sugar and a pinch of nutmeg or allspice. Cover with pastry and bake for 30 minutes in a hot oven. Serve hot with whipped cream.
MILK CAP 111	Vegetable Stews Flavoring	All parts (mostly the caps)	*Milk Mushroom à la Bordelaise* Remove the stalks from 1 lb (½ kilo) of milk caps and place in a frying pan containing a little cooking oil. Add a cupful of well chopped onion and fry for 10–12 minutes, turning over the contents occasionally. When cooked, serve on hot buttered toast and sprinkle with parsley. Milk caps have a peppery taste so use no seasoning.
MILKWEED 27	Salads Vegetable	Leaves Pods	*Buttered Seed Pods* All parts are edible, the young leaves in salads and the seed pods, when young, are cooked like the asparagus pea. Remove before they form silk threads inside. Simmer for 20 minutes and serve with melted butter to accompany game or fish.

Plant Lexicon Number	Uses	Part Used	Recipes
MILLET 216	Vegetable Bread and cakes	Seeds (corn)	*Indian Cornflour Cake* Also known as Indian corn, it is baked into bread and cakes. To make Sand Cake, mix ½ lb (200 g) Indian cornflour with 1 oz (25 g) rice flour. Beat 6 oz (150 g) butter and 6 oz (150 g) sugar until creamy. Beat in 2 eggs separately, then add the flour mix. Put into a baking tin and bake in a moderate oven for 1 hour. If required, slice into halves and line with apricot jam and whipped cream.
MOREL 133	Vegetable	All parts	*Stuffed Morels* Steep for several hours in salt water before cooking and do not use them raw. Drain off the water, remove the end of the stems and cook in milk for an hour until tender. They can then be filled with a suitable stuffing of minced fried chicken or other meats for the caps and stems of morels are hollow. Re-heat for a few minutes and serve on buttered toast with brown sauce.
NARANJILLA 213	Tarts and flans Puddings Dessert Drinks	Fruit	*Naranjilla Pudding* To make a steamed pudding with naranjillas, split open the fruits and remove the stones, then cut into pieces. In a bowl, mix 10 oz (250 g) flour with 8 oz (200 g) suet and with a little water, work into a stiff paste. With it line a basin to the thickness of 1 in. (2.5 cm) and fill with fruit. Cover with paste. Place in a saucepan with a lid and steam for 2–3 hours when the paste will be firm and crusty. Serve with a suitable sauce.
NASTURTIUM 235	Salads Pickles	Leaves Flowers Seeds	*Pickled Seeds* To a liter of malt vinegar, add ½ oz (13 g) salt and peppercorns and boil for 20 minutes. When cool, strain into screw-top jars three-parts filled with green (fresh) nasturtium seeds. When cold, screw on the tops and stand in a cool place. Use the seeds as a substitute for capers after standing for 2–3 months, to accompany fish dishes.
NUTMEG, MACE 138	Flavoring custard, pies, fruits	Fruit	*Baked Custard* Simmer ½ liter of milk with a bay leaf or two and the rind of a lemon for 15 minutes. Add ½ oz (13 g) of butter and the same of sugar. Mix a teaspoonful of flour with a little milk, pour into the pan, stir and bring to the boil. Beat 2 eggs, remove the pan from the flame for the contents to cool and add the eggs. Then pour the ingredients into a pie dish, add a pinch of nutmeg and bake in a slow oven for 40 minutes until set. Serve hot or cold with fresh or stewed fruit.
NUTMEG PLANT (Nigella) 141	To flavor cakes and bread	Seeds	*Nutmeg Buns* The nutmeg flavored nigella seeds are used for flavoring bread and cakes where nutmeg is unavailable. To make 12 buns, beat 4 oz (100 g) of butter to a cream and add 4 oz (100 g) sugar when doing so. Mix in 2 oz (50 g) flour and an egg, then a further 2 oz (50 g) flour and another egg. Add ½ teaspoonful of the seeds and stir in a tablespoon of milk to bring to a smooth consistency. Place the mix in bun trays and bake in 380°F (190°C) for 15 minutes. Add raisins or chopped cherries to the mix if required. When cool, dust the buns with icing sugar.
OAT 31	Bread Puddings Biscuits	Seeds	*Oatmeal Pudding* Mix 8 oz (200 g) of oatmeal and the same of flour, a teaspoon of ground ginger and one of baking powder, 4 oz (100 g) of sugar, 8 oz (200 G) of finely chopped suet and a cupful of golden syrup. Beat up an egg and stir it into the mixture, together with a little milk to bring it to a nice smooth consistency. Turn it into a pie dish and bake for 1½ hours in a hot oven. Serve with warm golden syrup.
OKRA 101	Salads Stews	Fruits	*Stewed Okra* Handle the fruits carefully for if carelessly cut or damaged the thick syrup-like juice will be lost in their cooking and this will greatly reduce the flavor. Carefully tail the pods, leaving the top uncut, then stew slowly in a roux until tender. Serve on slices of buttered toast, pouring the juice over. Another method is to drop the pods into boiling salted water and after 7–8 minutes, to remove them and serve with Hollandaise sauce. This is made by beating an egg yolk into 4 oz (100 g) of butter and adding the juice of half a lemon.
OLIVE 145	Salads Pickles Oil for cooking	Fruit	*Olive and Parsley Salad* Stone and cut up about 20 green olives and chop finely a large handful of fresh parsley and a cupful of chives. Place in a salad bowl and mix in 2 cupfuls of sprouting soya bean or alfalfa seeds. Season and sprinkle over the juice of a lemon and 4 tablespoons of olive oil. Mix well before serving.
OREGON GRAPE 122	Tarts and flans Pies Preserves	Fruit	*Oregon Grape Preserve* Gather the fruit when ripe but not too soft. To each lb (½ kilo) allow half the quantity of sugar. Place the fruit and sugar in a preserving pan in layers and it will set better if 4 oz (100 g) of apple is added to each lb (½ kilo) of fruit. Bring slowly to the boil and simmer for about an hour until it sets when a little is put on a saucer. As it cools, pour into screw-top jars and use with meat or game.
ORPINE 207	Vegetable Salads Pickles	Leaves	*Pickled Orpine* The young pickled leaves are piquant served with cold meats. Wash and chop (like pickled cabbage) and place in a large jar and to each 2 in. (5 cm) layer give a sprinkling of salt. Continue until the jar is filled to within 1 in. (2.5 cm) of the top. In a saucepan boil ½ liter of malt vinegar with several hot peppers and a tablespoon of allspice berries for 5 minutes and when cold strain and pour over the orpine.

Plant Lexicon Number	Uses	Part Used	Recipes
PAPAW 15	Pies Preserves Chutneys	Fruit	*Baked Pawpaw Pie* Obtain the pulp of several ripe pawpaws removed when the fruit has turned deep yellow and simmer for a few minutes before placing in a pie dish. To each cupful of pulp, add 2 oz (50 g) of sugar and a cupful of milk. Stir in the yolks of 2 eggs, then the whites previously whisked. Add a pinch of nutmeg. Cover the pie dish with pastry and bake in a hot oven for 30 minutes. Serve hot with whipped cream.
PARAGUAY TEA 106	Drinks	Leaves	*Yerba Mate* It is the New World's counterpart of Indian tea of the Old World and is used in the same way. The leaves are harvested all year and dried in the sun. They are then ground and from them a tea made by pouring boiling water onto the leaves and sweetening with honey or burnt sugar. If the powdered leaves are let drop into hot water and stirred, the brew is known as cha maté.
PARSLEY 159	Sauces Salads Stews Soups	Leaves	*Parsley Sauce* Parsley has many uses for garnishing but as a sauce to serve with fish, it has few equals. It also brings out the flavor of broad beans. Melt 1 oz (25 g) of butter and stir in 1 oz (25 g) flour. Cook for 2 minutes. Add a cupful of stock and one of milk, season, bring to the boil and simmer for a few minutes. Then add a cupful of finely chopped parsley, mix in well and simmer for several minutes. The sauce should be of a smooth consistency when ready to serve.
PASSION FRUIT 155	Confectionery Preserves Drinks	Fruit	*Passion Fruit Cake* To the juice of 6 ripe passion fruits (or granadillas) whisk in the white of an egg beaten to a froth, then as much icing sugar as it will absorb. Divide into two parts, spreading a thick layer on the lower half of a cake sliced into halves. Put over it the other half and top with the rest of the mix. Cover with whipped cream and serve as a pudding.
PEA 170	Vegetable Soups Rissoles	Seeds	*Green Pea Rissoles* Boil 1 lb (½ kilo) of fresh peas with a small sliced onion and a large handful of wild lettuce or spinach leaves. When the peas are nicely cooked, rub the whole through a sieve and mix into the purée a cupful of breadcrumbs, a tablespoon of nut meat and one of finely chopped chives. Add a pinch of winter savory and 2 small pats of soft butter and work the ingredients well together. Make into balls, dip into egg yolk and breadcrumbs and fry to golden brown. Serve with sauté potatoes to accompany game or meats.
PEACH 181	Tarts and flans Preserves Chutney Dessert	Fruit	*Peach Cheese Cake* To make a peach filling for a flan case, beat the yolks of 2 eggs with 1 oz (25 g) of sugar and a small cupful of milk until thick and creamy and put in a double saucepan containing boiling water. Add 1 oz (25 g) gelatine previously dissolved in 2 tablespoons of peach syrup. Remove from the cooker, mix in 6 oz (150 g) cream cheese and the grated rind and juice of a lemon. Add a teaspoonful of vanilla essence and when cool, fold in the egg whites whipped with 1 oz (25 g) sugar and a custard mixture. Place in the refrigerator to chill and set, then top with sliced peaches and whipped cream.
PEAR 185	Tarts and flans Preserves Chutney	Fruit	*Spiced Pears* Peel the pears, leave whole and place in a large fire proof dish which will take 8–10 fruits. Into a saucepan, put 2 large cupfuls of cider; 4 oz (100 g) of sugar; a teaspoonful of cinnamon and bring to the boil. Add a little vanilla essence and pour the contents over the fruit. Then place the dish in an oven heated to 250°F (120°C) for 3 hours. Drain off the liquid into a saucepan. In a cup, mix a tablespoonful of arrowroot to a paste then add it to the liquid. Bring to the boil and pour the syrup over the pears. Place in the refrigerator and before serving, sprinkle with chopped nuts and decorate with whipped cream.
PECAN 48	Puddings Confectionery Dessert	Nut	*Nusspudding* Moisten 8 oz (200 g) of breadcrumbs and wring out in a cloth. Beat 4 oz (100 g) of butter to a cream, add 4 oz (100 g) caster sugar and the yolks of 4 eggs, one at a time, and with each mix in tablespoonful of breadcrumbs so that the mixture is firm yet smooth. Then work in 8 oz (200 g) of finely milled pecan (or hazel) nuts and the stiff egg whites. Turn into a pie dish, cover with well greased paper and then tin-foil and place in a large pan containing water. Steam with a lid on for about 3 hours and add more boiling water if it evaporates. Serve with hot chocolate sauce.
PERSIMMON 78	Cakes Puddings Preserves	Fruit	*Persimmon Cake* The fruit will not be ready to use until frosted. First cook for 10 minutes, then put through a sieve to remove seeds and skin and let cool. Make a Genoa cake by placing 4 oz (100 g) of butter and 4 oz (100 g) caster sugar into a basin and beating to a cream. Then beat in 2 eggs separately and a little milk. Mix in 6 oz (150 g) flour, and pour into a greased baking tin. Bake in a rapid oven for about 15 minutes. When cool, slice the cake into halves and line with the persimmon purée, adding more to the top and a topping of whipped cream.
PINEAPPLE 12	Trifles Mousse Cakes Preserves	Fruit	*Pineapple Mousse* Remove the outer husk from a ripe pineapple, slice and core and put through a blender to make into purée. Place 1 oz (25 g) of gelatine in a pan with a small cupful of the purée and put the rest in a saucepan. Stir in 2 tablespoons of honey, dissolving it over a low flame. Beat in the yolks of 2 eggs (separately) until the mixture thickens. Melt the gelatine and purée and stir it in. Remove the pan from the heat and fold in a small cupful of yogurt and the whipped egg whites. Place in the refrigerator for 2 hours before serving.

Plant Lexicon Number	Uses	Part Used	Recipes
PINE-NUT 166	Dessert Nut meat Confectionery	Nuts	**Pine-nut Galantine** Grind 4 oz (100 g) each of pine nuts and cashew nuts and place in a large basin. Add 8 oz (200 g) of breadcrumbs, a small finely chopped garlic clove, a dash of Bechamel sauce (see Bay Laurel), an egg and seasoning and mix into a paste. Shape into a roll, tie in a cloth and steam for about 2 hours. Place in a bread tin overnight for it to cool so that it will retain its shape or that of the tin. Then remove the cloth and cut into slices to serve with salad.
PISTACHIO 169	Confectionery Cremes	Nuts	**Pistachio Cream** Place sponge finger biscuits in the grooves around a jelly mold. Mix a tablespoon of corn-flour with a little milk and boil a cupful with a tablespoon of sugar and the rind of a lemon. Strain, add the blended cornflour, boil for 2 minutes and allow to cool. Whip a cupful of cream and stir in; add a small glass of pale sherry and pour into the mold so that only the tops of the sponge fingers are left uncovered. Cover the top when cold and it has set with grated pistachio nuts, and keep in the refrigerator until ready to serve.
POKEWEED 163	Vegetable Salads	Young shoots	**Pokeweed Mayonnaise** The root is poisonous but the young shoots are tasty in a salad or as a vegetable. They should be boiled in two waters to remove any acidity. Boil for 10 minutes in a little water and drain off, then add a little fresh water and steam for 20 minutes, until tender. Serve hot with melted butter like asparagus, to accompany meat or game; or cold in a salad with mayonnaise sauce.
POLE BEAN 160	Vegetable Salads	Beans (pods)	**Savory Beans** Pick the beans when young (before the seeds show in the pod), top and tail, removing the "string" that runs down one side, slice thinly and steam in a pie dish containing a little butter until tender. Sprinkle with lemon juice and grated nutmeg and serve hot with meat or cold in a salad.
POMEGRANATE 184	Syrups Drinks Dessert	Fruits	**Grenadine Syrup** The name is from Grenada in Spain where the fruits were introduced by the Moors. The syrup is poured over stewed fruits, puddings and ices. The seeds are covered in a sweet pink pulp and are removed from inside the hard skin taking care not to include the bitter pith. Place the pulp in a saucepan with a little water and boil for 7–8 minutes. Strain the juice through muslin, put back in the pan with 2 tablespoons of sugar for each cupful of juice and simmer for 10 minutes more. Use the warm syrup to pour over steamed sultana puddings.
POTATO 214	Vegetable Soups	Tuber	**Stuffed Potatoes** Take several large potatoes, peel and slice off the tops. Hollow out the insides and fill with chopped mushrooms that have been fried until tender in a little butter. Cover with a small strip of bacon, place in a warm oven and cook until browned, then serve hot with mushroom juice poured over.
PRICKLY PEAR 146	Jellies Preserves Drinks	Fruit	**Prickly Pear Jelly** Remove the spines from 4½ lbs (2 kilos) of prickly pears, cut them into halves and place in a preserving pan. Add a liter of water, the juice of 2 lemons and 3½ lbs (1½ kilos) of sugar. Bring to the boil and simmer for 2 hours, removing any scum. When a little placed on a saucer sets, it is done. Allow to cool a little before pouring into screw-top jars. Use as a conserve.
PURSLANE 175	Vegetable Soups Salads	Leaves	**Purslane and Pea Soup** Soak 1 lb (½ kilo) of dried peas for 12 hours, drain and put into a saucepan. Add 2 large cups of chicken stock, a handful of chopped purslane leaves, a finely chopped onion and 2 large well chopped carrots. Simmer for 3 hours. Put through a sieve, return to the saucepan, season and mix in 1 oz (25 g) of flour to thicken. Serve with small pieces of bread fried in bacon fat on top.
QUINCE 72	Tarts and flans Preserves Chutney	Fruit	**Quince Conserve** Gather 2 lbs (1 kilo) of ripe fruits, chop up and place in a preserving pan. Add a liter of water and simmer until the fruits are soft. Put through a sieve and to every cupful of pulp add 4 oz (100 g) of sugar. Add the juice and grated rind of a lemon and an orange then boil for an hour until the contents have almost set. When cooler, pour into screw-top jars.
RADISH 187	Salads	Roots	**Radish and Fish Salad** To make a fish salad, cook 2 herrings or 2 cod cutlets and when cold, divide into flakes, removing bones and skin. Chop up 8 oz (200 g) of cooked potatoes and the same of apples; a dozen radishes including leaves, roots and seed pods, a small onion or a few chives and a tablespoon of parsley and mix with the fish. Serve with salad oil and tarragon vinegar or mayonnaise sauce.
RAMPION 41	Vegetable Salads	Roots	**Rampion Roots in Cheese Sauce** Wash and scrape the roots of several plants and steam for about 30 minutes in a little salted water until tender. Drain and serve hot with cheese sauce made by melting ½ oz (13 g) of butter in a saucepan, adding the same of flour and seasoning. Simmer for a few minutes then stir in a cupful of milk, simmer for 10 minutes more and add a tablespoonful of grated cheese. Pour over the boiled roots while hot and serve with meat.
RED ELM 238	Beverage Soups	Bark	**Slippery Elm Gruel** The inner bark or bast is dried and ground to a powder or the bark is cut up and boiled. The grains swell in water or in hot milk, to which a pinch of cinnamon or a few drops of vanilla essence is added and a spoonful of honey to sweeten. A teaspoonful of slippery elm, as it is called, makes a nourishing and mucilaginous drink, being especially useful in the diet of invalids. Mix the red elm with a little water, then add the milk and flavoring. An egg can be eaten with it if desired.

Plant Lexicon Number	Uses	Part Used	Recipes
RED POPPY 154	Bread and cakes	Seeds	*Oatmeal and Poppy Bread* Put 8 oz (200 g) of oatmeal into a basin, pour onto it a cupful of milk and let soak for 30 minutes. In another basin dissolve a teaspoonful of sugar with 2 of dried yeast in a cupful of warm water. Put 12 oz (300 g) flour into a bowl with a teaspoonful of salt and one of red poppy seed. Mix well and make a hole at the center. Add here the oatmeal and yeast which will be frothy and 2 tablespoons of cooking oil and mix to a stiff but smooth dough, kneading it for 10 minutes. Leave it to rise, then place half in each of 2 greased bread tins and scatter more poppy seed over the top. Allow to rise, then bake in a hot oven for 30 minutes and for 30 minutes more in a lower temperature. Use like bread when cold.
REED MACE 237	Vegetable Salads	Young shoots	*Reed Mace and Crab Salad* The young shoots are removed when 6 in. (15 cm) high. Take off the outer leaf sheath when the inside is pale green and succulent. It is boiled and served with melted butter or chopped raw into a crab salad. Include watercress or field cress and mix in crab or lobster meat after removing from the claws and shell. Serve with tarragon vinegar and brown bread and butter for hors d'œuvre.
RHUBARB 188	Pies Tarts Jellies Jams	Leaf stems	*Rhubarb Jelly* Place a cupful of water in a saucepan and bring to the boil. Cut up 1 lb (½ kilo) of rhubarb stems into 1 in. (2.5 cm) pieces, discarding the leaves, and add the rhubarb to the water. Cover with sugar and simmer for 10 minutes until cooked though the pieces should retain their shape. Strain off the liquid and let cool. Into a bowl place ½ oz (13 g) of gelatine and dissolve in a little hot water. Squeeze the juice from 6 oranges into the gelatine, stir and add the rhubarb. Then pour the contents into a jelly mold and allow 2 hours in a refrigerator to set. To turn out the jelly, dip the mold into warm water for a few seconds and turn upside down onto a dish.
RICE 150	Vegetable Curries Sweets	Seeds	*Siam Rice* A favorite dish of S.E. Asia to be made in a skillet and to serve 4 people. Put in 2 tablespoons of peanut oil and make hot. Add 2 cups of chopped onion and 2 cups of boiled rice. Stir in 2 eggs beaten up with 2 tablespoons of soy sauce. When assimilated, stop stirring or the rice will become sticky. Add a cupful of cooked chicken finely chopped and one of alfalfa or mung bean sprouts. Season and cook until heated through. Serve hot.
ROCKET 82	Salads Vegetable	Leaves	*Rocket and Potato Salad* Dig and wash 1 lb (½ kilo) of new potatoes, lightly scrape them and boil in a little water over a low flame for 30 minutes. Drain and when cool, slice into a salad bowl lined with lamb's lettuce and watercress. Mix in sliced tomato, finely chopped chives, parsley and only a few rocket leaves for they have a sharp bitter taste. Add 2 tablespoons of salad oil and vinegar dressing and seasoning. If required add sardines or tuna fish.
ROSEMARY 193	To flavor meat; pickles; wine; salads	Flowers Leaves	*Rosemary Wine* Cut up the young shoots when in bloom and place in a large pot or jar. Pour over white wine and leave in the sun for 2–3 days, stirring often. Strain into bottles and drink ice cold with a meal. To make a "tea" to take hot at night, infuse the tops in hot water in a covered saucepan for an hour and sweeten with a little honey.
ROWAN 215	Tarts and flans Preserves Mincemeat Drinks	Fruit	*Rowanberry Mincemeat* Gather 2 lbs (1 kilo) ripe berries and the same of either blackberries or elderberries. Put in a preserving pan with the juice of 2 lemons and a large cupful of water. Simmer until the fruit is soft. Put through a sieve to make a purée. Peel, core and well chop 1 lb (½ kilo) of crab or cooking apples and add to the purée. Have ready to mix in 4 oz (100 g) each of raisins, sultanas and currants which have been soaked in water overnight. Mix in together with 4 oz (100 g) chopped nuts, ½ oz (13 g) ground ginger, 1 lb (½ kilo) sugar; and a half teaspoonful of ground cinnamon. Mix well and put in jars to use in mince pies and tarts.
RUE 196	To flavor soups; stews; omelettes	Leaves	*Green Rue Omelette* Almost fill a saucepan with spinach or any plant that boils down to a purée. Add a pinch of chopped fresh rue and when soft, drain the spinach and put through a sieve. Whip 6 eggs, pour into an earthenware pot, stir in the purée and 2 oz (50 g) of grated Parmesan cheese and 2 oz (50 g) minced lean bacon (uncooked). Cover with a lid and cook for about 50 minutes in 300°F (150°C). Serve hot or cold, garnished with sliced cucumber to serve 4.
SAFFRON 67	Flavoring cakes; pies; puddings	Stigma	*Saffron Cake* Dissolve ½ oz (13 g) yeast in a cup of warm water. Put in a basin and stir in enough flour to make a soft dough. Leave in a warm place for an hour. With 2 lbs (1 kg) of flour, make a circle in a mixing bowl. In the center put 12 oz (300 g) butter and 8 oz (200 g) sugar. Mix until smooth then add 4 eggs and dough and work it in with the flour, at the same time adding a cupful of warm water to which a teaspoonful of saffron was added. Mix in ¼ lb (100 g) of stoned raisins, then turn it into a cake tin (or 2 tins) and bake in a moderate oven for 2 hours.
SAGE 200	Flavoring soups; stews; stuffings	Leaves	*Sage Stuffing* For pork and sausage meat, to take away the richness, slice several large onions into a saucepan, just cover with water and simmer for 10 minutes then drain. Melt 2 oz (50 g) of butter and fry in it the onions but do not let them brown. Add a tablespoon of finely chopped sage previously dried in a warm oven; a cupful of breadcrumbs and seasoning. Mix well with the fried onion and it is ready to use.

Plant Lexicon Number	Uses	Part Used	Recipes
SALOP 147	Thickening for soups; stews; drinks	Tubers	*Milk Salop* The tubers of many wild orchids can be used to make a hot nourishing drink but they are now protected plants in many countries. Lift the tubers in late summer and immerse for 10 minutes in boiling water. Drain off and when cool, rub off the skins. Then place in a hot oven 30 minutes to dry. Store for several days, then grind to a powder. Put a teaspoonful in a cup and mix to a paste. Pour hot milk over, stir well and sweeten with a little honey. It is mucilaginous and sustaining.
SALSIFY 231	Vegetable Salads	Root	*Salsify Salad (Salade de Salsifis)* First scrape the roots and cut into 2 in. (5 cm) pieces. To prevent them turning dark colored, place in cold water containing lemon juice at once. To each 2 lbs (1 kg) of roots, give a tablespoon of salt; 1 oz (25 g) butter and boil about 30 minutes until tender. Serve hot with meat or when cold, place in a salad bowl with winter radishes, lamb's lettuce and a tablespoon of pickled capers or nasturtium seed. Sprinkle with tarragon vinegar.
SAMPHIRE 66	Pickles Vegetable Sauces Salads	Leaves	*Pickled Samphire* This aromatic herb is boiled in a little water and served as a vegetable, or is pickled to serve with cold meats. To do so, gather the succulent leaves when young and steep 24 hours in salted water. Drain and then chop into a large jar, pouring over each 2 in. (5 cm) layer hot spiced vinegar. Allow to stand several days before using.
SASSAFRAS 202	Soups Stews Drinks	Bark Leaves Roots	*Sassafras Gumbo* A "tea" is made from the bark and roots and the dried leaves are included in gumbos (thick soups) which contain the mucilaginous okra. Cut up 8 oz (200 g) of okras and 6 tomatoes, 4 oz (100 g) pole beans and cook for about 50 minutes in meat or vegetable stock in a low oven. Then put through a sieve, re-heat, add seasoning and a teaspoonful of dried sassafras leaves that have been pounded in a mortar. Do not bring to the boil but serve hot with croutons of fried bread.
SAVORY 203	Flavoring soups Stuffings Sauces	Leaves	*Savory Sauce* Wash and scrape a piece of horseradish, chop up a small onion and put in a stewing pan. Add 6 cloves, the juice and peel of a lemon, a handful of savory or of mixed herbs, including savory, marjoram and basil; a cupful of malt vinegar and 2 cups of water. Simmer for 30 minutes and when cool strain into screw-top bottles and use a teaspoonful to flavor soups and stews.
SCOLYMUS 204	Vegetable Stews Soups	Root	*Scolymus Soup* The flavor of the roots is brought out to the full in soups though they can also be used as a vegetable. First boil or steam the roots until tender. Then make a roux which is the base for all sauces and soups by mixing together 1 oz (25 g) each or less of butter and flour over a low flame and make into a smooth paste. Then rub the still warm cooked roots through a sieve but not the hard center core. Add to the roux and stir in a half cupful of cream and ½ liter of water. Season and bring to the boil, stirring all the time. Serve hot.
SCORZONERA 205	Vegetable Omelettes	Roots Flower buds	*Scorzonera Flower Omelette* Steam and peel the roots and serve with white sauce or melted butter to accompany meats but the flowers are also delicious used in an omelette. Gather a cupful when in bud and cook in a little olive oil until brown. For an omelette, mix the buds into 2 well beaten eggs, add a pinch of salt and a tablespoonful of cream. Heat 1 oz of butter in a frying pan, pour in the mixture and stir until set. Then fold over the omelette, scatter grated cheese on top and serve at once.
SCURVY GRASS 57	Salads Drinks	Leaves	*Sardine and Scurvy Grass Salad* A decoction of the leaves with orange or lemon juice is a valuable spring purifier; or include it fresh in salads with sardines or shrimps. Fill a salad bowl with the leaves, add a tablespoonful of pickled capers, a few stoned and chopped olives; a chopped beetroot, kept in store and which has been cooked; a sprinkling of chopped chives and mix in 4 oz (100 g) sardines or shrimps. Sprinkle with lemon juice before serving.
SEA BUCKTHORN 102	To flavor meats; drinks	Berries	*Steak Diane* The orange berries have a piquant taste and are served with barbeque steaks. For Steak Diane, fry ½ lb (200 g) pieces of filleted steak on both sides in a little butter. When cooked, pour over the rest of the butter from the pan and 1 oz (25 g) of sea buckthorn berries, either fresh or dried. Serve with sauté potatoes sprinkled with parsley.
SEA HOLLY 83	Sweetmeat Vegetable	Roots	*Kissing Comfits (Eringoes)* It was Shakespeare's name for the candied roots which can also be boiled and steamed and served as a vegetable with a sauce. To candy the roots to eat as a sweetmeat, clean and boil them until tender though still firm. Pour off most of the water, cut the roots into small pieces and cover them with 1 lb (½ kilo) of sugar dissolved in a cupful of water. Simmer for 10 minutes and leave overnight for the roots to absorb the sugar and for it to harden. Place the pieces in jars to eat as required.
SEAKALE 64	Vegetable	Blanched shoots	*Seakale and Cream Sauce* Blanched seakale is the most tender and has the best flavor. It is grated raw into a salad or used hot as a vegetable. To retain its unique flavor, place several "heads" in a casserole dish, cover with a cupful of chicken stock and stew in a medium oven for 40 minutes. It will toughen if cooked too long. Serve with sauce made by mixing the yolk of an egg with a tablespoon of cream. Stir into the liquid drained from the seakale and stand in a pan of hot water until it thickens but do not let it boil or it will curdle. Serve the seakale on buttered toast or with meats and pour the sauce over it.

Plant Lexicon Number	Uses	Part Used	Recipes
SEA SPINACH 199	Salads Vegetable Sauces	Leaves	*Saltwort and Gooseberry Sauce* The saltworts can be pickled, served raw in salads or as a vegetable. Gather the thin round succulent leaves when young, wash and fill a saucepan. Add a cupful of water and boil or steam for an hour. Drain and serve with gooseberry sauce to accompany meat or fish. Top and tail 1 lb (½ kilo) part ripe gooseberries, put in a saucepan with a cup of water, a table-spoon of sugar and 2 oz (50 g) butter. Simmer 30 minutes, put through a sieve and serve with the saltwort.
SESAME 208	Salads Cakes Pickles	Seeds	*Sesame Salad* A delicious winter salad is made from sprouting soya or mung bean seeds, mustard and cress, grated carrot and a small finely chopped garlic clove. Place in a salad bowl, mix well and over the contents pour 4 tablespoons of sesame oil and the juice of a lemon. Place a handful of sesame seeds into a frying pan and heat a minute or two until brown. When cold, scatter the seeds over the salad and serve with cold chicken.
SKIRRET 210	Vegetable	Roots	*Skirret Pie* Boil 2 lbs (1 kilo) of washed skirret roots, scrape them and cut into 2 in. (5 cm) pieces. Beat to a cream 8 oz (200 g) butter or margarine and the yolks of 2 eggs and pour over the skir-ret. Add several boiled and well chopped chestnuts, put in a pie dish and bake for 30 min-utes in a hot oven. Serve with Béchamel or cheese sauce.
SNAKEROOT 26	Biscuits Puddings	Root	*Snakeroot Biscuits* It is the New World's alternative to ginger but it is used at double the strength. The roots grow just beneath the soil. Wash and scrub them but do not peel. Then bake in a warm oven for several hours or use fresh, grating them to make ginger puddings or biscuits. Mix in a bowl 1 oz (25 g) of ground snakeroot with 4 oz (100 g) butter. Work in ½ lb (200 g) of flour and 4 oz (100 g) sugar and at the center, break in an egg. Work into a firm smooth consist-ency, using a little milk to do so, then roll out ½ in. (1.25 cm) thick and cut out the biscuits with a metal cutter, place on a well greased tray and bake in a cool oven for 5–10 minutes.
SOLOMON'S SEAL 172	Vegetable Salads	Young shoots	*King Solomon's Pudding* The young shoots are removed when 6 in. high. Cut 8 oz (200 g) of shoots into small pieces and put in a basin, together with 2 beaten eggs, 2 tablespoons of flour, 1 of minced or chopped bacon and 1 oz (25 g) butter. Mix well and add a little milk to bring to a thick con-sistency. Season, cover the basin with a cloth and place in a large saucepan half full of water and boil for 2 hours. Turn out and serve hot.
SORREL TREE 152	To flavor soups; stews; drinks; stuffings	Leaves	*Sharp Sauce (Sauce Piquante)* To serve with pork or duck, chop a small onion and place in a saucepan with a cupful of vinegar. Simmer 10 minutes. Strain the vinegar into another pan, add 3 chopped gherkins, a tablespoon of chopped capers or pickled nasturtium seeds and one of sorrel tree leaves. Pour over a cupful of meat stock and simmer for 5 minutes. Strain and add a cupful of white sauce to thicken, stirring briskly for a few minutes and serve hot.
SOYA BEAN 95	Vegetable Salads Cooking oil	Seeds Bean shoots	*Soya Alfredo* A nourishing dish to accompany cold meats is made from soya bean sprouts steamed for 20 minutes to cook through but are not ''soggy''. Drain and put in a pan which is placed in a larger pan filled with boiling water. Sprinkle over the sprouts half a cupful of grated cheese and a tablespoon of instant dry milk. Mix well into the sprouts, add a knife point of butter and another half cupful of cheese and keep the water in the larger pan boiling. After a few minutes, toss the contents of the inner pan and serve with sauté potatoes and soya sauce.
SPEARMINT 129	Flavoring pickles; sauces; confectionery	Leaves	*Mint and Gooseberry Jelly* To accompany cold meats or roast lamb or mutton, top and tail 4 lbs (2 kilos) of ripe goose-berries, place in a saucepan with a liter of water and simmer until cooked. Rub through a sieve and to each cupful of purée add 4 oz (100 g) of sugar. Put in a preserving pan and add 12–20 stems of mint tied up in a muslim bag. Boil till the jelly sets, remove the mint and when it begins to cool, pour the jelly into screw-top jars.
SPINACH 217	Vegetable Soufflés Salads	Leaves	*Spinach Roulade (Soufflé)* Place 2 large handfuls of wild spinach with a little butter or margarine in a saucepan and simmer for several minutes until cooked (add little or no water). Mix in the yolks of 4 eggs and a little grated cheese. Whip the egg whites and fold into the spinach, then spread onto a tin and bake in a hot oven for 10 minutes. Spread over the contents a layer of cooked and peeled tomatoes or field mushrooms, allow a few minutes more in the oven and serve hot.
SQUASH 69	Vegetable Stews Jellies Dessert	Fruit	*Squash Casserole* Cut up a large squash (marrow), place in a bowl and sprinkle with salt. Let stand for an hour, then grease a baking pan and place in it the squash, a small chopped onion, and a cupful of lentil or soya bean sprouts. Sprinkle over some grated cheese and some finely chopped chives. Then beat together 2 eggs and ½ cupful of sour cream and pour over. Bake for 30 minutes in 350°F (180°C) until lightly browned. Serve hot.
STAGHORN 190	Jellies Preserves Tarts and flans Drinks	Fruit	*Sumac Jelly* The small red berries, borne in upright clusters, can be made into a jelly or ''teas.'' Place 4 lbs (2 kilos) in a preserving pan, just cover with water and boil for 30 minutes. Strain through 2 layers of cloth to remove the tiny hairs. Return the juice to the pan and for every liter allow 12 oz (300 g) sugar. Add the juice of a lemon and boil for 30 minutes until the jelly sets, stirring continuously and removing any scum. Use the jelly in place of cranberry or red currant jelly with turkey or mutton.

Plant Lexicon Number	Uses	Part Used	Recipes
STAR-OF- BETHLEHEM 149	Vegetable Bread Pudding	Bulbs	*Arabian Tart* The bulbs are roasted and ground into flour or to serve as a vegetable or in puddings where they are used as a substitute for sweet chestnuts and have a similar taste. But first put in a warm oven and roast for 30 minutes, then boil for 20 minutes in a pan of water and drain away the liquid to remove any toxic properties. Put through a sieve and the purée into a basin. Simmer a cup of milk and the rind of a lemon for 20 minutes, then strain over 2 oz (50 g) breadcrumbs. Bring 1 oz (25 g) butter and 1 oz (25 g) sugar to a cream, beat in the yolks of 2 eggs and the lemon juice. Then add the purée and breadcrumbs. Put into a dish lined with pastry and place in a hot oven for 25 minutes. Whisk and put on the egg white and return to the oven until it sets.
STRAWBERRY 87	Tarts and flans Preserves Ice Cream Drinks	Fruit	*Strawberry Flan* To make a flan case of pastry, line a 1 in. (2.5 cm) deep cake tin with pastry ¼ in. (about ½ cm) thick and bake in a brisk heat. Allow to cool and remove from the tin. The raised border is held in place by fastening on the inside, a strip of grease-proof paper and filling with rice which is emptied after the flan is cooked. Fill the flan case with fresh ripe wild strawberries, cover with caster sugar and over the top put a thick layer of the whisked whites of 2 eggs. Place in a cool oven until the meringue hardens and serve hot or cold, topped with whipped cream.
SUGAR CANE 197	Sweetening puddings; sauces; preserves	Stem syrup	*Oranges in Syrup* Remove the skin and pith from the oranges (allow one orange per person) but leave them unquartered. Place in a saucepan, cover with water and simmer for 10 minutes. They should retain their shape. Remove them and add 8 oz (200 g) sugar to the liquid. Bring to the boil and simmer until the liquid becomes a syrup. Put in the oranges and simmer for 7–8 minutes then lift them out and place on a dish. Sprinkle over them grated peel and serve with the orange flavored syrup.
SUGAR MAPLE 1	Sweetening food Drinks	Syrup	*Waffles and Maple Syrup* To serve 4 people, beat 2 oz (50 g) of butter to a cream and to it add a cupful of sugar, a little grated nutmeg, a pinch of salt and ½ a teaspoonful of baking powder dissolved in a little milk. Beat in 2 eggs and add as much flour as to make a thick smooth batter. Put 2 tablespoons onto a waffle-iron and cook over a full flame for several minutes until brown. Serve hot with warm maple syrup and whipped cream.
SUNFLOWER 97	Cooking oil Cakes and bread Coffee substitute	Seeds	*Beef and Potato Pie* Oil from the seeds is the purest of vegetable oils and in the New World is used instead of olive oil as a salad oil or for frying. Fry 1 lb (½ kilo) finely chopped beef with a tablespoon of sunflower oil until the meat is nicely brown. Stir in a large cupful of meat stock, bring to the boil and simmer for 20 minutes. Add 2 oz (50 g) each cooked diced carrots and peas and transfer to a casserole dish. Place cooked mashed potato all round the dish, sprinkle with paprika and grated cheese and place in a hot (400°F – 200°C) oven for 5 minutes. The seeds are also ground and used as a coffee substitute or as flour.
SWEET CHESTNUT 49	Cakes Puddings Pickles Dessert	Nuts	*Chestnut Cake* Boil 1 lb (½ kilo) of sweet chestnuts until tender and while still warm, remove the hard shell. Rub the chestnuts through a sieve and mix in a cupful of sugar and half a teaspoonful of vanilla powder. Work in the yolks of 3 eggs and whip the whites until stiff. Fold into the mixture then pour into a greased cake tin and bake for about 45 minutes in 350°F (180°C). When cool, cut across into halves and spread with cream and sieved chestnut purée. Sprinkle caster sugar over the top.
SWEET CICELY 139	Vegetable Salads	Leaves Roots	*French Salad* The roots of sweet cicely can be boiled and used as a vegetable or the leaves, with their slightly sweet taste included in a salad. Cook ½ lb (¼ kilo) of French beans and 2 or 3 celery stems. When cool, shred the beans and celery, add the chopped leaves of wild lettuce and several of sweet cicely. Mix well and serve with mayonnaise sauce.
SWEET CORN 249	Vegetable Salads Bread	Seeds	*Corn Cob Salad* An American salad for late summer to be enjoyed with cold meats. Cook a corn-on-the-cob which should be plump and ripe, boiling it in a saucepan half filled with water for 8–10 minutes. Add no salt, which will cause the kernels to harden. Drain and remove the kernels from the cob. Shred 2 lb (1 kilo) red or green cabbage, put in a bowl and add an oil and vinegar dressing. Mix in a sliced cucumber, add the corn when cold, the grated rind of half a lemon and sprinkle with a tablespoon of honey and vinegar. Serve from the refrigerator.
SWEET POTATO 107	Vegetable Salads	Tubers	*Sweet Potato Salad* The waxy tubers have a slightly sweet taste and are served hot with meats or cold in a salad. Wash and boil 1 lb (½ kilo) of the roots until tender, then cut into slices and place in a basin. Fry a rasher of lean bacon, cut up and chop up a small onion. Mix with the sweet potatoes and mix in a tablespoon of finely chopped parsley. Season and stir in a tablespoon of mayonnaise mixed with one of vinegar. Serve with cold meats.
SWEET RUSH 3	Vegetable Sweetmeat	Roots	*Candied Roots* The roots were once used to clarify ale; now they are candied to enjoy as a sweetmeat. Dig up and wash the roots and cut into slices. Place in a saucepan, just cover with water and simmer about 30 minutes until tender. Drain off any moisture and cover the pieces with birch or maple syrup. Simmer for 10 minutes more and let cool. Leave several hours for them to dry and candy.

Plant Lexicon Number	Uses	Part Used	Recipes
TAMARIND 221	Stews Chutney	Fruit	*Mutton Swartzuir* Place a kilo of mutton cut small into a stew pot, add ½ liter of boiling water and a large sliced onion, 1 oz (25 g) of stoned tamarinds, 4 cloves, a teaspoonful of brown sugar and seasoning. Cook in a warm oven for 1 hour. Take off a cupful of liquid, place in a saucepan, add ½ cupful of flour and seasoning and stir until cooked. Work in 2 beaten eggs to make dumplings of the size of a small hen's egg which are added to the stew pot and cooked for a further 10–15 minutes. Serve hot as a nourishing winter meal.
TAMARISK 222	Sweetening	Gum	*Tamarisk and Apricot Tart* The honey tasting gum exuded from the bark is used for sweetening fruits and drinks. Boil for 10 minutes 1 lb (½ kilo) of fresh or dried apricots (after stoning) in a little water. Add a small measure of tamarisk gum and after 10 minutes tip the fruit and syrup into a pie dish lined with pastry and distribute evenly. Cover with pastry (or leave open), brush lightly with water, sprinkle with caster sugar and bake in a hot oven for 40 minutes until done. Serve hot or cold, topped with whipped cream.
TANSY 224	Herb "butters" Fritters Salads	Leaves	*Tansy Butter* Finely chop 2 or 3 leaves of tansy and several leaves of balm and sage. Make soft a ½ lb (¼ kilo) of butter and mix in the leaves, using a wooden spoon to do so and until the butter takes on a creamy consistency. Use as a spread for sandwiches or to butter hot toast to accompany cooked mushrooms or tomatoes.
TARRAGON 22	Sauces Vinegars	Leaves	*Tarragon Mayonnaise* To make a sauce to serve with fish, take 2 tablespoons of cream, add a pinch of mustard powder, a teaspoonful of sugar and 2 tablespoons of olive oil. Stir until it thickens, add a few drops of lemon juice and a teaspoonful of tarragon vinegar. This is made by placing several handfuls of tarragon leaves in a jar and covering with malt vinegar. Allow to stand for 14 days, then strain into screw-top jars and keep in a dark place.
TAWA 34	Dessert Pies and flans Cakes Preserves	Fruit	*Tawa Pie* The stones are removed from the damson-like fruits which are then part-boiled for 20 minutes and drained. Line a pie dish with pastry to a thickness of ¾ in. (2 cm), keeping some for the top. Place 1 lb (½ kilo) of tawas in the dish after mixing with them 2 oz (50 g) sugar, the grated peel of an orange or grapefruit and 2 tablespoons of flour. When in the pan, add several small pats of butter, moisten the edge of the pastry and put over the pastry covering. Make a small hole at the centre and bake for 10 minutes in a hot oven, reducing to 350°F (180°C) for a further 30 minutes. Serve hot with whipped cream or orange sauce.
TEA 227	Drinks Crèmes Jellies	Dried leaves	*Crème au Thé* Boil ½ liter of milk and pour over 1 oz (25 g) of Indian tea in a jug. Allow to stand for 20 minutes then strain and add a cupful of cream. Dissolve 1 oz (25 g) of gelatine in boiling water, sweeten with a tablespoon of honey and add to the other ingredients. When almost cool, whip another cupful of cream and stir in, then pour into a jelly mold and place in the refrigerator to set. Serve with fresh strawberries or other fruit in season.
TEA TREE 117	Sweets Drinks	Leaves	*Iced Cream Tea* The dried leaves are a substitute for the tea of commerce, taken hot or cold. They also make a delicious crème. Place 2 tablespoons of dried tea tree leaves in a pan and 1 in. (2.5 cm) of vanilla pod. Over it, pour 1 pint (½ liter) hot milk, cover and leave for 5 minutes and strain. Beat 4 oz (100 g) caster sugar with 2 eggs until stiff, then add the tea. Place in saucepan and stir slowly over a low flame until it thickens. Add a cupful of stiffly whipped cream and place in the refrigerator. Serve with fresh or stewed fruit.
THISTLE 45	Stews Salads Vegetable	Young shoots	*Thistle and Tomato Salad* The young shoots with their stem-clasping leaves make valuable pot-herbs to include in stews or to serve as a vegetable. Simmer for 30 minutes in a little stock and serve with sauce or melted butter; or when cool, the shoots are used in salads. Have them radiating from the center of a large dish and fill in the spaces with tomatoes cut into quarters. Sprinkle with parsley and chopped chives and serve with cold potatoes.
THYME 229	Flavoring soups; stews; stuffings	Leaves	*Thyme and Parsley Stuffing* To accompany pork or veal, mix together a cupful of fresh breadcrumbs; half a cupful of finely chopped suet; a tablespoon of chopped parsley and one of grated lemon peel; a teaspoonful of dry thyme; a pinch of nutmeg and seasoning. Mix in an egg and sufficient milk for the whole to bind and it is ready to use.
TOMATO 121	Salads Chutneys Sauces	Fruit	*Stuffed Tomatoes* Take a small slice of skin off top of several large red tomatoes and scoop out some of the flesh. Finely chop ½ cupful of mung bean sprouts and ½ cupful of chives and add the tomato pulp removed. Mix in a tablespoonful of olive oil and season, then stuff the tomatoes with the mixture and serve chilled from the refrigerator to accompany cold meats.
TRUFFLE 236	Vegetable Salads	All parts	*Truffles à l'Italienne* To prepare fresh truffles to serve with meat or game, peel and slice them into a pie dish. Moisten with salad oil, put in a small onion and a sprinkling of parsley, season and bake for 30 minutes. Sprinkle with lemon juice before serving hot.

Plant Lexicon Number	Uses	Part Used	Recipes
TURMERIC 71	Flavoring curries	Root	*Savory Onions* Fry 2 sliced onions in a little margarine and add 4 sliced tomatoes, a small teaspoonful of turmeric (or curry powder containing it) and a sprinkling of salt. Simmer for 5 minutes, then add a cupful of stock, bring to the boil and simmer for a further 15 minutes. Add 3 or 4 large chopped mushrooms, mix thoroughly and simmer 15 minutes more. Serve hot.
VANILLA 242	Flavoring	Pod	*Vanilla Crème* Beat the yolks of 2 eggs and add to 1 liter of milk almost brought to the boil but not quite. Stir and add 1 oz (25 g) caster sugar and let cool. Dissolve ½ oz (13 g) of gelatine in a tablespoon of water and stir into the mixture, with a teaspoonful of vanilla essence. Whip a cupful of cream and stir in. Pour into a jelly mold to set and serve cold.
VIOLET 246	Confectionery Salads	Flowers	*Candied Violets* The flowers, included in salads, look most attractive. They are also crystallized to decorate cakes and chocolates. To candy, gather the flowers when fully open but while still fresh. Place on trays for several hours in a cool but airy room away from the sun to dry off. Then dip the flowers into a solution of gum arabic and rose water, holding the spur with tweezers to do so. Replace them on the tray and while wet, sprinkle with fine sugar and place in a slightly warmed oven (with the door left open) to dry. Place in boxes on layers of tissue and use as required. They retain their purple color and almost dissolve in the mouth when eaten.
WALNUT 108	Salads Cakes Pickles Dessert	Nuts	*Walnut Salad* Chop up a small red or green cabbage and a large onion and place in a salad bowl. Mix in a small handful of stoned raisins and a cupful of chopped walnuts and over the whole sprinkle the juice of a lemon mixed with a tablespoonful of olive oil. Mix well and serve with cold meats.
WATER CHESTNUT 79	Soups Vegetable Salads	Tubers	*Water Chestnut Soup* Boil the tubers until tender then strain off surplus liquid. Add a thinly sliced onion, a knife-end of butter, a finely chopped carrot, ½ cup of chopped parsley and seasoning. Add 2 pints (1 liter) of chicken stock and simmer until the ingredients can be emulsified. Then stir in a cupful of cream and serve hot with toast or fried bread.
WATERCRESS 140	Soups Salads	Leaves	*Watercress Soup* Take 2 large onions, peel and slice and place in a saucepan with 2 oz (50 g) of butter. Add 4 potatoes after peeling and slicing and 4 pints (or 2 liters) of chicken stock. Bring to the boil and simmer for 10–12 minutes. Wash and chop 2 handfuls of watercress and add to the pan. Simmer for another 10 minutes then blend in a mixer or pass through a sieve. Return to the pan, season and simmer again. Beat up the yolks of 4 eggs with a cupful of cream, mixing in a little soup to prevent it curdling. Then add to the soup, stirring it in as one does so and continue for another 5 minutes. Serve hot or cold.
WATERMELON 55	Hors d'œuvre Dessert	Fruit	*Watermelon and Shrimps* Take a small melon, cut into quarters and remove the seeds. Cover the melon slices with fresh shrimps or prawns, or thawed after freezing. Decorate with finely chopped chives or parsley and squeeze over, the juice of a lemon. Serve chilled as hors d'œuvre.
WHEAT 234	Bread Cakes	Seeds	*Wheat and Nut Bread* A delicious and nourishing bread is made from 2 cupfuls of wholewheat flour and 2 of white flour, and a cupful of finely chopped alfalfa sprouts. Place in a large bowl and mix well. Stir in 2 teaspoons of baking soda and 1 of salt, together with ½ cupful of honey. Fold in a cupful of finely chopped walnuts. Place into a greased bread tin and bake for 1 hour in 350°F (180°C).
WILD ARUM 24	Thickening for soups; drinks	Tubers	*Portland Sago* The potato-like roots must be treated before using to rid them of poisonous alkaloids. Boil the tubers for 10 minutes and drain. Then cut into slices and bake in a warm oven until quite dry when the substance of the tuber is left as starch. When peeled and powdered, it can be used in puddings; in soups as a thickener or to make a nourishing drink. Mix a teaspoonful with a little milk in a cup and fill up with hot milk. Sweeten with honey or sugar.
WILD CHERRY 179	Sauces Pickles Preserves	Fruit	*Cherries and Gammon* Gather ½ lb (200 g) ripe sour cherries and remove the stones. Chop a small onion and place in a pan with ½ oz (13 g) margarine. Cook gently for 5 minutes and remove. Add the cherries and a cupful of stock and seasoning. Simmer for 15 minutes until the cherries are soft. Grill 2 gammon steaks 5–6 minutes on both sides, covering them with a little margarine. Add a teaspoonful of white vinegar to the cherry mix, stir and cook gently for several minutes, adding a teaspoon of sugar if too sour. Then pour over the grilled gammon and serve with sauté potatoes and watercress.
WILD LETTUCE 112	Salads	Leaves	*Wild Lettuce Hors d'Œuvre* Shred the lettuce leaves into individual hors d'œuvre dishes and over them slice a tomato and place a small handful of chopped chives. Over them sprinkle grated cheese or add a spoonful of cream cheese and top with orange or grapefruit segments. Dress with a teaspoonful of grapefruit or lemon juice and olive oil. Serve cold from the refrigerator.

Plant Lexicon Number	Uses	Part Used	Recipes
WILD PARSNIP 156	Vegetable Fritters Soups Stews	Root	*Cod and Parsnip* Place the cod cutlets in a frying pan containing a little olive oil and cook for 20 minutes over a low flame. At the same time, cut the parsnips lengthwise into two and boil separately until tender (wild parsnips take longer to cook than garden varieties). Make an egg sauce by boiling 2 eggs until hard, remove the shells and separate the whites from the yolks. Chop up the whites and add to a large cupful of heated butter, together with a teaspoonful of lemon juice and seasoning. Serve the cod cutlets with the drained parsnips on top, cover with soy sauce and garnish with the egg yolk and chopped parsley.
WILD PLUM 180	Tarts and pies Preserves Pickles	Fruit	*Wild Plum or Damson Preserve* Place the ripe fruits in a pot or jar and cover before placing it in a warm oven for several hours until the fruits become soft. Then rub through a sieve to remove the stones and skins. Put the pulp in a preserving pan and to each cupful of pulp add a cupful of sugar. Boil until the pulp has become stiff, stirring frequently and removing any scum. Allow to cool and pour into screw-top jars and store in a cool place.
WILD RAISIN 244	Confectionery Puddings Cakes	Fruit	*Wild Raisin Cake* Beat about 1 lb (½ kilo) of butter to a cream, then add 1 lb (½ kilo) of castor sugar and a small teaspoonful of nutmeg. Whisk in 4 eggs separately, then mix in 1 lb (½ kilo) of flour into which a teaspoonful of baking powder has been mixed. Then add the stoned and chopped raisins and bake in a greased tin for 1½ hours in a moderate oven.
WILD ROSE 192	Preserves Tarts and flans Drinks	Fruit	*Rose Hip Tart* A delicious conserve is made from rose hips and crab apples while they also make a tasty flan or tart. Gather when fully ripe. Top and tail the hips and peel and core the apples. Place an equal weight of both in a saucepan with a cupful of sugar for each 1 lb (½ kilo) of fruit and a little water and simmer for 20 minutes. Strain and cover a dish lined with pastry (or use a flan case) with the pulp which should be a deep red color. Bake the pastry for 20 minutes in a warm oven until done and serve hot with lemon juice, or cold topped with whipped cream.
WILLOW HERB 81	Vegetable Salads	Young shoots	*Willow Herb Salad* The young shoots make a tasty vegetable cooked like asparagus or sliced raw into a salad. They make an interesting jelly salad to serve with cold meats. Dissolve a lime jelly in a pint or ½ liter of hot water in a jelly mold. Add a cupful of wine vinegar and a tablespoon of sugar and stir in. When part-set, drop in sliced pieces of willow herb and diced and peeled cucumber which will be suspended in the jelly. Place in a refrigerator to finish setting and serve with watercress or early salad greens.
WORMWOOD 21	Flavoring meats; soups; stews	Leaves	*Sausage Meat* Wormwood, used sparingly with sage, will impart its pleasant bitterness to sausage meat and take away its richness. Finely chop 2 lbs (1 kilo) lean pork meat and 1 lb (½ kilo) beef suet and mix together. Add a cupful breadcrumbs and the grated peel of ½ a lemon, a pinch of allspice and a tablespoon of finely chopped wormwood, sage and marjoram mixed together. Mix in well and make into small ''cakes,'' then fry in a little fat for 10–15 minutes. Serve with potatoes and other vegetables.
WOUNDWORT 218	Vegetable Salads	Young shoots Roots	*Woundwort and Lemon Sauce* The young shoots, after boiling in two waters to remove their strong smell, are included in salads. Simmer for 30 minutes until tender and when cold, cut up and include with cress and tomatoes. The fleshy roots are boiled and also included cold in a salad; or hot with chicken. Serve with white or lemon sauce. To make, simmer the rind of a lemon for 10 minutes with a cupful of chicken stock and one of milk. Melt 1 oz (25 g) of butter in a saucepan and mix in 1 oz (25 g) flour. Stir over a low flame for 5 minutes. Pour in the stock, bring to the boil and simmer for 15 minutes. Add lemon juice and seasoning.
YAM 77	Vegetable Chutneys	Roots	*Baked Yam* Yams are boiled and served with cheese sauce but never taste better than when baked liked potatoes. Do not peel but place in a moderate oven for about 40 minutes until soft. Then serve with ham or pork meat with melted butter and seasoning. Baking brings out their unique flavor to the full and retains their pleasant sweetness.
YUCCA 248	Vegetable Salads	Flowers Seeds	*Yucca Seed and Egg Sauce* Petals from the white flowers are included in salads and the flat seeds, green when young (when they are used), are served with white sauce as a vegetable. Slit open the pods to extract the seeds which are flat and nutty when cooked. Steep them overnight and cook for 40 minutes in a little water. Drain and serve with egg sauce to accompany fish or chicken.
ZAPODILLA 2	Sweets Preserves Chutneys	Fruits	*Zapodilla Brulée* Remove the thin brittle skins (like litchees) and place in saucepan with a cupful of water. Simmer for 10 minutes, add 2 oz (50 g) brown sugar and stir a tablespoon of arrowroot (or other thickener) which has been dissolved in a little water. Bring to the boil and pour into small fire-proof bowls. Top with yogurt or sour cream, add a pinch of cinnamon and sprinkle with brown sugar. Then place under a grill for 30 seconds for the top to harden and serve hot.

Nature also Breeds Poisons

When collecting wild plants, care must be taken not to confuse edible with poisonous varieties. This chapter describes some plants which, although highly toxic, have important medicinal properties when administered carefully and in small doses. An example is Henbane, *Hyoscyamus niger (below)* which was used as a local anaesthetic as long as two thousand years ago.

While nature has given man all the plant foods he needs for a healthy body, it has also provided mankind with poisonous plants. Though they may cause violent death if eaten, these plants are of the greatest importance in medical practice if administered with care. Early man could not have come to

mulcent which invalids find easily digestible; or it may be used as blanc-mange. And yet, the species *Maranta malaccensis,* native of Southeast Asia, is used by Borneo tribesmen to poison their arrows, for the roots are among the most dangerous that nature produces.

Other poisonous plants are used to obtain toxic substances used for spearheads, or as a test of innocence in ordeal trials, such as the flowers of *Acokanthera venenata (right)* which contain the poison *ouabai.*

understand how to use them to treat his simple ailments except by trial and error, which must often have resulted in death. Even within the same genus, there are some species which provide man with nourishing foods while others are deadly poisonous. One example is Indian arrowroot *(Maranta arundinaceae),* so called from the Aruac Indians of South America where the plant is indigenous. These Indians use its rhizomatous roots as an antidote for poisonous arrows. It is also used the world over as a nourishing food and de-

As another example, the field or Flanders poppy, *Papaver rhoeas,* an attractive weed of cornfields with its vivid red petals, produces edible seeds used for flavoring and to make an edible cooking oil. Yet *P. somniferum,* indigenous to Asia Minor and India, contains highly poisonous alkaloids – though when used under medical supervision, it must be included among the most valuable natural products known to medical science. The plant is grown in large numbers in Iran, India and China, for opium is extracted from the green seed

No, no, go not to Lethe,
neither twist Wolf's-bane, tight rooted,
for its poisonous wine.

JOHN KEATS
(Ode on Melancholy)

The field poppy, *Papaver rhoeas (above)* provides edible seeds, while the opium poppy, Papaver somniferum *(below)* contains poisonous alkaloids. Its most highly refined extract is heroin, a powerful and widely abused narcotic.

heads. The white juice, obtained by making slits in the unripe seed capsule, is scraped from the capsule when partially dry and made into latex cakes. When chewed or smoked, by which methods it is consumed in large quantities in the East, it is narcotic and causes addiction. Its use for this purpose is now widespread. But from opium, the alkaloid Morphine is obtained and is the most valuable of all sedatives, used throughout the world by the medical profession to relieve pain. It is administered by injection in cases of severe injury or terminal cancer. It is also the best of all astringents in cases of diarrhea and dysentery. From the seeds, a quick-drying oil is obtained and used by artists in their paints and a syrup is obtained to use in cough mixtures. Tincture of opium is called laudanum. The juice of opium yields codeine, another valuable alkaloid, used by the medical profession to ease headaches. The opium poppy also produces heroin, which also causes addiction.

Only rarely do different varieties of the same species show poisonous and non-poisonous characteristics, but such is the case with the almond. Both the sweet and bitter almond are different varieties of *Amygdalus communis;* the bitter almond *var. amara* contains the poisonous Prussic acid. Even so, and in spite of its rapid action on the system, spirit of almonds is widely used in confectionery

for flavoring, yet if taken in quantity will cause giddiness and dimness of sight.

The snakeroot of North America is also a plant of many qualities. The dried roots have the bittersweet taste of ginger and are used in cooking as a substitute fo that product. They contain the bitter principle Aristolochin as well as starch and phosphate of lime. It is a tonic and sharpens the appetite. It also aids the digestion and for centuries has been used as an antidote for snake bite. But excessive use of the root can cause serious irritation of the gastro-intestinal tract, and it should be consumed only in small amounts.

Nature has produced no plants which show greater diversity in this regard than those of the genus *Solanum*. Of the 85 genera and more than 2000 species, many are among the most poisonous of all plants. Yet among those species native of the New World are the potato, tomato, eggplant and pepper (chili), mostly present in Chile and Peru, edible plants of the greatest economic importance. Also among the edible species are the winter cherry and cape gooseberry and *Lycium chinense,* native of South East Asia, where it is known as the tea-plant.

Another genus of the family Solanaceae is the tobacco, *Nicotiana tobaccum,* also of considerable economic importance and a plant of the New World. It contains the alkaloid Nicotine which,

Eating berries or leaves of the yew tree, *Taxus baccata (right)* can cause a fatal slowing of the heart.

The potato plant, *Solanum tuberosum (center right)* is an edible member of a family containing many poisonous plants.

Lily-of-the-valley, *Convallaria majalis (far right),* despite its sweet smell, contains extremely powerful cardiac glycosides.

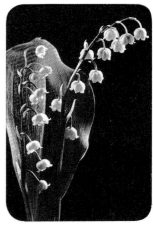

A depiction of *Canna indica rubra* from the "Hortus Eystettensis" of Basilius Besler, 1613 *(left)*.

The columbine, *Aquilegia vulgaris (below)* was once considered to be a favorite food of lions as, when rubbed on the hand, it gave a lion's courage. Although it is poisonous, its properties have not yet been isolated. In some countries an infusion of its seeds is used as a medicine, but this has been claimed to kill small children. All parts of the plant are suspect.

after the leaves are dried and smoked, yields the poisons hydrocyanic acid and carbon monoxide. Highly poisonous nicotine smokes are used in horticulture, to clear glasshouses and mushroom houses of insects, there being no more powerful insecticide. Other poisonous plants of the family include deadly nightshade, which yields the powerful alkaloid Atropine, a drug so deadly the one tenth of a grain is sufficient to cause severe poisoning and twice the amount may result in death. The root is still more poisonous than the fruits, while the leaves should never be handled by anyone who has cuts on the hands. Yet, used under medical supervision, it is one of the most effective plants known to science.

It is from the fresh leaves and the root that the green tincture is prepared. It is used as an antidote for opium poisoning and to allay palpitation of the heart. It is used to treat whooping cough in children, and older people suffering from

pneumonia or typhoid fever, while it is in constant use by occulists throughout the world. Before testing the eyes for glasses, the occulist will place a drop of Atropine in each eye to dilate the pupils. It is so powerful that only $\frac{1}{5000}$ of a grain is used for this purpose and only $\frac{1}{200}$ of a grain whenever taken internally.

Datura stramonium, the thorn-apple, and *Hyoscyamus niger,* the henbane of the same family, which inhabit the warmer parts of Europe, Asia and America, are both highly poisonous plants but also have considerable medicinal value. Like belladonna and many other poisonous plants, they have an unpleasant appearance and usually an equally unpleasant smell when approached. Tincture of henbane is used by the medical profession everywhere, to relieve pain and in cases of epilepsy, as Dioscorides prescribed 2000 years ago, when these highly poisonous plants were used before surgery, as anesthetics to dull the senses.

The death cap or fly agaric, *Amanitas muscaria* is a highly toxic hallucinogenic. It contains an alkaloid which interferes with the nervous system.

Four poisonous plants *(below, left to right).*

Cowbane, *Cicuta virosa*, all parts of which are highly toxic. A piece of its root the size of a walnut is said to be enough to kill a cow.

Tobacco, *Nicotiana tabacum*, is originaley from South America. It contains poisonous nicotine, a powerful insecticide.

The thorn-apple, *Datura stramonium*, contains alkaloids which are used in tinctures and anti-asthma cigarettes.

Deadly nightshade, *Atropa belladonna*, from which the important yet deadly drug atropine is produced.

The white bryony, a hedgerow plant of Europe and Asia, has all the characteristics of a poisonous plant. A member of the Cucumber family, its leaves and stems are covered in stiff hairs which makes them rough to the touch and the greenish-white flowers emit an unpleasant smell. They are followed by small bright red berries which emit a nauseous smell when crushed. They are emetic and poisonous, the large parsnip-like roots being even more so, releasing a milky juice when cut which produces blisters on the skin. It is used under medical supervision for heart trouble and in cases of dropsy.

Not all poisonous plants reveal their properties by their unpleasant appearance: plants of the Ranunculus family are among the most handsome of all wild plants when in bloom, yet their appearance belies their dangerous qualities for their roots are among the most poisonous of all. Among them is the aconite, *A. napellus*, with its turnip-like root. Barbarous tribes of Europe and

Opposite page:
The famous poisoner Lucia Borgia is said to have used an *anello della morte*, a ring that pierced the finger of its wearer and injected a deadly poison. She also allegedly applied poisons to clothes.

Asia used the juice and the pollen of its flowers on their arrows, hence its botanical name which is derived from the Greek *akontion*, "dart." Its medicinal qualities were discovered by Dr. Stoerck, the German physician who first prescribed its use for rheumatism and arthritis.

Salzburg is the main center for root collection, which takes place in October when the stem dies down. Young or "daughter" roots which grow around the "mother" root are the most wanted for they are the most active. They contain the alkaloid Aconitine, one of the most deadly of all poisons; but, used under medical supervision, it brings many benefits to mankind and is prescribed in cases of pneumonia and heart failure.

The black hellebore, *Helleborus niger*, takes its name from the Greek *cleine*, "to harm," and *bora*, "food," an indication of the poisonous qualities of its tuberous root if eaten. But its large white flowers appear in mid-winter, hence their name Christmas rose. They are the most handsome of all winter flowers and are attractive when used for indoor decoration. The roots contain the poison Helleborin, a narcotic which under medical supervision is used to treat heart disease and hysteria.

Another flowering plant whose beauty belies its poisonous qualities is

Two important figures from the history of medicine. Dioscorides *(below)*, the Greek physician of the 1st century A.D., and *(right)* the Swiss Paracelsus (1493–1541).

(This page and opposite page, below left to right)

Meadow saffron, *Colchicum Autumnale,* from which colchinine, an effective pain killer for gout and rheumatism, is extracted.

Almonds, the bitter variety of which contains the highly toxic prussic acid.

Hemlock, *Conium maculatum,* despite its delicate appearance is deadly poisonous.

The ordeal bean, *Physostigma venenosum.* Some tribes in tropical West Africa hold trials in which those who survive eating a few seeds are considered innocent.

Black hellebore, *Helleborus niger,* is also known as the Christmas rose. Its root contains a poisonous narcotic.

Laburnum, *L. anagyroides,* whose pea-like pods attract children and, in Britain, cause more deaths than any other plant.

the Colchicum whose roots provide medical science with the drug Colchinine, which has been used since the ancient Egyptians made use of it to treat gout and rheumatism. Modern science has found a new use for Cholchinine for it has the ability to increase the number of chromosomes in a plant so that hybrids which are sterile may be made fertile.

With certain plants, some parts are edible while other parts are poisonous, though they may be only mildly so. The rhubarb is an example: the stems (which are the leaf stalks) are edible, containing an easily digested sugar similar to that of the grape, though the leaf is mildly poisonous. Yet the flower in the bud state has often been enjoyed au gratin, as an alternative to cauliflower in the spring.

There are certain plants which yield food only after the part to be used has first been treated. With some plants, spinach for example, it is advisable to remove its high oxalic acid content, which to certain people acts as a mild poison, by cooking in two waters, pouring away the first after boiling for a few minutes, then simmering in its own juice until tender. The pokeweed too should be boiled in two waters to eliminate the large amounts of phytolaccic acid present in the leaves, though only small quantities are present in young leaves.

The wild arum or wake robin, a plant of hedgerows and open woodlands, advertises its poisonous qualities by the unpleasant smell of its flowers. It is a plant of the Aroid family, most of which are tropical and evil-smelling. The lower flowers are followed by a cluster of poisonous green berries, while the leaves yield the poisonous Prussic acid. And yet the large tuberous roots, which are poisonous until treated, yield starch and sugar and the salts of potassium and calcium. After peeling and soaking, then baking or boiling to remove the poisonous juice, they are highly nutritious.

Almost all those plants which are edible are either without smell or emit a pleasing fragrance either from their flowers or leaves. This is often a wholesome resinous smell rather than a sickly perfume as with rosemary, hyssop and thyme. Canadian bergamot, *Monarda didyma,* releases a sweet aromatic scent when handled and so do leaves of the walnut tree. There are varieties of pelargonium which, when pressed, release the refreshing scent of lemon, orange or

The exotic passion flower *(left),* used in small doses, makes an excellent sedative.

The foxglove, *Digitalis purpurea (below)* produces digitalis which, although highly toxic, is a substance of great importance in combating heart disease.

nutmeg. Cloves scent the air with their aromatic fragrance when being gathered and dried. The sweet bay also releases the unique sweetly resinous scent of its leaves whenever the sun shines upon them and releases the fragrance stored up in the oil glands. Always it is a wholesome smell. With poisonous plants it is entirely the opposite: their smell is usually nauseating and the appearance of the growing plant confirms their poisonous qualities. The same may be said of fungi. Those which are edible, the field mushroom and milk mushroom, the orange agaric and the chanterelle with its smell of ripe apricots and nutty taste, all have a wholesome, slightly aromatic smell, the appetizing scent of damp woodlands and meadows. They have dry caps and often pink gills beneath and are mostly found in open spaces. They look good to eat.

With the poisonous Amanitas or death caps, the cap is often of an unpleasant green, yellow, brown or orange-red coloring and is covered all over with white warts to give it a most unattractive appearance. As it opens, it becomes sticky or slimy and often emits the nauseating sweet, sickly smell of the early stages of putrefaction. They inhabit damp woodlands and are never found in open spaces.

Most highly poisonous fungi are either of the Aminita or Coprinus groups, the latter being known as ink-caps with thin stems and pointed caps shaded with black. Fungi of the Lactarius group are also poisonous. They have an unpleasant fishy smell, but with *Lactarius deliciosus,* the saffron milk cap, the smell is pleasantly aromatic, and as would be expected, it is delicious and safe to eat.

The papaya or melon tree of South America and the West Indies bears large melon-like fruits whose flesh, enjoyed as dessert, contains large amounts of vitamins A and C. The dry latex of the unripe fruits contains the enzyme papain which is used in brewing and for tenderizing meat. The juice is used for drinks and preserves, yet the leaves contain the poisonous alkaloid carpaine, which acts on the heart exactly like digitalis (obtained from the European foxglove) and though highly poisonous, when given under medical prescription stimulates the heart muscle and corrects an irregular pulse. It is also used in the treatment of kidney diseases and in cases of epilepsy. Both the papaya and foxglove, so different in their botanical characteristics and habitat, are among mankind's most valuable plants and an example of how nature in her wisdom provides for all her peoples through edible and poisonous plants which are distributed everywhere.

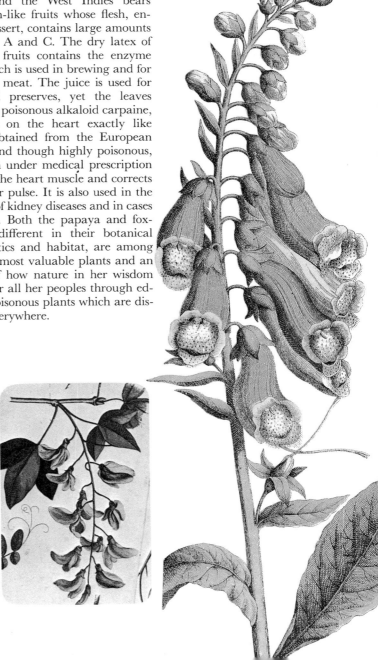

Epilogue

As modern man continues to destroy the hedgerows and primeval forests at an ever-increasing rate, he may eventually bring about his own destruction. This could be done by the elimination of the carbon cycle, for the carbon that is contained in plants and animals today is the same carbon which has been used to support all forms of life since the beginning of time, and without which life cannot exist. Carbon in the form of carbon dioxide (CO_2) is exhaled into the air by animals for plants to convert into food required for their own healthy growth and that of man; for carbon is present in all foods, whether proteins, fats or carbohydrates, each of which is needed by man for his survival. Plants assimilate carbon in their leaves by photosynthesis and make it a source of energy for man to use as carbohydrates. In addition, through the decomposition of dead leaves and animal matter in the soil, more carbon dioxide is returned into the atmosphere for plants to convert into more food. Thus, when large areas of forest are removed, nothing is left to convert the carbon dioxide of the atmosphere into oxygen and food, while soil erosion by wind and heavy rain completes the devastation. Virgin forests are composed of three layers. At the top is the canopy formed by the silk cotton and other trees which reach a height of 100 ft (30 m) or more. Below them grow smaller palms and other less vigorous trees, and below is a dense undergrowth of ferns nourished by the fallen leaves of the plants above them. The heavy rain reaches the soil only indirectly, thus preventing it from being washed away – which happened to the now desolate area watered by the mighty Tigris and Euphrates rivers. Once known as the Fertile Crescent, this area provided early man with all his requirements. Today, nothing grows there.

The same thing that happened to the Fertile Crescent 2,000 years ago is taking place in South America, to the once luxuriant jungles of the Amazon where grow many of nature's most important food and medicinal plants.

Wild food plants grow in the presence and protection of each other. They flourish in soil that through centuries has seen an accumulation of humus and plant food. Plants growing in woodlands and hedgerows have no need for man-made fertilizers. Nature provides their every need, but the continued destruction of natural resources – the removal of hedgerows and the felling of trees in the drive for greater efficiency as on the corn-bearing lands of North America, in North Africa and in India – leads only to the creation of desert lands where water evaporation exceeds the rainfall; only a few plants and humans can survive such conditions.

Natural foods are the only plants left to man that contain all the ingredients for a healthy body, for they have been grown in soil that needs no help from man. He will destroy them at his peril.

EMB Archives, Lucerne: 2, 9, 10, 11 12/13, 12 bottom, 14, 15 top and right, 16, 35 bottom, 38 (1 and 2), 40 (9 and 12), 41 (15 and 16), 42 (17), 44 (25, 26 and 27), 45 (30), 46 (32), 47 (36), 51 (48), 52 (53 left), 53 (55), 54 (60), 57 (68), 58 (70 and 71), 59 (74), 60 (77 and 79), 61 (82 and 83), 63 (90), 64 (92), 65 (98), 66 (102), 68 (107 and 110), 71 (119 and 120), 72 (123), 73 (125 and 126), 75 (132, 133 and 135), 79 (146 and 147), 80 (149), 81 (153 and 155), 82 (158), 85 (166 and 168), 87 (174), 88 (178), 89 (181), 91 (185 and 187), 92 (188, 189 and 190), 95 (198 and 199), 96 (202), 98 (206 and 208), 99 (212), 100 (214), 101 (216), 104 (227), 105 (231 and 232), 108 (240 and 243), 109 (244), 111 (250), 114 left, 114/115, 115 (all from top to bottom), 116 bottom left, 116/117 top, 121, 122 bottom, 129, 194 bottom center, 196 top, bottom center left, 199 below far left

Freeman, John R. & Co. Ltd, London: 125 below center and right

Fuchs, Leonard, *New Kreuterbuch,* Basel 1543: 5

Genders, Roy: Worthing: 127, 155 top, 198 bottom left

Gould, Prof. Richard A., Providence: 155 right

Gremper, Zebedäus, Malters: 34

Jacana, Paris (PH: Michel Viard): 50 (45), 70 (116), 111 (251)

Köhler, *Medizinal-Pflanzenatlas,* Gera-Untermhaus 1887: 39 (79), 41 (14), 42 (19), 45 (29), 50 (46), 53 (54 and 56), 61 (84), 65 (96), 69 (114), 70 (118), 74 (129), 84 (164), 85 (167), 86 (171), 88 (179), 91 (186), 93 (193), 94 (196), 103 (225), 194 top

Leuenberger, Hans, Yverdon: 193 right

Lonicero, Adamo, *Kreuterbuch,* 1679: 30 left, 31 top and right

Losch, F., *Les Plants Medicinales,* Bienne: 38 (4), 42 (18), 52 (53 right), 64 (93 left), 67 (104), 68 (109), 84 (165), 88 (177), 89 (180 bottom), 104 (230), 105 (233), 107 (239), 109 (246), 199 bottom center left

Magnum, Paris: 113 (PH: Henri Carter Bresson)

Mattioli, *Commentaires,* Lyons 1579: 198 bottom center

Metropolitan Museum of Art, New York (The Robert Lehman Collection, 1975): 8

Museum für Völkerkunde, Basel: 154 left (PH: A. Foote-Baldinger)

Natural History Photographic Agency, Baltwood/Kent: 126 center left

Natural Science Photos, Watford: 199 top (PH: Gil Montalverne)

Österreichische Nationalbibliothek, Vienna: 198 center

Picturepoint, London: 39 (6)

Rauh, Prof. Dr. W., Institut für Systematische Botanik und Pflanzengeographie der Universität Heidelberg: 47 (37), 49 (41), 51 (50), 52 (52), 54 (58), 55 (61), 56 (66), 58 (69), 59 (73), 63 (91), 64 (94), 65 (95), 66 (101), 67 (103 and 106), 69 (112), 70 (115), 72 (122), 76 (137), 78 (142), 86 (172), 87 (173), 94 (195), 100 (213), 103 (226), 116 bottom right, 117 bottom center left and far right, 120, 122 top and center, 126 top, above left and below left, 194 bottom left and right, 196 bottom center right.

Reichenbach, Dr. A. B., *Volks-Naturgeschichte des Pflanzenreichs,* Leipzig 1837: 33, 90 (184), 124 below, 126 below right

Reinhard - Tierfoto, Heiligkreuzsteinach: 161 left

Royal Botanic Gardens, Kew: 76 (136), 102 (222)

Rüedi, Ruth, Lucerne: 13 below, 117 bottom left and bottom center right, 124 above, 162 all, 163 all, 164 all, 165 all, 166 all, 167 all

Schlapfer - Color, Lucerne, 168

Schöffer, Peter, *Gart der Gesundheit,* Mainz 1485: 119

Schröder, Johann, *Höchstkostbarer Arzney-Schatz,* 1685: 17

Schulthess, Emil, Forch/Zurich: 156/157

Smith, Harry, Photographic Collection, Chelmsford: 60 (80), 65 (97), 101 (219)

Städelsches Kunstinstitut, Frankfurt: 197

Topham, John, Picture Library, Edenbridge: 62 (86), 66 (100), 69 (113)

Von Schuberts, Prof. Dr. G. H., *Naturgeschichte des Pflanzenreichs,* Esslingen 1853/1887: 39 (8), 40 (10 and 11), 43 (21 and 23), 44 (24), 45 (28), 47 (35), 49 (40 and 42), 50 (44), 52 (51), 54 (57 and 59), 55 (63), 56 (64 and 65), 59 (75), 61 (81), 62 (87), 63 (88), 67 (105), 71 (121), 72 (124), 73 (127), 74 (130 and 131), 75 (134), 77 (140), 78 (144), 80 (150 and 151), 81 (154), 82 (156), 83 (160 and 161), 84 (163), 85 (169), 86 (170), 87 (176), 89 (180 above), 92 (191), 93 (192), 94 (194), 95 (197), 97 (205), 99 (209), 100 (215), 101 (217 and 218), 102 (220), 103 (224), 104 (228), 106 (234 and 235), 107 (237), 108 (241), 109 (245), 110 (247), 111 (249), 116 bottom center, 193 left, 195 below, 196 bottom left and bottom right, 198 bottom right, 199 bottom center right, and far right

INDEX